*Electrical Appliance Service Manual*

# Electrical Appliance Service Manual

*by* **WILLIAM L. GABBERT**

*The David Ranken, Jr.,*
*School of Mechanical Trades*
*St. Louis, Missouri*

*Technical Division*
**Rinehart & Company, Inc.**
*New York*

*Printed in the United States of America*
*Library of Congress Catalog Card Number: 52–5783*

**to** *the four women in my life who,*
*ingenuously or ingeniously, I know not which,*
*maintain that "Daddy can fix anything,"*
*this book is affectionately dedicated.*

# Preface

Early in 1946, the David Ranken, Jr., School of Mechanical Trades in St. Louis, Missouri, undertook to offer a course in electrical appliance servicing to be taught as part of a World War II veteran training program. The author, who had had a number of years' experience in appliance repairing, was assigned to prepare and subsequently to teach this course.

For the first year that the appliance servicing course was in progress, the class worked mainly from lecture notes and without the benefit of textbooks other than standard works in electrical theory, because no book on electrical appliance repairing existed. During this year the author prepared a series of papers relating to appliance theory, operation, and servicing. These were mimeographed at Ranken and used as the textbook for the appliance course.

When it became apparent that this material was to be published, it was rewritten and expanded, first, to make the content, originally intended only for classroom use, equally suitable for the homemaker who would repair his own appliances (thus the inclusion of the servicing charts, one for each type of appliance) and, secondly, to incorporate into the text the result of experience gained in the actual teaching of appliance repair. The author sincerely believes that these changes have made the revised version more useful for its purpose—the teaching of the fundamentals of appliance repairing.

The student is not the only person who learns in the classroom; the teacher learns too. One such lesson gleaned from the teaching of the course in appliance repairing is that the student's main requirement is assurance—the confidence that what he is doing is correct—the conviction that there is no mystery to any mechanism; that each is governed by certain basic mechanical or electrical principles which, once learned, can be applied with the certainty that the repairman can be master of the appliance—not vice versa.

Thus, in this book, operating principles are stressed. No brand names are mentioned for the sake of the brand name itself, for it will be found that once the principles are understood, the brand makes little difference in the method of repair to be followed. For example, an electric fan moves air because of a motor-driven blade, regardless of the legend on the name plate. Of course, one must not overlook the fact that a man who has repaired thousands of appliances is more familiar with what he is doing and consequently more adept than the person who is working on his first appliance; for, as with any other craft, experience is of recognized benefit in the appliance field. On the other hand, the beginner need not necessarily do a poorer job just because he is a novice.

Many persons are "afraid of electricity." Undoubtedly, electricity can be a tremendously destructive force, but so can fire be destructive, and as with fire, comprehension causes fear to vanish. It is to be observed that the intelligent electrician recognizes the hazard of electricity and uses the wisdom he has learned in working on and with electrical apparatus. For this reason, the initial chapters in this book have been devoted to the theory of electricity, with the hope that an understanding of how electricity behaves, how to control and govern it, will eliminate the hesitancy to repair a device just because it is "electrical."

Although actually a part of the field of appliance repair, the topics of refrigeration, motor winding, and radio and television repair have deliberately been omitted from this book. The reason is simple; all these subjects are adequately covered by many fine publications. The interested reader will find no shortage of information in these fields.

The author extends his thanks to the students whose efforts have aided materially in the assembling of diagrams and material for this book, to the instructors and staff of The David Ranken, Jr., School of Mechanical Trades for their willing help and advice, and to the manufacturers who so liberally contributed the sketches and photographs which illustrate this manual.

*William Lee Gabbert*

*St. Louis, Missouri*
*July, 1954*

# Contents

*Electrical Appliance Service Manual*

*chapter* **1**

# Basic Electrical Principles

Electricity is a term familiar to most of us, since so many of the things we use are electrically operated. In order to understand how electricity causes appliances to do what they are intended to do, it is not necessary to have a deep understanding of what electricity is; but it *is* important to understand the behavior of electricity and the fundamental laws that govern it.

## 1.1. The Electric Circuit. Conductors. Insulators

In order to have an electric current, we must have a source of electric force, or voltage, to drive current through the electric circuit. Two of the most common ways of obtaining electric voltage and current are from electric generators and from electric batteries. Generators convert mechanical power sent into their shafts into electric current and voltage, representing electric power. Batteries convert chemical energy into electric current and voltage.

But to have an electric current, we must have, in addition to a source of voltage, a complete electric circuit. That is, there must be a complete path of material through which current can flow out of the voltage source through the path and back to the voltage source again. A good example of an electric circuit is a flashlight battery connected to a flashlight lamp.

A substance which will carry electricity is called a conductor. Most metals are relatively good conductors. Some nonmetals (carbon and certain liquids) are also good conductors. Copper is one of the best, and for that reason (together with its comparative cheapness) most wires are of copper. Other metals which are good conductors and consequently are encountered in electric circuits are silver, aluminum, and lead (as found in solder).

In order to confine the electric current to its circuit and prevent it from following conducting paths where damage might occur, the conductors and other parts of the circuit are surrounded by materials that will not conduct electricity. Such nonconductors are called insulators. Some materials that make good insulators are rubber, cloth, paper, fiber, plastics, and, where heat is present, asbestos, mica, and porcelain.

## 1.2. Resistance

It cannot be said that all substances are either conductors or insulators. Some materials allow a limited amount of current flow, yet not to the extent that they may be called conductors. These materials do, to a greater or lesser extent, *resist* a current flow. Therefore they are classified as *resistors,* and are said to possess the electrical quality of *resistance*. Commonly used resistance materials are carbon, tungsten, nichrome, and iron.

Resistance is a physical quality of a material; it does not vary with change of other circuit components. Increasing or decreasing the flow of current does not (for all practical purposes) change the value of the resistor through which this current flows, unless there is a considerable temperature change.* The value of the resistor does depend upon the size and shape of the resistance material. If a 10-foot length of iron wire has a certain resistance, obviously a 20-foot length of the same wire possesses

*If there is a considerable change in temperature most metals change their resistance enough to alter circuit conditions appreciably. Some metals (special alloys) are available with a very low temperature coefficient.

twice as much resistance. A little thought on the matter will lead to the correct conclusion that doubling the size (cross-section area) of the wire will halve the resistance.

## 1.3. The Ohm

The unit of measure of resistance is the ohm. A short length of the type of wire used in house wiring may have a resistance of a small fraction of 1 ohm, whereas the insulation on this wire will have a resistance of many millions of ohms. The wire itself resists current flow only to a very slight degree; the insulation resists current flow to a point where the flow is negligible.

When the *quantity* of resistance of a device is to be expressed in ohms, the Greek letter Ω (omega) is often used as an abbreviation of the word "ohms." For example, 20 ohms may also be written 20Ω. This should not be confused with the *symbol* for resistance, *R*, which is used to designate a specific resistance or resistor. For example, if there are two resistors in a circuit, we might refer to one as *R1* and the other as *R2* so we can easily identify which one we are talking about.

The resistance material most familiar to the appliance service man is nichrome, an alloy of nickel and chromium. This alloy, in wire form, is used for heating elements in irons, toasters, hot-pads—in fact, any appliance in which heat is produced electrically.

## 1.4. The Ampere

The unit of measurement of the rate of current flow in an electric circuit is the ampere. There is a precise scientific definition of the ampere, but for our purpose it is more practical to state that one ampere is approximately the quantity of current required to operate a 100-watt bulb in a house-wiring circuit. The letters *amp* are used as an abbreviation for amperes, in the same way as Ω is used for ohms. Currents are designated by the letter *I* in the same way as resistors and resistances are identified by the letter *R*. For example, 15 amperes can be written 15 amp, and two currents can be designated $I_1$ and $I_2$ to distinguish between them.

## 1.5. Current and Electron Flow

In the early days of electrical science, when the terminology of units of electricity was in the making, the exact nature of electricity was controversial, and theories were prevalent which by present standards seem somewhat inadequate. For example, the term *current* was given to the *rate* of flow of electricity, and its *direction* of flow (externally) was arbitrarily expressed as being from the positive to the negative terminal of the source. Although still a perfectly satisfactory convention, this notation became less popular with the advent of electronics, and has now been partly supplanted by the concept of electron flow, externally from negative to positive.

All matter consists of minute particles called molecules. If it were possible to break up a piece of glass (for example) into the *smallest* fragment which had all the properties of glass, though submicroscopic in size, that fragment would be a molecule. Molecules are comprised of atoms. The distinction between a molecule of glass and that of some other substance, such as wood, lies in the type and quantity of atoms which make up the molecule. The familiar chemical formula for water, $H_2O$, indicates that a water molecule is a combination of two hydrogen atoms ($H_2$) and one oxygen atom (O).

The electrical and chemical behavior of atoms has given clues to the probable nature of the too-small-to-be-visible atom. The suggested scheme of an atom's structure is shown in Figure 1-1, where it is seen to resemble a miniature solar system. Analogous to the planets are *planetary electrons,* shown on the diagram as small dots. The minus sign placed beside each electron shows that it is a negative particle of electricity. The outer circles represent the circular or oval paths or *orbits* around which the electrons are in constant motion. Within the central circle are placed a number of plus signs (corresponding with the number of minus signs denoting electrons) to indicate that the core or *nucleus* of the atom contains particles of a positive electrical nature called *protons.* Actually the atomic picture is much more complex than here shown; the only parts we are interested in are those which have to do with fundamental electrical theory.

The mass or weight of the positive proton is more than 1,800 times greater than that of the electron. Because of this difference, the electron is capable of greater mobility than is the proton. That force which we call electrical voltage is capable of causing electrons of certain substances to move from one atom to another; such materials are electrical conductors. Copper, whose atoms contain 29 protons and electrons, behaves in this manner and, as has already been stated, is known to be one of the better conductors. Conversely, the type of atom in which it is difficult to set electrons in motion toward other atoms is that of an insulator. Resistance materials are such that the electrons *can* be set into motion, but with difficulty. Thus it is seen that an electric current consists of a concerted drift of electrons through a metallic substance; the direction of motion is dictated by the rule that like charges repel, unlike charges attract. From this rule we may judge that the flow of electrons will necessarily be externally from the negative terminal to the positive terminal of the electrical source: battery, generator or whatever it may be. Therefore, when placing an arrow to indicate electrical flow upon a circuit diagram, it is wise to designate in some fashion whether the older idea of current (externally from positive to negative) or the newer electron theory (from negative to positive) is that employed. In this book we will consider direction of electron flow, negative to positive, as direcion of current, and all diagrams and explanations will follow this convention.

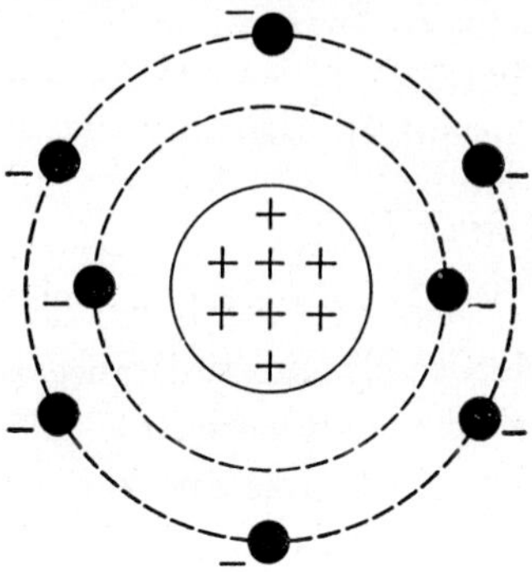

FIG. 1-1.

## 1.6. The Volt

In order that this electric current (electrons) may flow in a circuit, there must be a force or pressure causing it to move. This pressure is called the electromotive force, or, more familiarly, the voltage. It is common knowledge that our homes are wired for 110 to 120 v. The symbol for voltage is $E$. The abbreviation for volts is v. The electrical pressure in volts is measured between two points in a circuit; thus, voltage exists *across* a circuit. It is wholly incorrect to refer to the voltage as "going through the circuit."

*Ohm's Law*

So far, we have discussed three distinct qualities of the electric circuit; resistance (ohms), current (amperes), and electrical pressure (volts). These three qualities have a definite relationship to one another, and this relationship is called "Ohm's law." Ohm's law, in its simplest form, states that "the voltage applied to any circuit is equal to the current in that circuit multiplied by the resistance of that circuit," or

$$\text{VOLTS} = \text{AMPERES} \times \text{OHMS}.$$

Mathematically, this is stated as $E = IR$, where

$E$ is the voltage,
$I$ is the amperes of current, and
$R$ is the ohms of resistance.

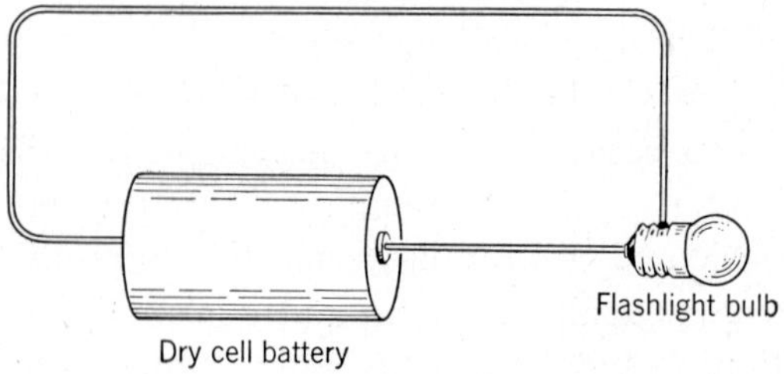


FIG. 1-2.

EXAMPLE 1: In the circuit of the flashlight, shown in Figure 1-2, there is 0.5 amp of current flowing through the bulb. The resistance of the bulb is 3Ω. What is the battery voltage?

SOLUTION:

$$E = IR,$$
$$E = \text{amp} \times \text{ohms},$$
$$E = 0.5 \times 3,$$
$E = 1.5$. The voltage of the battery is 1.5 v.

Ohm's law may be expressed in two other forms. They are

**1. The current in a circuit is directly proportional to the voltage applied to that circuit, and inversely proportional to the resistance of that circuit.**

More simply,

AMPERES = VOLTS divided by OHMS.

Mathematically, this is stated

$$I = \frac{E}{R}.$$

And, finally,

**2. The resistance of an electric circuit is directly proportional to the voltage applied to that circuit, and inversely proportional to the current flow in that circuit.**

Or,

OHMS = VOLTS divided by AMPERES.

Mathematically, this is stated

$$R = \frac{E}{I}.$$

We are now equipped with three statements concerning the behavior of the three qualities of an electric circuit. These statements enable us to find any one of the three qualities if the other two are known.

EXAMPLE 2: If, in Figure 1-2, the battery is rated at 6 v, and the bulb has a resistance of 3Ω, what will be the amount of current flow?

In this problem, the unknown quantity is the current. One of the equations of Ohm's law states that $I = E/R$. Filling in the known values, this becomes $I$ (current) $= 6/3 = 2$ amp. The current flow in the circuit is 2 amp.

EXAMPLE 3: If, in Figure 1-2, the battery voltage is the same as in the preceding example, 6 v, and 0.15 amp of current is flowing, what is the resistance of the bulb while glowing?

The unknown quantity is the resistance. Using the form of Ohm's law that states $R = E/I$, and filling in with known values, $R = 6/0.15 = 40\Omega$. The bulb resistance is 40Ω.

EXAMPLE 4: An electric toaster has stamped on its name plate the information that, when plugged into a 120 v circuit, the appliance will draw 10 amp of current. What is the resistance of the heating element in this toaster?

This problem is the same as the one in Example 3, except that now the source of voltage is a generator instead of a battery.

$$R = E/I = 120/10 = 12\Omega.$$

## 1.7. Electric Symbols

In Figure 1-3 is a group of the most commonly used electric symbols and the electric components which they represent. The proper use of these symbols greatly reduces the labor involved in preparing a scheme of the electric circuit within an appliance. The following remarks concerning the symbolic representation of a circuit diagram—or, as it is sometimes called, a "schematic"—will serve as a guide.

1. Since the symbols given in Figure 1-3 are standard, use these rather than "homemade" symbols (as they are sometimes called), recognizable only to their inventor.

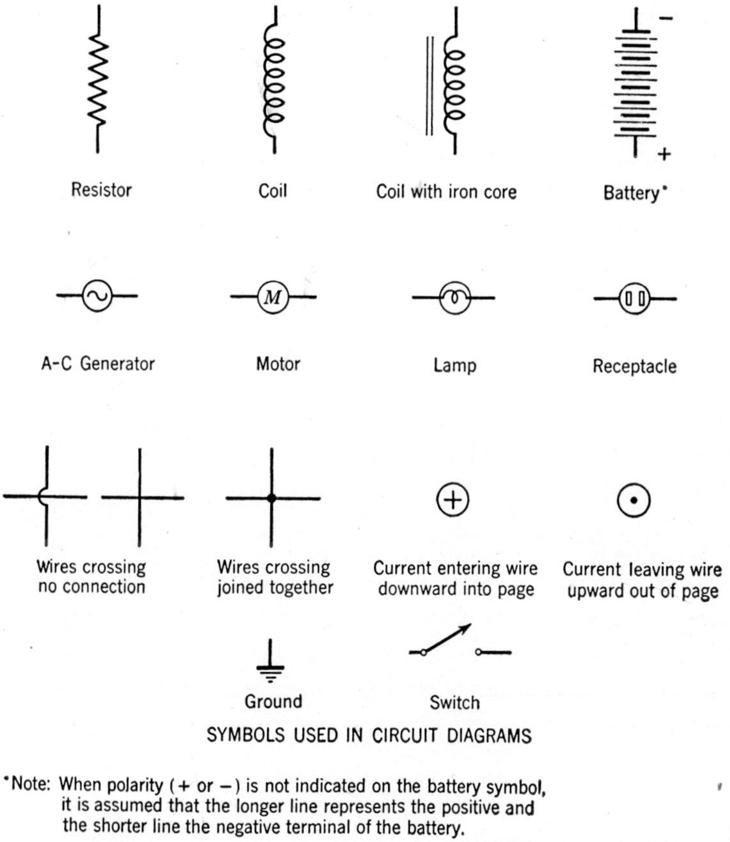


FIG. 1-3.

2. Attempt to arrange the layout of symbols representing parts, and lines representing wiring, in a horizontal and vertical pattern, with as few crossovers as possible.

Do not attempt to show the physical position of these parts and wires; this practice inevitably leads to a confused and disorderly diagram. The circuit diagram can do only so much. It cannot show electrical and mechanical details simultaneously. If the electrical plan is readily apparent from the diagram, the intelligent repair man will be able to make a satisfactory placement of the parts and wiring.

3. Do not attempt to show parts values by relative size of symbols. That is, do not draw a small or short resistance symbol to represent low ohms, and a large zigzag for high ohms. Use the same size symbol for each, and mark beside it the value to be used.

4. Draw the circuit diagrams of a few appliances for practice in the use of electric symbols. Compare your drawings with those in manufacturers' literature. Within a short time it is possible to become fairly proficient in the use of symbols and in the making of acceptable circuit diagrams.

In Figure 1-4, the flashlight bulb and battery are represented by these symbols. Figure 1-5 is the diagram of the circuit of the toaster described in Example 4, with the use of symbols rather than pictures to depict the parts of the circuit.

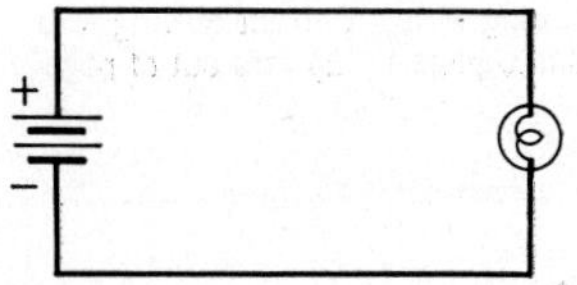


FIG. 1-4.

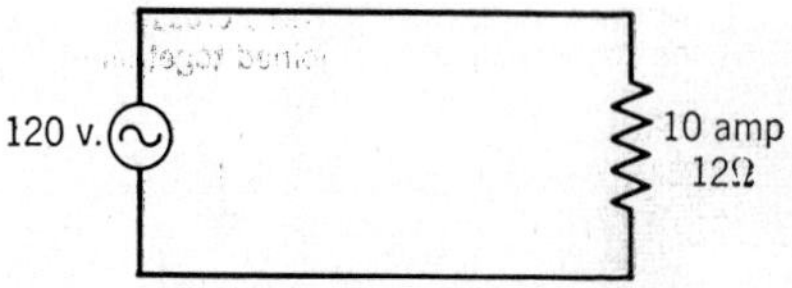


FIG. 1-5.

The value of a circuit diagram, properly made, cannot be overestimated. Often it is necessary to completely disassemble an appliance having an intricate electrical circuit. If a diagram of the circuit is made while disassembling the appliance, it will be unnecessary to rely upon memory alone for proper reassembly. Frequently a considerable period of time elapses between disassembly and repair; it may be necessary to obtain repair parts from the manufacturer in another city. Should memory fail, the circuit diagram will facilitate proper rewiring of the appliance.

## 1.8. Series and Parallel Circuits

Not all circuits are of the simple type, as shown in Figures 1-4 and 1-5; in fact, a circuit may become quite complex. However, the *parts* of a circuit may ordinarily be individually analyzed as being either *series* or *parallel.*

In Figure 1-6 (which might be the circuit diagram of two electric irons, plugged into a duplex outlet receptacle) there are two paths for the current; the resistors are said to be *in parallel.* In Figure 1-7, the same two resistors have been rearranged so that there is but one current path; this is a *series arrangement.*

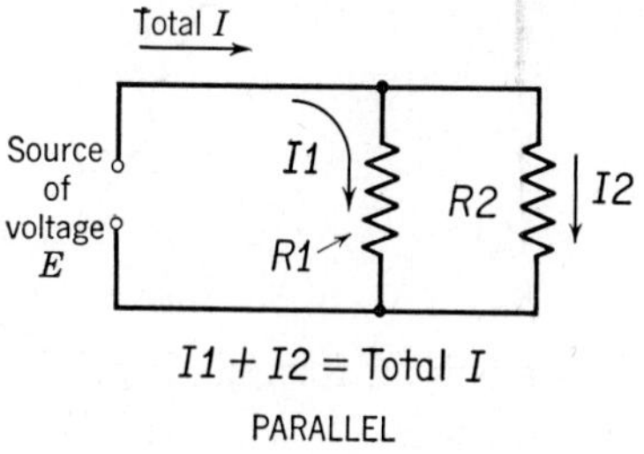


FIG. 1-6.

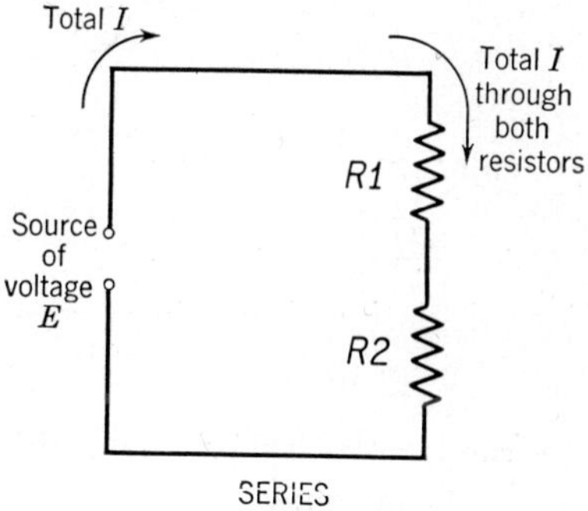


FIG. 1-7

Some Christmas-tree lamp sets are series connected; ordinary house wiring is parallel connected.

The series circuit of Figure 1-7 lends itself to an easy analysis. The flow of current is limited, not by one, but by two resistors, *R1* and *R2*. The total resistance in the circuit is the sum of the two resistors. According to Ohm's law, the current in the circuit, *I,* equals

$$\frac{E}{R1 + R2}.$$

The rule for series resistance is

**The total resistance, $R_t$, is the sum of the individual series resistors:**

$$R_t = R1 + R2 + R3 \cdots.$$

The parallel circuit, in Figure 1-6, possesses two current paths; consequently, the current flow will be greater than with either of the two resistors in an individual circuit. It is apparent, from Ohm's law ($I = E/R$), that this increase in current is accompanied by a decrease in resistance, the voltage remaining constant. Therefore, two parallel resistors offer less resistance to current flow than either resistor alone. The rule for finding the total resistance of resistors in parallel is as follows:

**The total resistance is equal to the reciprocal of the sum of the reciprocals.**

Or the total resistance (Fig. 1-5) equals

$$\frac{1}{\dfrac{1}{R1} + \dfrac{1}{R2} + \cdots}.$$

For calculations involving two resistors only, a formula involving less figuring than the preceding may be used.

**The total of two parallel resistors is equal to their product divided by their sum:**

$$R \text{ total} = \frac{R1R2}{R1 + R2}.$$

EXAMPLE 5: Two appliances, a toaster whose resistance is 15 ohms, and a coffee maker, whose resistance is 20 ohms, are plugged into a receptacle supplying 110/120 v. What is the total resistance across the 110/120-v line?

$$R \text{ total} = \frac{1}{\dfrac{1}{R1} + \dfrac{1}{R2}} = \frac{1}{\dfrac{1}{15} + \dfrac{1}{20}} = \frac{1}{\dfrac{4}{60} + \dfrac{3}{60}}$$

$$= \frac{1}{\dfrac{7}{60}} = \frac{60}{7} = 8.57\Omega.$$

ALTERNATE SOLUTION:

$$R \text{ total} \frac{R1R2}{R1 + R2} = \frac{15 \times 20}{15 + 20} = \frac{300}{35} = 8.57\Omega.$$

## 1.9. The Watt

The Underwriters Laboratories require the manufacturers of appliances to place on the name plate information concerning the power consumed by the appliance. Generally, this information consists of a listing of the watts of electric power required to operate the appliance. The watt is the unit of electric power, and is equal to the product of volts and amperes.

$$\text{WATTS} = \text{VOLTS} \times \text{AMPERES} = EI.$$

As with Ohm's law, there are three forms of the equation for determining the power in watts in an electric circuit. The other two are

$$\text{WATTS} = \text{VOLTS}^2/\text{RESISTANCE} = E^2/R.$$

$$\text{WATTS} = \text{CURRENT}^2 \times \text{RESISTANCE} = I^2R.$$

## 1.10. Heat and Electricity

This last equation, WATTS $= I^2R$, is important to the appliance repair man. What this equation means, from an appliance standpoint, is that when, in an electric circuit, there is current through a length of resistance material, some electric power (watts) is consumed. This power does not remain within the resistance material, but is released as heat. It is this electrically produced heat which toasts bread, presses clothes, cooks food, and performs the myriad tasks assigned to the heater-type appliances.

There is a direct relationship between the wattage of an heating element and the heat produced by that wattage. If the wattage is doubled, the heat is doubled; if the wattage is halved, the heat is halved; and so on. With this information, it is possible to predetermine the heat produced by any particular heating element. Nichrome wire is employed as the resistance material in electric appliances. The table on page 14 lists the resistance of nichrome in the various wire sizes. From this table it is possible to determine the correct length of whatever size wire is to be used.

## Nichrome Wire-Resistance Chart

| B & S GAUGE | OHMS PER 1000 ft. | B & S GAUGE | OHMS PER 1000 ft. |
|---|---|---|---|
| 1 | 7.1 | 21 | 738 |
| 2 | 9.0 | 22 | 937 |
| 3 | 11.4 | 23 | 1174 |
| 4 | 14.4 | 24 | 1485 |
| 5 | 18.1 | 25 | 1872 |
| 6 | 22.8 | 26 | 2373 |
| 7 | 28.9 | 27 | 2971 |
| 8 | 36.6 | 28 | 2778 |
| 9 | 46.1 | 29 | 4698 |
| 10 | 57.6 | 30 | 6000 |
| 11 | 72.4 | 31 | 7575 |
| 12 | 89.9 | 32 | 9375 |
| 13 | 115 | 33 | 11904 |
| 14 | 146 | 34 | 15113 |
| 15 | 184 | 35 | 19108 |
| 16 | 230 | 36 | 24000 |
| 17 | 296 | 37 | 29702 |
| 18 | 375 | 38 | 37500 |
| 19 | 463 | 39 | 49180 |
| 20 | 586 | 40 | 66666 |

for heating element. If the line voltage is known, the wattage may be derived from the formula $E^2/R$. A formula for converting wattage into its heat equivalent is

$$\text{CALORIES OF HEAT} = 0.24 \times \text{WATTS} \times \text{TIME IN SECONDS.}$$

The heat thus produced may be considered as being generated by the friction resulting from a current flow through a wire made of a material that resists the current's flow. However, it is not usually true that an increase of resistance (causing an increase of friction) will produce more heat. On the contrary, since voltage across the resistance is ordinarily constant, *less* heat is produced because of a reduction of the current flow. Remember that the watts which cause this heat equal $I^2R$, not $IR$.

For example, if, in a circuit containing 10 ohms, 10 amp is flowing, the wattage is $10^2 \times 10$, or 1,000 w. Now, if the resistance is doubled, the current will be halved (Ohm's law), and the wattage will then become $5^2 \times 20$, or 500 w. The increase in resistance results in a decrease of wattage, and vice versa.

The extent to which the resistance may be reduced, thus increasing the heat output in an electric appliance, is limited by the size of wire used in building construction, and the size of fuse allowable for this wire size. The National Electric Code requires the installation of a branch circuit for appliances consisting of No. 12 wire, fused for 20 amp. If a number of appliances are to be used on this circuit simultaneously, such as a refrigerator, radio, toaster, and fan, the total current for all these appliances must not exceed 20 amp. Therefore, each appliance should be designed so as to make the most efficient use of the current it requires. This fact should be kept in mind when replacing a heating element in a defective appliance.

The wattage of an appliance is dependent upon the applied voltage ($W = E^2/R$), and will change if the appliance is operated at other than its rated voltage. The wattage changes more rapidly than the voltage. For example, if a waffle iron is rated at 120 v, 500 w, its wattage (and heat output) will double if the voltage is increased to only 179 v. This increase of heat output may perhaps be of advantage in providing a faster-acting appliance. However, the more intense heat may materially shorten the life of the appliance.

If a moderate increase in voltage results in a severe increase in wattage and heat, in like manner an appliance operating on a low-line voltage may be unable to produce sufficient heat to perform its appointed task. A common complaint about irons, toasters, waffle makers, and other heat-producing appliances is that they will not get hot enough, or that the heating is uneven. This is caused, in many instances, by the fact that the appliance is operating on too low a voltage. Either too low a line voltage, or excess resistance introduced by poor attachment plug, cord, or insecure internal connections, is a contributing factor, producing low-operating voltage for the heating element in the appliance. In Chapter 2 are detailed the types of electrical measuring instruments for checking line voltage, and the methods of use of such meters.

### 1.11 Magnetism

With the exception of electronic devices, all electrical appliances operate on one or the other, or a combination of, two principles. One is the production of heat by a current flow through a wire having resistance; the second is electrically produced magnetism. Magnetism results when a current flows through a coil. In the first category are such appliances as electric irons, waffle makers, toasters. The electric motor and doorbell are examples of appliances operating by magnetism. The electric ironer and circulating heater, containing both motor and heating element, represent a combination of the two principles heat and magnetism.

The average home will contain more appliances operating on the magnetic principle than those containing heating elements. For this reason, if for no other, it is important that the appliance repairman have an understanding of the principles underlying electrically produced magnetism.

Many years ago, in the country of Magnesia, in Asia Minor, a shepherd discovered (or so the story goes) that a certain rock exhibited the peculiar property of "holding on" to the metal end of his crook. This stone was given the name of "magnet" after the country in which it was found. It is now known that this substance is an iron ore, commonly called magnetite, and is the familiar lodestone.

The behavior of the magnet is familiar to every one. It has a selective attraction for certain metals: namely, iron (and steel), nickel, and cobalt. A favorite child's toy is the brightly painted horseshoe-shaped magnet. This is a bar of hard steel which has been magnetized. If the magnet is covered with a piece of paper, and iron filings sprinkled on the paper, the filings will arrange themselves as shown in Figure 1-8A. The pattern formed by the iron filings shows the shape and extent of the magnetic influence.

This is called a magnetic *field,* or *flux,* and may be seen to consist of lines stretching from one end of the magnet to the other.

The ends of the magnet are called *poles.* The earth itself is a huge magnet, its magnetic and geographic poles being in the same vicinity. A magnet, delicately suspended, will align itself on

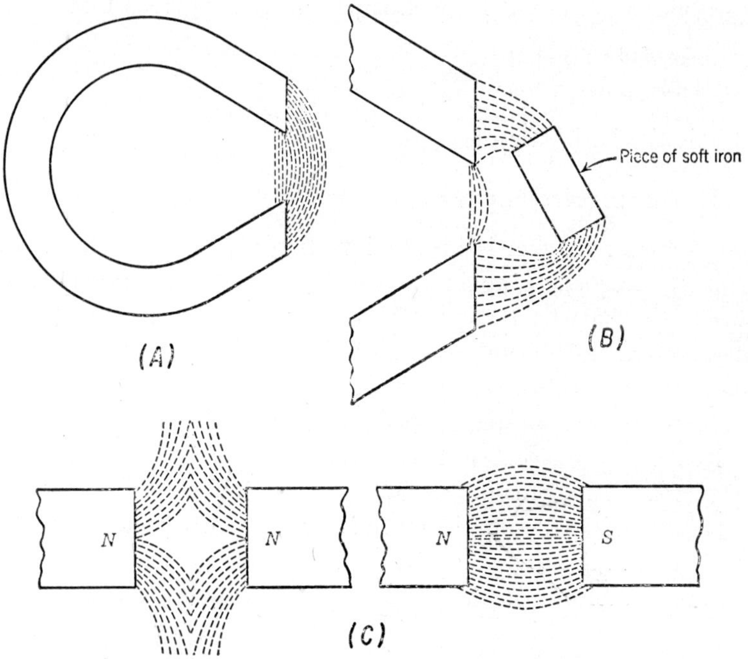


Fig. 1-8.

a line between the earth's magnetic poles; it then becomes a *compass.* The pole of the magnet which points north is called its north pole. The lines of magnetic flux emanate from the north pole of the magnet and enter the south pole of the magnet.

The magnetic materials (iron, cobalt, nickel) offer an easy path for the magnetic flux, much more so than air. Consequently, when a piece of magnetic metal is placed near a bar magnet, the lines of flux from the magnet become distorted, as shown in

Figure 1-8B, so as to pass through this easy path. However, the magnetic lines of flux behave much like stretched rubber bands in that they will try to shorten themselves if possible. As a result, the piece of metal is drawn toward the magnet.

Figure 1-8C shows the fields resultant from placing together the like poles of two magnets, and the field of two unlike poles when placed adjacent. From this pattern it is obvious that

**Like poles repel.**
**Unlike poles attract.**

This is the basic law of magnetism.

## 1.12. The Electromagnet

If a bar magnet is broken into two pieces, each piece will remain a magnet. If, again, the smaller magnets are broken, each piece will behave as a magnet. If this process is carried to its ultimate extreme, the smallest particle into which the bar could be broken would still be a magnet. The smallest particle of any substance which retains the properties of that substance is called a molecule. The molecules of the steel bar forming the permanent magnet are small magnets. The combined effect of all of these small magnets makes up the much stronger bar magnet.

Because the molecules of any bar of iron or steel are magnets, each molecule has a north and a south pole. Normally, the molecules are not in any particular arrangement with respect to one another, and the magnetism of the molecule is not apparent. When, however, the bar is magnetized, the north poles of all the molecules point in one direction; the south poles point the opposite way. Thus the combined effect of all the molecules in the bar constitutes a strong magnet.

A magnetic field exists around a wire carrying a current as indicated by holding a pocket compass above or below it. (Fig. 1-9A.) The small magnet that is the compass needle will align itself with the direction of the magnetic flux around the wire. Figure 1-9B shows that the direction of this magnetic flux depends upon the direction of the current flow. Figure 1-9C illustrates a simple rule for determining the direction of the magnetic flux around a wire if the direction of current flow is known.

> Grasp the wire with the left hand, the thumb pointing in the direction of electron flow. The fingers will then point in the direction of the magnetic flux.

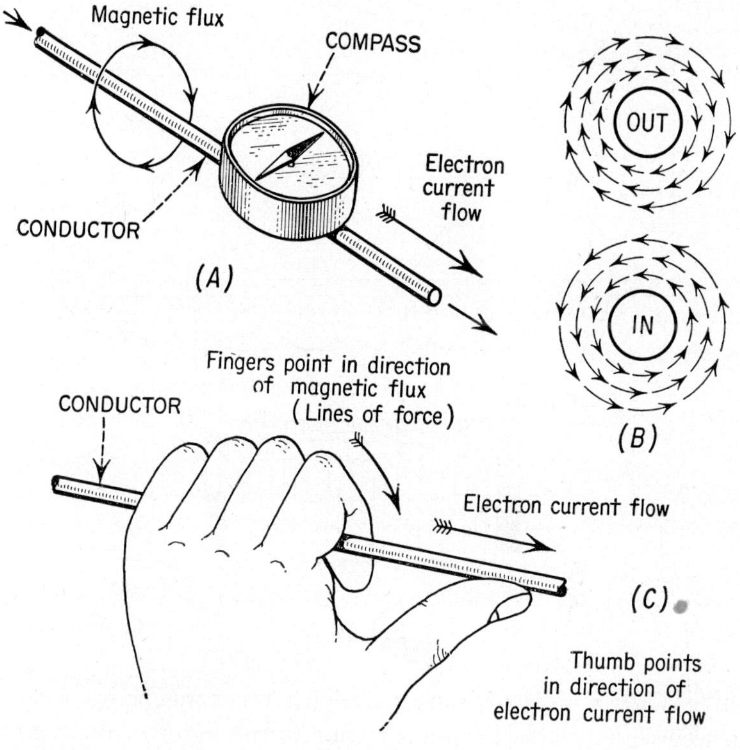


FIG. 1-9.

Now, if a wire is formed into a coil (Fig. 1-10) and connected to a source of voltage, the current flow through the individual turns of the coil will produce a magnetic field, as shown. This composite flux is seen to emanate from one end of the coil and enter the other. Because of this, the coil behaves in the same manner as a permanent magnet, and attracts magnetic materials.

The strength of the magnetic flux produced by the coil is directly proportional to the current flow through the coil; that is, if the current is doubled, the magnetic "pull" of the coil will be doubled. This is a *solenoid.*

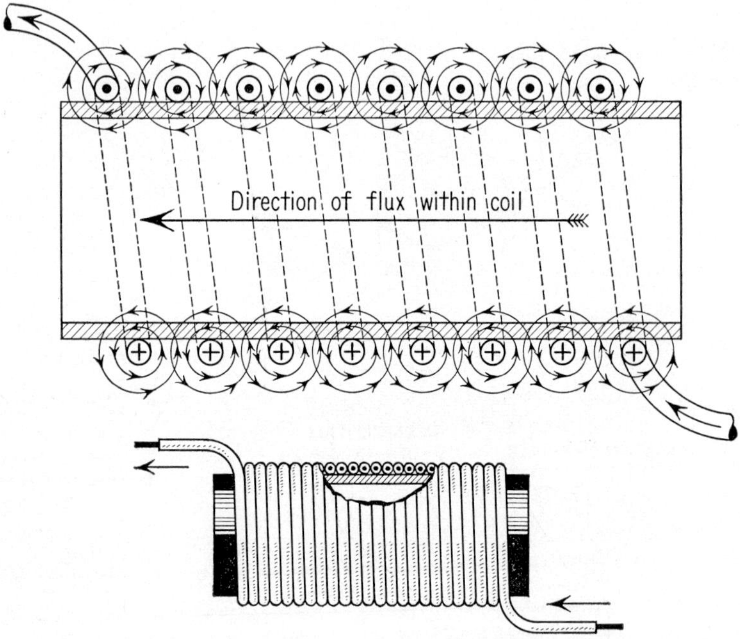


FIG. 1-10

When a piece of iron or steel (or other magnetic metal) is placed within the coil and a current sent through the coil, the flux lines within the coil will cause the molecules of the metal to align themselves with north poles in the same direction, and the south poles combine their effect in the other direction. The metal piece in this condition is a magnet. Because of the very nature of the metal itself, the molecules of a hard steel bar will retain their magnetic alignment when the current is interrupted. Therefore, hard steel is used for permanent magnets. The same is not true of soft iron. As long as the current flows through the surrounding coil, the soft iron piece will be a magnet. When the current ceases, the molecules of the soft iron bar become rearranged to their former nonmagnetic state.

The soft iron bar with a coil surrounding it is called an electromagnet (Fig. 1-11). As the name implies, the iron bar is a magnet only when the current is flowing through the coil. Perhaps the most common example of the use of an electromagnet is the familiar doorbell. When the bell button is depressed, it com-

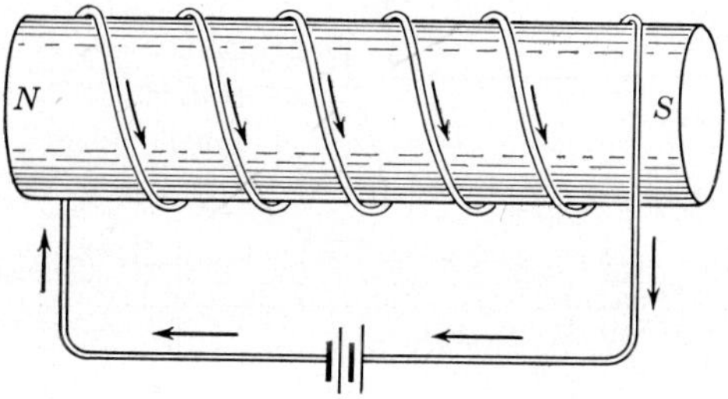


FIG. 1-11.

pletes the circuit through the doorbell electromagnet. The electromagnet draws the iron bar to which is attached the bell clapper. The circuit is broken by the motion of the bar toward the magnet; the resulting vibration of the bar, "making" and "breaking" the circuit, produces a continuous ringing of the bell.

Every motor contains one or more electromagnets. The field piece and armature core are soft iron through which the field coils and armature windings form electromagnets. The interaction of these electromagnets causes the motor to rotate when connected to a source of current.

## 1.13. The Generator

Electricity is a form of energy. It can be obtained only through the expenditure of some other form of energy. The dry cell converts chemical energy into electrical energy. The generator produces electricity from the mechanical energy of its prime mover. Electricity also may be obtained from light energy (photoelectric cell), heat energy (thermocouple), or from the pressure or torsional force applied to certain chemical salts (piezo-electric crystal). The electricity which operates appliances is obtained from the generator.

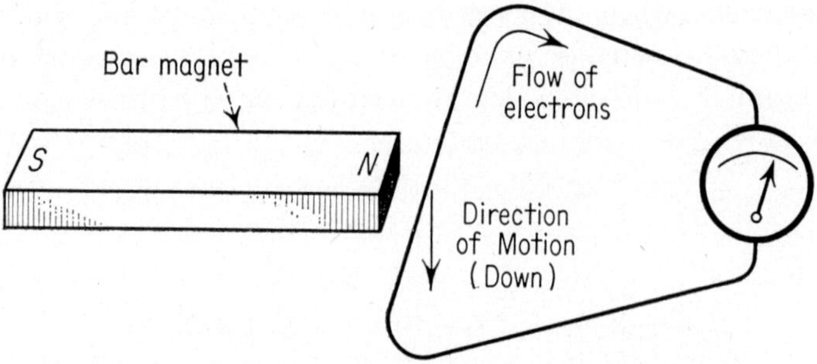


FIG. 1-12. Electromagnetic Induction. If the conductor is passed through the field of the magnet, a current will flow through the conductor.

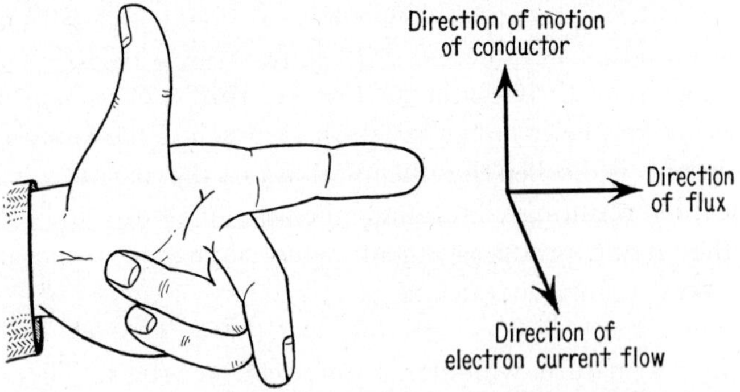


FIG. 1-13

The electromagnet produces magnetism from electricity. The generator produces electricity from magnetism. If a wire is moved through the field of a magnet, a voltage will be *induced* across the terminals of a wire; and if a complete circuit is provided, current will flow through the wire. This is electricity by induction. The presence of an induced voltage may be easily demonstrated by connecting the ends of a wire to a sensitive meter (galvanometer) and swinging the wire past a magnet pole. A deflection of the meter needle indicates the presence of a current through the meter (Fig. 1-13).

In accordance with Ohm's law, the amount of current flow depends upon the resistance in the circuit and the voltage of the circuit. The magnitude of the induced voltage depends upon the rate of speed at which the wire moves and the number of series conductors cutting through the magnetic flux. Thus, if a coil of many turns is moved past the magnet pole (or the magnet plunged into the center of the coil), the voltage generated will be greater than with the single conductor.

The direction of the current thus produced depends upon the relationship between the direction of the motion of the conductor and the polarity of the magnet. Moving a wire downward past a north pole produces a current flow in one direction; moving the wire upward past the same north pole will cause current to flow in the opposite direction through the conductor. Alternately, moving the conductor downward past a north pole produces a current flow in one direction; moving the wire downward past a south pole results in a current flow in the opposite direction. Fleming's rule, also called the left-hand rule for generated voltages, provides a method for determining the direction of current flow, direction of motion of conductor, or direction of flux if only two of these factors are known. It is, as illustrated in Figure 1-12:

> With the left hand extended so that the thumb, index finger, and middle finger are all at right angles to one another, point the thumb in the direction of the motion of the conductor, and the index finger in the direction of the magnetic flux (from north to south poles). The middle finger will then point in the direction of the induced electron flow.

This is the principle of the operation of the electric generator.

Notice that in the foregoing rule the words "motion of the conductor" are underscored. It is not absolutely necessary to move the conductor to produce the induced voltage. The magnet pole may be moved instead, and the result will be the same. It is the *relative motion* between conductor and flux that produces the current generated. This fact must be considered when applying the left-hand rule, and the thumb pointed in the direction of the equivalent motion of the conductor. For example, if the wire is stationary, and the magnet pole moved upward, the thumb will indicate the equivalent motion of the conductor as downward.

Figure 1-14 illustrates the fundamental generator. It consists of two magnet poles (produced by electromagnets) and a single loop of wire rotated past the poles. The source of motion may be an engine, turbine, or any device producing rotary motion. As one half the loop moves past the north pole, the other half tra-

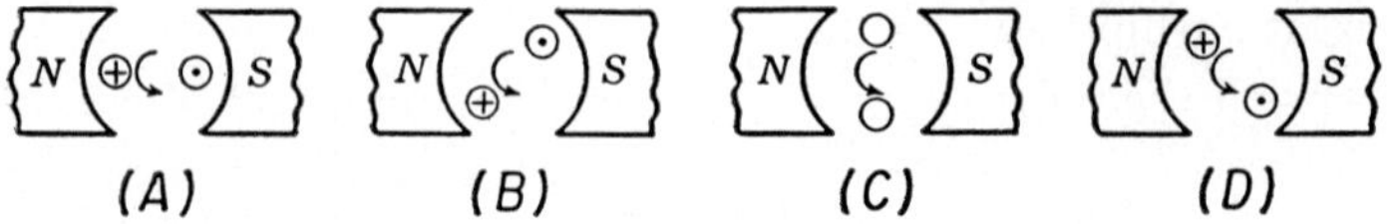


FIG. 1-14.

verses the magnetic flux of the opposite south pole. The generator rule applied here will indicate the direction of the current in each half of the coil. It will be seen that the current directions are such as to be aiding, not opposing, in the entire loop. Slip rings and a load complete the circuit of this generator. In practice, a portion of this current may be used to supply the coils of the electromagnet poles.

As the generator coil continues its rotation, the conductor will assume a position where the lines of flux are no longer cut through but are paralleled by the motion of the conductor (Fig. 1-14C). The principle of induced currents applies only when the conductor actually cuts through lines of magnetic flux, and at this point of rotation there will be no voltage generated; no current flowing. The left-hand rule just won't work when applied to this situation, as it is impossible to have the thumb and forefinger at right angles and yet pointing in the same direction. As the coil side approaches this zero or neutral spot, the angle through which it cuts flux lines becomes progressively less than a right angle, the number of flux lines traversed fewer, and the generated voltage and current smaller in magnitude.

Past the neutral point, each coil side cuts through the field flux of a pole opposite to that through which it has just moved. Again applying the left-hand rule, it will be seen that the current flow through each coil side has now reversed; current flow through the external circuit is reversed.

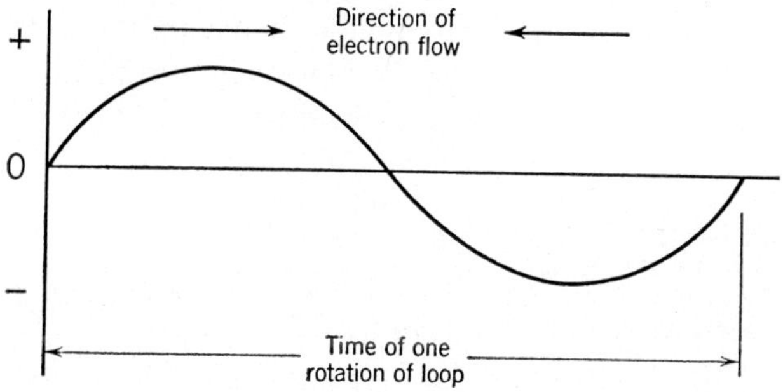


FIG. 1-15.

Figure 1-15 shows graphically the amplitude and direction of the current on the vertical axis; the time of one complete revolution of the rotating coil is plotted on the horizontal axis. This is the familiar "sine wave" associated with alternating current. The voltage varies from zero to a certain positive value, again through zero to a negative value and back again to zero. The current varies in like manner, the graph indicating that it goes first in one direction and then in the other. This series of events is called a *cycle*. Ordinary house current goes through 60 such cycles per second, and is said to have a *frequency* of 60 cps (cycles per second).

The basic generator is seen to produce alternating current. To make it produce a direct current, it is necessary to equip the rotating coil, or armature, with a reversing switch, designed to reverse the connection from the armature to the external circuit at exactly the instant that the current direction in the armature coil reverses, thus sending current in the same direction through the external circuit at all times. Such a reversing switch is called a commutator. As a general rule, a piece of electrical machinery operates from direct current if it is equipped with a commutator. Exceptions to this rule are the universal motor and the repulsion-induction motor.

The basic generator used as an illustration here contains two poles and one moving coil. A practical generator may contain many more than one pair of poles, and the armature consist of as many coils as is consistent with the design of the slots in the armature. Larger machines are designed with a revolving electromagnet, and the wires into which the generated current is induced are wound in slots in the stationary member.

## 1.14. Alternating Current

The a-c voltage available in homes for use with electrical appliances is 120-v, 60-cycle. Referring to the sine wave graph of alternating current in Figure 1-16, the value representing 120 v

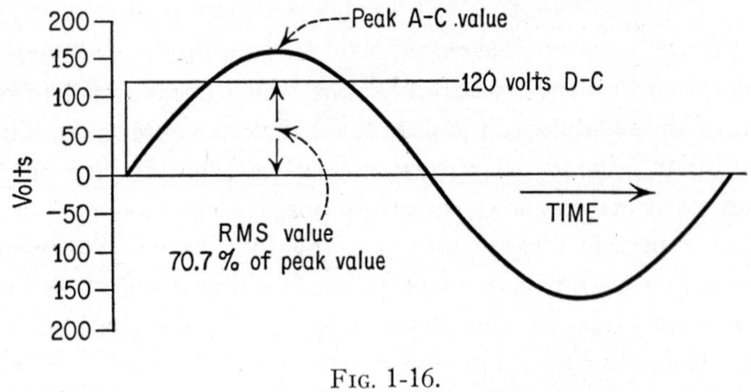


FIG. 1-16.

is not readily perceptible. A direct current graph of 120 v would have as its vertical plotted value 120 on a voltage scale. The same is not true of the a-c graph, as the value of the 120 v a-c is in excess of 120 v at its peak. Wherein, then, is the relationship between a-c and d-c of the same rated value?

If a lamp bulb is connected across 120 v a-c, it will glow just as brightly as on 120 v d-c. Your electric soldering iron produces just as much heat, in the same length of time, on a-c as on d-c. In fact, whenever a circuit contains a "resistive load"—one which produces only heat from electricity—the effect of a current is the same regardless of whether it is a-c or d-c. This is the basis of comparison of an alternating current and a direct current. 120 v is the *effective* value of the a-c voltage. It is also called the RMS value. RMS stands for "root, mean, square," an abbreviation of a mathematical method of proving the equivalence of the effective a-c voltage or current to the same d-c value.

Any appliance, then, which contains a heating element will operate just as well on d-c as on a-c. If, however, it is thermostatically controlled, the thermostat will last longer if a-c is applied. Motors, being a magnetic or inductive load, behave differently, some operating on a-c only, others on d-c. The a-c induction motor will be destroyed if connected across a d-c line.

An electromagnet will produce a flux if the coil is energized with a-c. Unlike that produced by d-c, this will be an alternating flux: that is, it will build up and collapse along with the alternating current producing it. Since this flux is in constant motion, it is constantly cutting through the wires forming the coil. Applying the left-hand rule, it is found that the current generated by this moving flux opposes the current producing the flux, or a voltage is generated whose polarity is opposite that of the applied voltage. This back voltage, more properly called the *counter emf,* subtracts from the applied voltage, leaving a smaller net voltage to force current through the coil. The result is a measurably smaller current flow through the coil from a-c than from d-c. The coil is said to "choke back" the current flow when a-c is applied. For purposes of calculation, the coil is considered as having acquired some additional *inductive* ohms. The combination of the resistance and the inductive ohms is called the *impedance* of the coil. Ohm's law, when applied to a-c circuits, states that the impedance

$$Z = \frac{E}{I}.$$

In addition to the properties thus far described, the inductive quality of a coil is such as to cause the current in the coil to lag behind the voltage. If the coil had no resistance, the current would lag 1/4 cycle (90 electrical degrees) behind the voltage. The presence of coil resistance reduces the amount of lag. The greater the resistance, the less the amount of lag. This factor is important in the operation of the split-phase motor.

## 1.15. Grounding

A motor, or switch, or other electrical fixture, will be provided with an arrangement for fastening it to the appliance which it serves. The fastening device is generally a bolt or rivet, either of which is a metallic electric conductor. Consequently, the electrical fitting is actually electrically connected to the appliance, and any voltage applied to the frame of the electrical fitting will also be applied to the frame of the appliance. The appliance is considered to be normally at the same voltage level as the earth itself, and is referred to as being at *ground potential.* The term "potential" is synonymous with voltage. Now, if some portion of the electrical circuit should come in contact with the metallic frame of the fixture in which it is contained—as, for example, when the insulation on a motor coil wears off and the wire touches the pole piece—the electrical part acquires the same voltage level as the wire touching it; or, if the fixture is actually connected to the earth by means of a wire intended for that purpose, the electrical circuit will, at the point of contact, assume ground potential.

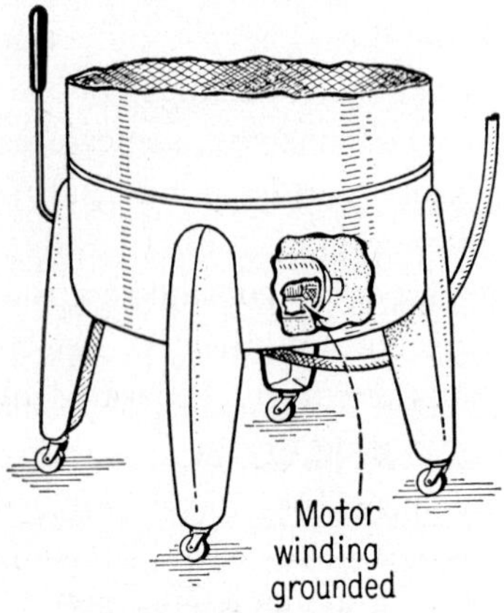


FIG. 1-17.

A case in point is shown in Figure 1-17. A washing machine, as shown, will often be used in a basement. If the floor is at all damp, it will be a good conductor to the ground. At the point marked in Figure 1-17 there is a defect in the motor winding, which makes contact with the motor frame. The motor is said to be grounded. If (as is the case in most systems) one of the house wires is also grounded, a portion of the motor winding will be shorted out. Another possibility, especially on the newer type of washing machine with rubber casters which insulate the machine from the floor, is that the operator of the machine, being at ground potential, will receive a severe shock when she touches the machine or even the water contained in its tub.

Unintended "grounds" are dangerous, then, both physically and electrically, and should be repaired whenever found. In Chapter 2 is shown a test instrument which will give evidence of the existence of such grounds.

## 1.16. Filtering

Everyone has observed how some appliances—especially those equipped with a motor—cause interference with radio and TV reception. The spark that occurs when a switch opens, or the sparking at motor brushes, is the cause of this interference, for the radiation created by an electric spark or arc is of the same nature as radio waves. Now that radio and TV have come into universal popularity this problem of interference has received much attention, with the result that methods have been developed to combat the nuisance of interference (more technically, man-made static). A device known as a filter is placed in the electric circuit of the offending appliance. There are many types of filters—almost as many types as there are types of appliances: some with intricate circuits, others with circuits that are relatively simple. The basis of the filtering is the application of the properties of an electric device called the *capacitor*. It is also often referred to—though incorrectly—as a condenser. A capacitor of the type used for static elimination is shown in Figure 1-18. It is made of two metal foil strips separated by a thin layer of some insulating material, usually paper, and rolled up into a tubular shape. A lead wire is attached to each foil strip, and brought out, one at each end. From an electrical standpoint this is an open circuit, for the paper insulation is between the foil strips at all points where they might otherwise touch.

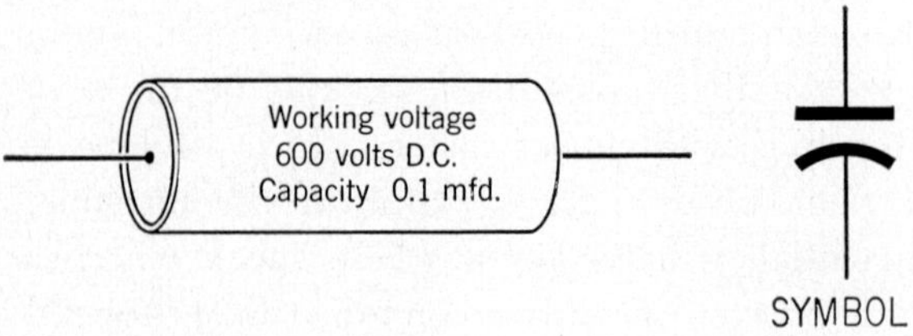


FIG. 1-18.

The capacitor has the electrical quality of being capable of holding a quantity of electricity. The quantity is proportional to the size and rating of the capacitor.* Since it can hold an electric charge, a current will necessarily flow in the circuit of the capacitor for the brief length of time it is charging (Fig. 1-19).

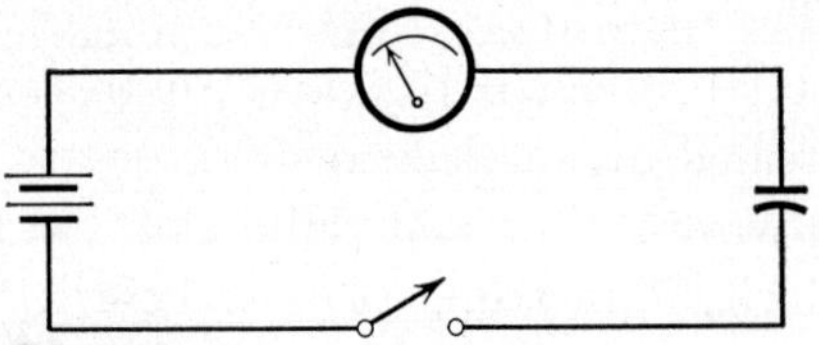

FIG. 1-19.

Therefore, although the capacitor does not complete the circuit in which it is located, it does permit a brief moment of current flow in that circuit. Now, look at Figure 1-20. Here is shown a capacitor connected across the terminals of a switch. With the switch closed, the capacitor is short-circuited, and has no charge, but when the switch opens there is a voltage across the switch terminals and a tendency to spark. The capacitor, however, keeps current flowing for a brief instant while it is charging, reducing the severity of the arc at the switch terminals, and meanwhile

*For a complete explanation of capacitor behavior, see any electrical textbook.

absorbs and eliminates radio interference. When used on a motor with arcing brushes, the capacitor is connected from brush to brush, as shown in Figure 1-21, where it acts as a momentary short circuit to the arcing as it occurs.

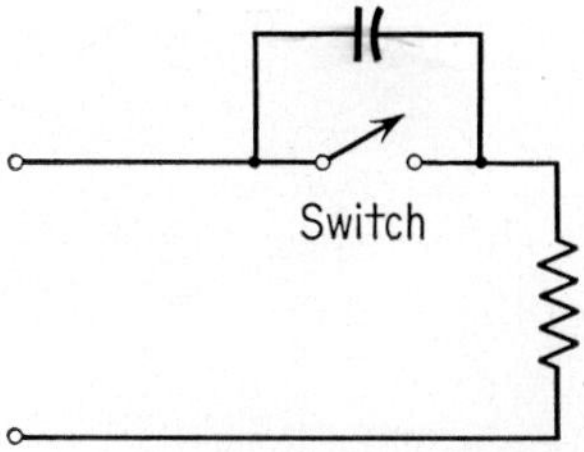


The capacitor reduces the severity of the arc when the switch is opened

FIG. 1-20.

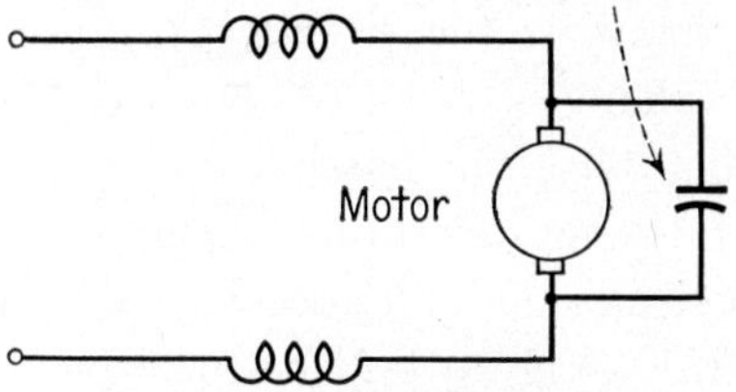


The capacitor eliminates radio interference produced by arcing motor brushes

FIG. 1-21.

The unit of measurement of capacity is the *farad*. This is much too large a unit with respect to the size of the capacitor itself, so a smaller unit representing a millionth of a farad, the *microfarad*, is used. It is abbreviated as mf. or μf. The values encountered in appliances range between 0.01 μf and 1 μf.

## Now that you have read this chapter, can you answer these questions?

**1.** What is the purpose of an insulator?

**2.** Which material would be the better insulator for the lead wires in an electric heater, cloth or asbestos? Why?

**3.** Is the filament of a lamp a conductor, a resistor, or an insulator? Explain.

**4.** Is it true that absolutely no current can flow through an insulator? Explain.

**5.** A 10-inch length of nichrome wire has a resistance of 1 ohm. A 600-inch length of copper wire of the same size has the same resistance. Why is the nichrome wire used as a heating element rather than the copper wire?

**6.** Why do you think it important that an appliance man commit Ohm's law to memory?

**7.** How can it be determined that a wire of too small a size is being used on an appliance?

**8.** An electric fan and a radio are plugged into the same outlet. Are the appliances in series or in parallel?

**9.** When a wall switch is flipped so as to turn off the lights in a room, is the circuit resistance being increased or decreased? Explain.

**10.** Why is it possible for an electric shock to be fatal?

**11.** What determines the upper limit of the wattage that an appliance can be built to consume?

**12.** In Figure 1-21, if the capacitor shown were internally short-circuited, what would be the effect, if any, on the motor operation?

**13.** What precaution should be taken when working on an appliance to avoid an electric shock?

**14.** Why should not a fuse be replaced with one of a higher ampere rating?

**15.** If a length of resistance wire 1/16-inch thick is replaced with an equal length 1/32-inch thick, will the resistance be decreased or increased, and to what extent?

**16.** It says on the name plate of a toaster that it draws 10 amp when used on a 120-v circuit. The burned-out heating element should be replaced with one of what resistance?

**17.** Will a 1,000-w, 120-v iron draw enough current to blow out a 10-amp fuse?

**18.** An automatic toaster contains three parallel heating elements. The outer two elements are 60 ohms each, and the center element is 30 ohms. What is the total resistance?

**19.** On which will a toaster produce a greater amount of heat, a-c or d-c?

**20.** On which will a doorbell ring louder, a-c or d-c? Why?

*chapter* **2**

# Test Instruments

The first step in servicing an appliance is to disconnect it from its source of power. The second step is a process of elimination: a series of tests to determine which part of the appliance is the source of trouble. Mechanical troubles disclose themselves by

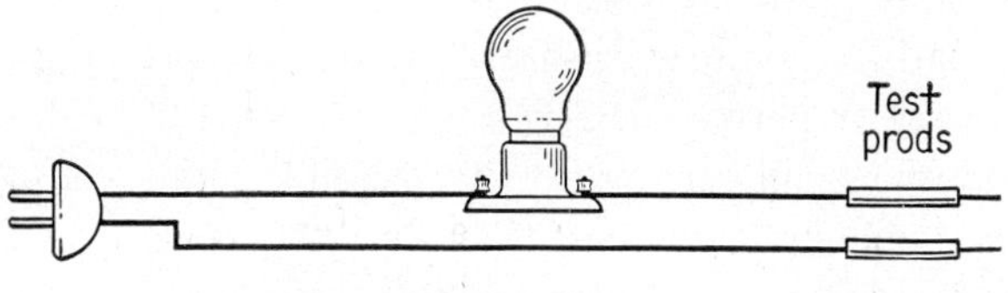


FIG. 2-1.

noisy operation, or an inoperative part. Electrical troubles are a bit more difficult to isolate. A most convenient device for tracing electrical circuits is the series test lamp, which is pictured in Figure 2-1.

## 2.1. Series Test Lamp

The series test lamp can be conveniently assembled from parts obtainable from any hardware store. Observe that it consists of a length of attachment cord with a lamp bulb in series, and two test prods which, when touched together, will behave as a switch to turn the lamp on. In fact, any time a conducting material is placed between the test prod ends, the lamp will burn. In Chapter 1 it was specifically stated that an electric circuit, in order to operate, must be complete. The electric circuit of any appliance may be checked for completeness, or, more properly, for *continuity,* by means of the test lamp. The test prods of the series are placed on the lugs extending from the attachment plug of the appliance being tested. If the series test lamp fails to burn, it is an indication of an open circuit. If the test lamp burns, the circuit is complete; however, it is possible to misinterpret this indication, since a short circuit is a complete circuit. If the appliance owner complains that it blows fuses, the test lamp will not provide evidence of the site of the trouble. Some appliances contain more than one circuit (ironer, range). The test lamp will aid in tracing the various circuits in these appliances. Each circuit, however, should be temporarily disconnected from all others while checking for continuity, since, if an open circuit is paralleled by another circuit which is complete, the combination will test continuous.

A small-size bulb works best in a series test lamp. One of 10-w or less, or perhaps a 2-w neon bulb, will provide a usable glow from the small current flow that results from testing a high-resistance appliance, whereas a larger wattage lamp will remain dark. Furthermore, the high-wattage lamp may allow enough current flow to operate the appliance being tested, which is not only a nuisance but may be dangerous, as for example an electric fan whose blades unexpectedly begin to spin while the motor winding is being checked for continuity.

The series test lamp may be used for testing an attachment cord as follows.

> Remove the cord from the appliance. Place the test prods of the series test lamp on the terminals of the plug cap of the cord under test. If the lamp glows, the cord has an internal short.
>
> Next, at the end of the cord formerly attached to the appli-

ance, connect the two wires together. Use the series test lamp at the plug cap as before. If the lamp fails to glow, the cord has a break, or is open-circuited.

## 2.2. Appliance Tester



In the pages that follow, repeated reference is made to the use of the apparatus whose picture and circuit are illustrated in Figure 2-2. We will refer to it as the *appliance tester.* Its purpose

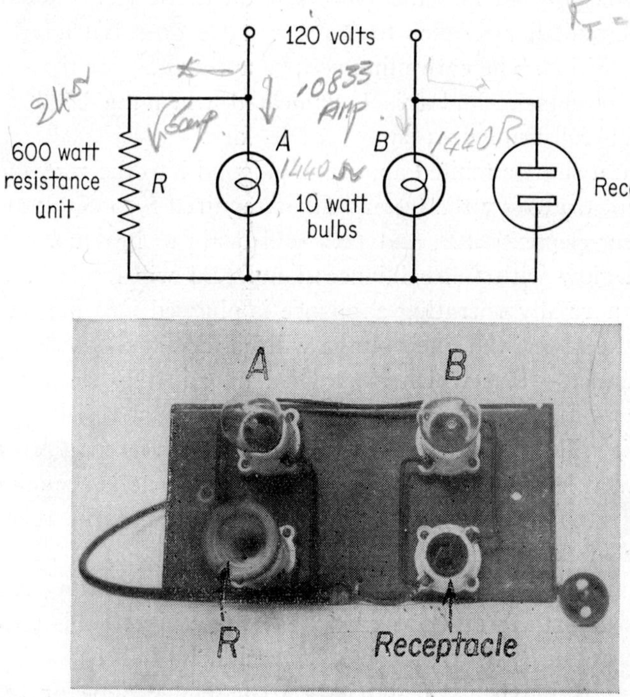


FIG. 2-2.

is to provide an instrument which will reveal the general condition of the appliance under test, and act as a guide in servicing procedure. Obviously, one could plug in an appliance and observe whether it blows a fuse, burns up, runs normally, or does nothing—but this would be a rather crude form of testing! The appliance tester will provide as much, and more, information, without damage to fuse or appliance. An examination of the circuit will show just how it performs.

Consider the circuit as consisting of resistance unit and receptacle only, in series across the a-c line. The two 10-w lamps draw so little current as hardly to disturb the series behavior of the circuit, and actually serve to indicate the voltage distribution across the 600-w heating element acting as a resistance unit and whatever is plugged into the receptacle on the tester. Attaching an open-circuited appliance to the receptacle does not alter the circuit condition. The entire line voltage appears across the open-circuited receptacle, and this is indicated when the lamp (B) glows with full brilliance; lamp (A) is dark.

With a short-circuited appliance plugged into the receptacle, the current drawn by the tester is that required for operation of the heating element (R), and (R) will begin to heat up. Lamp (A) will glow with full brilliance; lamp (B) will be dark.

If a normally operating appliance is plugged into the receptacle of the tester, the line voltage will be distributed across the two appliances—that which is plugged in, and the heating element (R)—in direct proportion to the individual resistance of each. This will be evidenced by the fact that both lamps (A) and (B) glow at less than full brilliance. In fact, if one is acquainted with the rated wattage of the appliance under test, the relative brilliance of the lamps can be taken as an indication of whether the appliance under test is operating at its correct wattage.

It is difficult to describe adequately the utility of this tester; the more one uses it, the more information its indications give. The tester is inexpensive and easy to assemble. One or more should be assembled by every appliance repair man for servicing convenience.

## 2.3. Meters

Although it is possible to make a number of tests on appliances with equipment of the type already described, these are but approximations. In many instances this is adequate. Occasionally, however, faulty appliance operation may be due to improper voltage and current, and it will then become necessary to measure these quantities. It will also be shown that a direct reading meter for measuring resistance is practical for use with appliances.

Meters are expensive and delicate instruments. In the hands of the inexperienced they can easily be destroyed. A knowledge of why an instrument operates enables the user to exercise the care necessary to insure its safety.

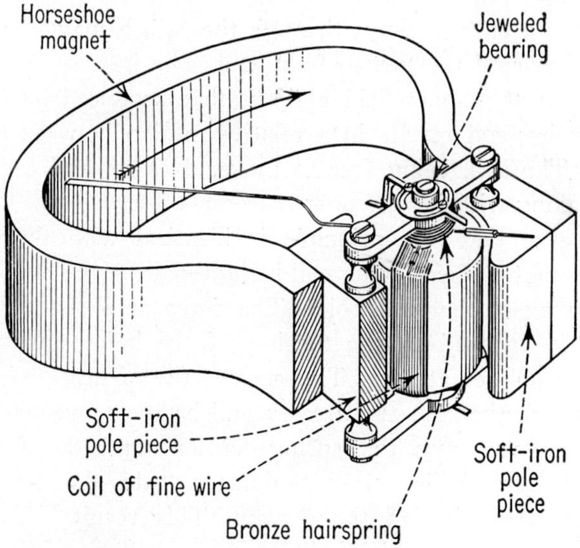


FIG. 2-3. (Courtesy, Weston Electrical Instrument Corporation)

## 2.4. Moving-Coil Mechanism

Fundamentally, the moving-coil meter operates on the same principle as the universal motor. Upon examination of the movement (Fig. 2-3) it will be seen that it contains a horseshoe magnet to which are attached two curved soft-iron pieces. Within the curved faces of the soft-iron pieces is a coil of fine wire, wound on a rectangular aluminum form and suspended by jeweled bearings. The coil is free to move through an arc of about 90°. A bronze hairspring is attached to either end of the coil assembly, and adjusted so as to hold the coil and an attached aluminum pointer at some one spot (zero on the meter scale). The springs also act as conductors to carry the current to be measured into the wire of the coil. Within the moving coil is placed a cylinder of soft iron. The only gap in an otherwise complete magnetic path is the air space wherein the moving coil is located. Construction such as this produces a strong magnetic field within the air gap.

When a current flows through the coil, a magnetic field is produced around the turns of the coil. The interaction between the permanent magnet field and the flux produced by the current-carrying coil results in a relative motion between coil and magnet. The coil, being free to move, does so, and carries the pointer along with it.

Observe that this principle is identical with that of the universal motor, the moving coil being the armature and the permanent magnet the field poles. The force applied to the moving coil is opposed by the tension of the hairsprings holding the meter pointer at zero. The greater the quantity of current flow through the coil, the greater will be the movement of the coil as it overcomes the spring tension, and the farther it will carry the needle across the meter scale, the force being in direct proportion to the current. This results in a *linear* meter scale: one on which calibrated values are equally spaced.

Present-day meter magnets are quite strong, and coil movements extremely lightweight. The result is that a very small current is adequate to provide full-scale movement of the meter needle. Perhaps the most commonly used movement is the one that will, with 0.001 amp (1 ma) of current flowing through the coil, have *full-scale deflection:* that is, the needle will move all the way across the meter dial to its farthest calibration point. This is called a "one-milliampere movement," or, more familiarly, a "one-mil movement." It is also referred to as a "thousand-ohm-per-volt" movement. According to Ohm's law, 1,000 ohms per v is equivalent to 1 ma.

Meters are made which operate on much smaller current values; the most sensitive require but .00005 amp for full-scale deflection. The smaller the amount of current a meter requires for its operation, the less it will alter the conditions in a circuit into which it is placed; however, the more sensitive a meter is, the more easily it can be damaged by excess current. The 1,000-ohm-per-v movement is adequate for appliance-circuit measurements.

## 2.5. The Voltmeter

Assume that a one-mil-movement meter is to be used to measure the voltage of a 6-v battery. If the meter is placed directly across the battery terminals, current will flow through the meter coil in accordance with Ohm's law. The meter coil has very few turns of wire, and the average resistance of such a coil is about 40 ohms. The current flow would be 6 v/40Ω, or 0.15 amp. But only 0.001 amp is required to operate the meter; any current in excess of this value will break the mechanism or burn out the delicate coil. Now, if the meter had a resistance of 6,000 ohms, a 6-v battery would send but 1 ma through the coil. So the difference between the 40-ohm coil resistance and the required 6,000 ohms, or 5,960 ohms, is placed in series with the coil, and the needle moves to full scale with only 6 v applied. The series resistor is called a meter multiplier, and is usually mounted inside the meter case. Its value will, of course, depend upon the full-scale reading of the meter and its *basic sensitivity* (1,000 ohms per v in the example just given). The voltmeter is always placed in parallel with the voltage to be measured.

## 2.6. The Ammeter

The ammeter, an instrument to measure amperes of current, must be inserted in the circuit through which that current is flowing. In other words, it is placed in series with the appliance or other load being tested. Thus it is connected so that all the current to be measured must flow *through* it before it can get to the rest of the circuit. A d-c ammeter has polarity, and must be connected so that electron flow is into the negative terminal and out of the positive terminal.

As with the voltmeter, if a 1,000-ohm-per-v movement is used, any condition causing a current larger than 0.001 amp to flow will be detrimental to the meter. Yet some appliances draw as high as 10 amp. To permit measurement of these large current values, it is necessary to divert all the current but 0.001 amp around the meter. Thus, if a meter is to measure up to 10 amp, its scale will be marked as such, and in parallel with the meter coil will be placed a "shunt" resistance of such value so that 9.999 amperes go through the shunt and only 0.001 amp through the coil. The meter coil will then carry the needle to full scale: 10 amp.

The value of the shunt to be used can be calculated by the formula

$$\frac{\text{Current through meter coil}}{\text{Current through shunt}} = \frac{\text{Resistance of shunt}}{\text{Resistance of meter coil}}.$$

If the meter coil in the preceding example is 40 ohms, use of the formula will indicate the value of the shunt to be 0.004 ohms.

The direction of movement of the meter needle when used as described is determined by the direction in which the current is flowing through the moving coil. The meter terminals are marked plus and minus or positive and negative, and, if the polarity of the d-c voltage is known, connecting plus of the line to plus of the meter, and minus to minus, will result in proper deflection. If the circuit polarity is not known, a quick check in a temporary meter hookup will instantly show if the connections are correct. If the needle moves backward, instantly open the meter circuit and reverse the meter leads. This check should always be made on the highest scale of the meter to minimize the probability of damage to the meter.

## 2.7. A-C Meters

The nature of alternating current is such that it would, if allowed to flow through the meter movement, cause the needle to move first in one direction and then an equal distance the other way. Household a-c, being at a 60-cycle rate, is varying at a speed

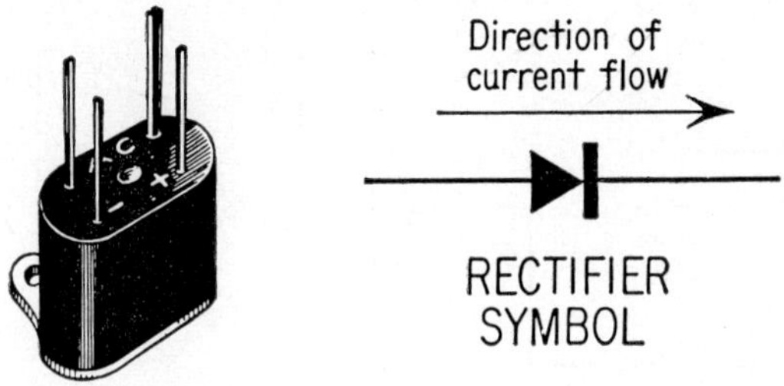


FIG. 2-4.

so rapid that the meter needle is unable to follow. Thus, if the meter is used to test a-c voltage or current, the result is no apparent movement of the needle.

The qualities of the moving-coil mechanism make it desirable to adapt it to measurement of a-c as well as d-c. To accomplish this, an auxiliary unit known as a rectifier is placed in series with the d-c movement to cause it to register when a-c is applied. The rectifier is a device which changes a-c to d-c. The type commonly used in meters is the copper-oxide rectifier. It consists of alternate disks of copper and copper oxide bolted together so as to assure good contact between the two materials. It is characteristic of this particular combination that current can flow from oxide to copper, but not in the reverse direction. Placed in an a-c circuit, the copper-oxide rectifier will allow a current flow on only one half of each a-c cycle. Current flow in one direction only is direct current, yet the rectified a-c does not have the steady quality of the d-c obtained from a battery. To distinguish between the two, rectified a-c is called *pulsating d-c*.

Pulsating d-c will cause a moving coil meter to respond with a movement of the needle proportional to the average value of the peaks of pulsating d-c. Thus, the greater the value of a-c, the farther the needle will swing across scale. Of course, the meter must be calibrated so as to compensate for the loss during the

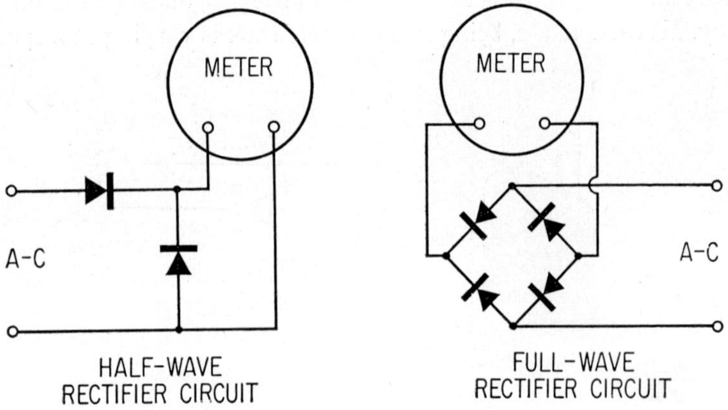


Fig. 2-5.

portion of the a-c cycle when the rectifier allows no current flow. The use of four rectifiers in a *bridge circuit* makes available both halves of the a-c cycle for measurement, with an improvement of the meter sensitivity. The direction of current flow through the meter depends upon how the rectifier is connected to the movement, so it is not necessary to observe polarity when connecting the a-c meter in the circuit (Fig. 2-5).

## 2.8. Moving-Vane Meters

The following experiment will vividly demonstrate the principle of the moving-vane meter. Within the core of a solenoid place two rectangles of thin transformer iron arranged so that one covers the other. Apply a current (either a-c or d-c) to the coil. The two pieces will fly apart and remain so until the current is interrupted.

When current flows through the coil, it magnetizes the two pieces of iron. The magnetic polarity of both pieces will be identical. Since the same end of each is a north pole and the other a

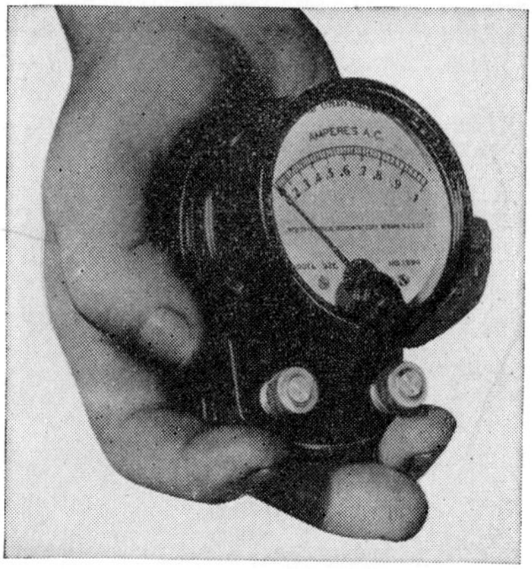

FIG. 2-6A. FIG. 2-6B.
(Courtesy, Weston Electrical Instrument Corporation)

south, the like poles will repel each other with a force dependent upon the amount of current and the number of turns of the coil.

When used in a meter, the coil carries the current to be measured. Within the coil one piece of iron is fastened in place, the other pivoted so as to move against the force of a hairspring when repelled by the first. To the *moving vane* is attached a pointer; a calibrated scale completes the meter. The voltmeter has a coil with many turns of a fine wire in order that it may draw very little current from the voltage source being measured. The ammeter has a very few turns of heavy wire which can adequately handle the current being measured without damage or

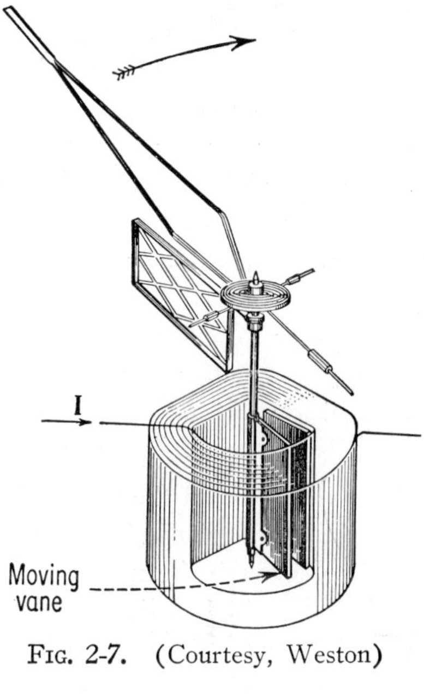


FIG. 2-7. (Courtesy, Weston)

overheating. The moving-vane mechanism will function with either a-c or d-c applied; therefore, no rectifier is needed.

The force with which the magnetized iron vanes repel each other depends upon the square of the distance they are separated. This results in a meter whose gradations are not evenly spaced; a nonlinear scale, it is called. The moving-vane meter is less sensitive than the moving-coil type, and in general is less expensive.

## 2.9. The Ohmmeter

Either the moving-coil or moving-vane movement may be used in the ohmmeter. To measure resistance it is necessary that a current be sent through that resistance, and its effect in limiting that current be measured by a meter movement. Thus, the ohmmeter contains its own source of current, a battery.

Assume that an ohmmeter is to be constructed with a 1,000-ohm-per-v moving-coil mechanism, and a single flashlight cell providing 1.5 v. The lowest value of resistance which will ever be measured is approximately zero ohms. This resistance value (short circuit) placed across the test leads of the meter will permit maximum current flow from the self-contained battery through the meter. As a 1-ma movement is being used, maximum current must not exceed that value. A 1.5-v battery will deliver 1 ma to a circuit of 1,500 ohms. To the coil resistance must be added a resistor whose value will bring the total circuit resistance to 1,500 ohms. A variable resistor whose maximum value is 1,500 ohms is mounted within the meter housing. The use of a variable resistor allows an adjustment to be made that will compensate for the reduction of battery voltage with age and use. The knob on the meter panel which controls this variable resistor is labeled "zero set." When the meter test leads are connected to each other, the current flow is just enough to cause full-scale deflection. This spot on the meter dial is calibrated zero. An insulator (open circuit) placed between the test leads will cause no current to flow through the meter, and this needle position is calibrated as infinitely high resistance ( $\infty$ ). Finite resistance values, when placed between the test leads, will cause a needle deflection between the extremes of zero and infinity, and are calibrated as such. The completely calibrated dial will appear as in Figure 2-8.

*This is important:* The ohmmeter battery supplies the right amount of current for meter operation; any excess current will damage the meter. *Never use the ohmmeter on a live circuit.* Be sure that the appliance being tested is not plugged in.

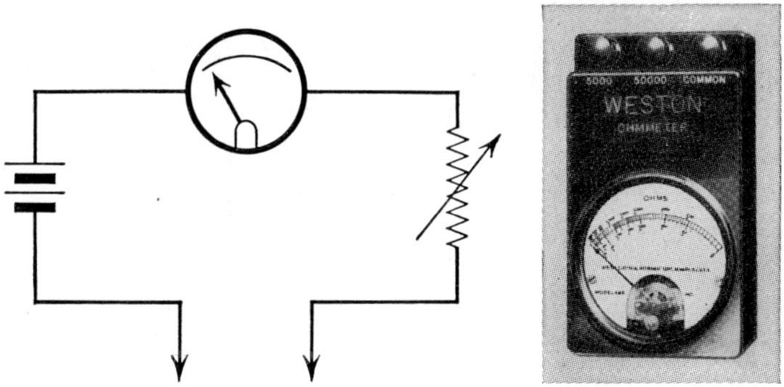


FIG. 2-8. (Courtesy, Weston Electrical Instrument Corporation)

The ohmmeter will detect open circuits, short circuits, and normal circuits with a high degree of accuracy. It will enable the user to distinguish between circuits whose resistance values differ by but a small amount, such as the starting and running windings of a split-phase motor. It may be used to test a capacitor as described in Chapter 7.

## 2.10. The Voltmeter-Ammeter Tester

Whereas the ohmmeter will supply the necessary information concerning the quality of the electric circuit of an appliance, it is often necessary to test the appliance while it is operating. For such tests the voltmeter and ammeter will supply the required information. Figure 2-9 shows a tester using these two instruments and into which the attachment cord can be conveniently plugged. The voltmeter range is 0–150 v and the ammeter has two scales: 0–3 amp, and 0–15 amp. An S.P.D.P. switch makes either ammeter range available. Fuses of the proper value have been placed in the ammeter circuits to prevent damage to the meter from overloads or short circuits. From the readings of the two meters can be determined the resistance of the appliance: $R = E/I$. The wattage, $P = EI$, can be compared with that stamped on the appliance name plate. An appliance with a thermostat can be checked, since the ammeter needle will swing back to

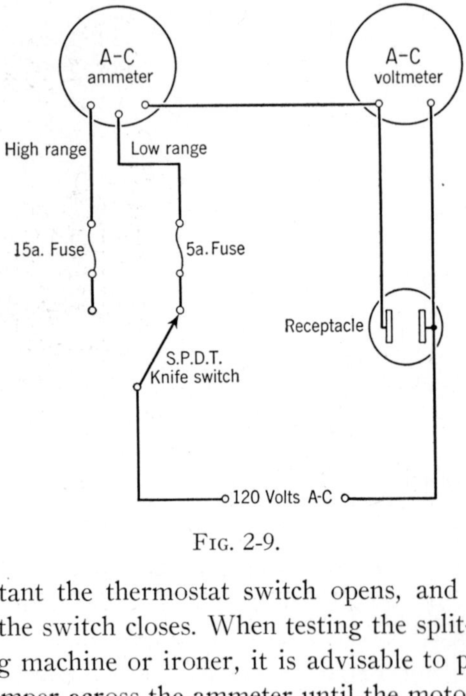


FIG. 2-9.

zero the instant the thermostat switch opens, and will register again when the switch closes. When testing the split-phase motor of a washing machine or ironer, it is advisable to place a short-circuiting jumper across the ammeter until the motor reaches full speed; the starting current of this motor may be in excess of the higher meter range. As a precaution, the appliance should be tested with an ohmmeter or test lamp to determine whether its condition is approximately normal, and the voltmeter and ammeter used only as a final check to compare the appliance operation with that listed on the name plate.

## 2.11. The Multimeter

An instrument which incorporates in one unit many of the meter functions mentioned in the preceding paragraphs is called a multimeter. A typical service man's portable multimeter is shown in Figure 2-10. The moving-coil mechanism is employed, usually with a basic sensitivity of 1,000, 5,000, or 20,000 ohms per v. In general, the greater the basic sensitivity figure, the more expensive is the instrument; however, the more expensive instrument is also more accurate and more delicate—that is, it is more likely to suffer damage from careless use. Usually the less sensitive instrument is adequate for appliance repairing.

FIG. 2-10. (Courtesy, Simpson Electric Co.)

The multimeter can be used as a voltmeter, a milliammeter, an ohmmeter, or as an output meter (for use in radio and TV servicing). These various scale types and ranges are obtained either by switching or by the use of several jacks on the front of the instrument. When a switch is used (Fig. 2-10), this switch connects into the circuit of the moving-coil multiplier, shunts, and batteries as needed. Also contained in the meter is a rectifier enabling the user to measure either a-c or d-c voltage. When several jacks are provided on the instrument, it is merely necessary to connect the test leads to the correct pair of jacks, and the instrument will function as indicated by the label beside the jacks.

Use of the instrument illustrated in Figure 2-10 is typical. One of the test leads is plugged into the terminals marked "common," located at the lower left side of the meter. The selector switch positions in the same vicinity are used when voltage is to be measured; the four switch positions allow a choice of voltage ranges of from 2.5 v to 1,000 v full-scale. The one most suitable for appliance work is the 250-v scale. The knob above the jacks should be placed in the a-c position. This connects the rectifier into the circuit, allowing use of the meter on a-c voltages.

The selector switch positions to the right of the knob are for resistance measurement. The same jacks are still used for the meter leads. The switch above the jacks is set on d-c. The test leads are touched together and the "zero ohms" knob is manipulated so that the meter needle is right on zero on the ohms scale. The instrument is now ready to be used for resistance measurement or continuity checking. The most convenient resistance range for appliances is the $R \times 1$ scale, in which the value of the resistance being measured is read directly on the meter dial.

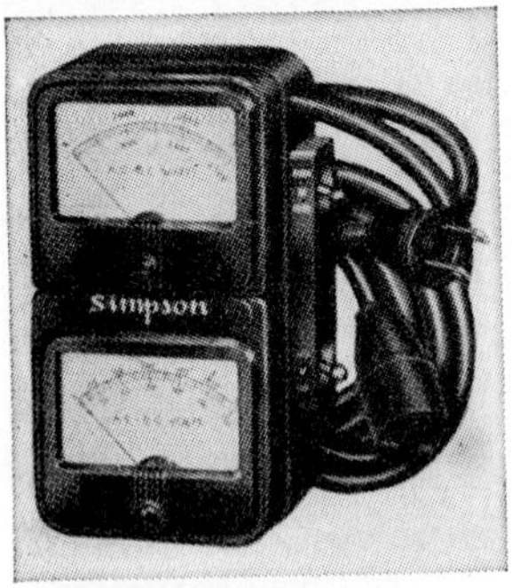

FIG. 2-11. (Courtesy, Simpson Electric Co.)

The other scales on the multimeter are used in fields other than electrical appliances (for example, in radio and TV servicing), and their performance need not be detailed here.

A multipurpose test instrument designed more particularly for appliance repair is the combination voltmeter-wattmeter shown in Figure 2-11. The appliance to be tested is plugged into a receptacle supplied with the meter, and the meter attachment cord plugged into the power line. Both voltmeter and wattmeter register, supplying the information necessary to determine whether the appliance is performing as it should. This instrument does not contain an ohmmeter, so continuity tests cannot be made with it.

## Now that you have read this chapter, can you answer these questions?

**1.** Describe the action of the moving-coil mechanism.

**2.** Describe the action of the moving-vane instrument.

**3.** Why will the moving-vane meter function on a-c without a rectifier?

**4.** Describe the action of a rectifier.

5. Why is the bridge-type rectifier superior to the simple half-wave rectifier?

6. What is meant by pulsating direct current?

7. Why is the moving-coil meter more sensitive than the moving-vane instrument?

8. Draw the circuit of a voltmeter and ammeter connected so as to measure the voltage and current of a universal motor.

9. What is a linear scale? A nonlinear scale?

10. Why does the moving-coil meter have a linear scale?

11. Why does not the moving-vane meter have a linear scale?

12. Although it contains a moving coil mechanism, an ohmmeter has a nonlinear scale. Can you explain why?

13. The ohmmeter's greatest accuracy is at mid-scale. Why would you imagine this to be so?

14. If the needle of a d-c voltmeter goes backward, the connections should be immediately reversed. Why is this unnecessary with the ohmmeter? Why is it unnecessary with an a-c meter?

15. What is meant by the basic sensitivity of a meter?

16. An 0–1-amp meter has 1 ohm of resistance. How would you extend its range to 10 amp? Give parts values.

17. A one-mil movement is used for a voltmeter. Its present range is 0–10 v. How would you extend its range to 1,000 v? Give parts values.

18. A toaster, plugged into the tester of Figure 2-9, draws 5 amp. The voltmeter registers 120. What is the resistance of the appliance? What is its wattage?

*chapter* **3**

# Tools and Wiring Problems

The problems encountered in servicing appliances are both mechanical and electrical in nature. Some problems are characteristic of an individual appliance, while others will pertain to many appliances. It is the latter type with which this chapter is concerned.

## 3.1. Attachment Cords and Plugs

Every appliance is fitted with a cord and plug cap. Repair and replacement of this cord set is one of the jobs most frequently encountered in the appliance shop. Although it is a simple task mechanically and electrically, the appliance man should nevertheless take pains to do it right. The very fact that this job is generally considered to require little skill is the reason why so many cord-set repairs indicate poor workmanship and are unsafe electrically.

Four cord types are used on appliances. They are shown in Figure 3-1. The first is type POSJ. This is the familiar small-size rubber-covered appliance wire. It is to be found on all appliances with a low-wattage rating. This includes table lamps, radios, small motor appliances (such as electric shavers), and desk fans.

Larger appliances are equipped with type SJ wire. This is a heavy-duty cord that will be found on washing machines, exhaust fans, mixers, and, in a smaller-diameter cord designated as SV, on vacuum cleaners.

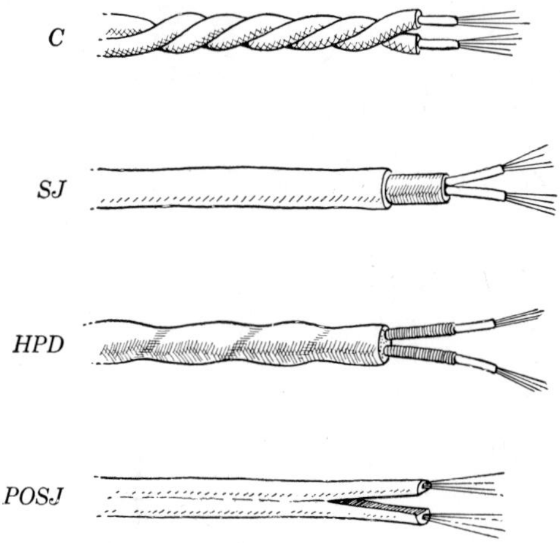


FIG. 3-1.

Any appliance containing a heating element is fitted with type HPD wire. This cord consists of a twin conductor, each conductor covered with a thin (and consequently fragile) layer of rubber insulation. This is surrounded by a liberal layer of asbestos, and the entire assembly is held together by a woven outer covering. Because of the large current requirements of the appliance with a heating element, and resultant heating of the appliance cord, asbestos insulation is ideally suited to this application.

An old favorite with repair men and appliance owners alike (except for use with heating appliances) is type C. This cord is quite rugged, and also easy to work with. All this, added to its reasonable cost and availability, makes it a cord that is popular as a replacement on any of the foregoing types except heating appliances, where it must never be used because of the rapid deterioration of its insulation due to heating of the conductor.

In all cases, the cord on an appliance should be replaced with the type *originally intended for that appliance.* Defective cords should be replaced, not repaired. A cord that has been subjected to wear or deterioration will, if patched, soon develop new breaks.

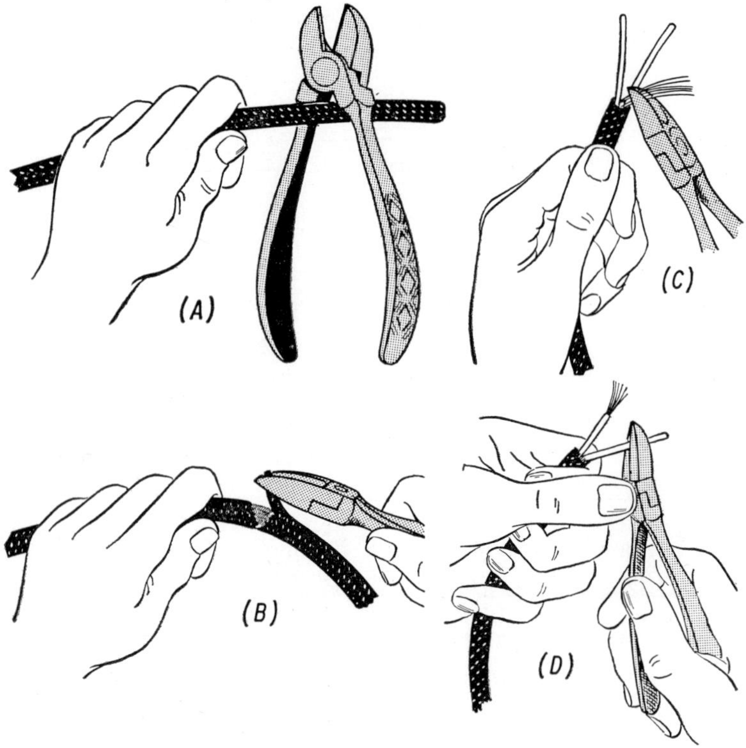


FIG. 3-2.

Furthermore, cord is inexpensive, and a new one is a wise investment in safety.

Experience has proved that the fastest and neatest way to prepare the ends of a length of cord is by the use of diagonals, or side-cutting pliers, rather than a knife. Figure 3-2 shows the steps in removing the insulation from the wire ends.

In Figure 3-2A the end of a length of SJ wire is placed within the back edge of the diagonals, and the outer covering crushed lightly from the end back about 2 inches. Figure 3-2B shows the "V" of the diagonals cutting away the outer rubber cover of this cord. Next, the cord filler is snipped off where it extends out of the insulation (Fig. 3-2C). Last, the cutting edges of the diagonals are placed on the individual conductors' rubber covering, and, by use of a light pressure, this rubber covering is torn away (not cut) and slipped off the end of the stranded conductor. The cord is now ready to be attached to plug cap or appliance terminals.

The other cord types are processed in a similar manner. Types POSJ and C will not require the step shown in Figures 3-2A and 3-2B. To remove the outer covering from type HPD,

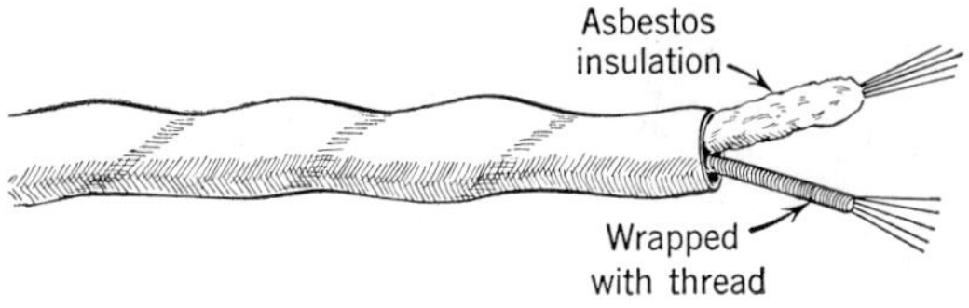


FIG. 3-3.

use the diagonals scissors-fashion and snip off the outer layer to the desired extent. This exposes the asbestos insulation, which can easily be loosed from the conductor and cut off. The asbestos covering remaining is quite loose (Fig. 3-3). Wrap the loose asbestos with thread so as to make it fit neatly and snugly around the wire.

Present-day manufacturers fit a special molded rubber or machine-attached plastic plug cap to the cord on their appliances. While it is possible to reuse many of these plug caps, often the time required to connect them to a cord is prohibitive. The screw terminal rubber or bakelite plug is more suited to the needs of the appliance repair man. Two things are important in connection with the installation of this plug cap. First, always loop the covered portion of cord around the lug that is a part of the terminal to which the wire is to be connected. This provides maximum separation of conductors in the plug cap, and minimizes the possibility of a short circuit. Second, be sure to loop the conductor under the terminal screw in the same direction as the screw turns. This will cause the loop in the wire to pull tighter as the screw is tightened. If looped in the wrong direction, the wire will loosen and slip out as the terminal screw is tightened. This is shown in Figure 3-4.

The cord should be removed from the receptacle by pulling out on the plug, not on the cord. By grasping the cord and pulling,

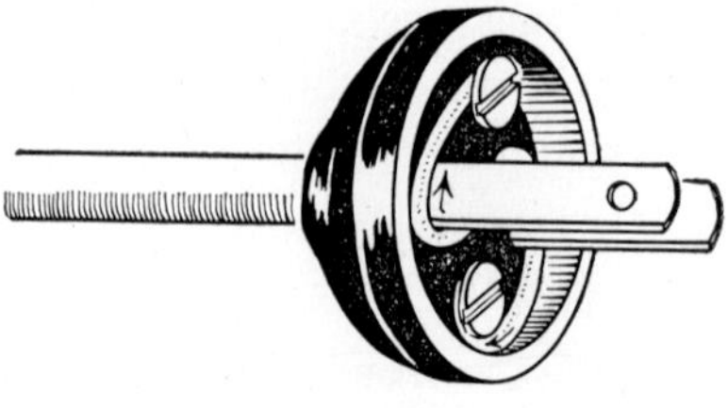

FIG. 3-4.

a short circuit is likely to be encouraged because of the loosening of the terminal wires.

So far, the cord connection to the plug has been considered; but what about the end that fits onto the appliance? This end will be prepared in the same manner as the other, but the method of attachment will depend upon the appliance. Some appliances require solder connections. Many are fitted with terminal screws. The cord may be fitted under these screws in a manner similar to fastening it to the plug cap. A neater and more durable attachment is obtained by placing an eyelet (connecting lug) on each wire end. The eyelet is a small metal ring caused to clamp around the wire by use of a plierlike tool. The hole within the eyelet allows the screw to pass through, and the screw head, pressing against the eyelet, assures good electrical contact. Eyelets and the tool for attaching can be obtained in a variety of sizes in kit form from appliance-parts outlets. Eyelets are inexpensive and easy to install. The improved neatness and electrical security obtained more than warrant the slight cost of their use.

## 3.2. Soldering

Soldering is often necessary in the appliance shop—not only on electrical parts; many mechanical connections are soldered. The most convenient soldering iron for the appliance shop is an electric iron, preferably of the type that has provision for an assortment of tips. The tip is the important part of the soldering iron; it must be properly prepared in order to do good work. In soldering, heat is transferred from the tip of the iron to the work, or joint, to be soldered. When the joint reaches the proper temperature, the solder applied to it will melt, and upon cooling hold the parts of the joint together. In order to heat up the work properly, the soldering tip must be tinned. This consists of melting a layer of solder onto the copper tip. The iron is heated and rubbed on a block of sal ammoniac. This cleans dirt and corrosion off the copper, allowing the solder to stick. The layer of solder aids in conducting heat onto the work. If solder is to cling to the work, it also must be clean. If the surface to be soldered is rusty, or corroded, it should be buffed or sanded until a bright metallic surface shows. Then flux should be applied.

Solder flux is a cleansing agent. It prevents oxides, which would prevent the solder from holding, from forming on the work while it is heating. Many different solder fluxes are used; muriatic acid, "cut" acid, solder paste, and rosin are the most common. Of these, only the last two are suited to electrical work. Rosin, being wholly noncorrosive, is preferable. Solder paste may be used, although it is mildly corrosive. Other fluxes are much too corrosive for electrical joints. A form of solder is sold which has a rosin core, and this is quite practical for electrical work.

Assuming that the job to be done is the joining of an attachment cord to a solder lug inside an appliance, the wire should, first, be fastened or twisted around the lug so that any mechanical strain will not depend solely upon the solder for strength. Next, hold the soldering iron *under* the joint until it is so hot that a piece of solder touched to the joint will melt and run. Allow the solder to permeate all the wires of the joint. A good solder joint will be completely covered with solder, yet the contour of every wire will be visible. When the solder is melted by the iron onto a joint that is still cool, the solder will not penetrate into the joint, and the result will be a "cold solder" connection which is neither mechanically nor electrically secure.

Allow sufficient time for the soldered joint to cool before disturbing. If the parts to be soldered together are moved while the solder is in a semifluid state, the soldered connection will be a poor one, and will loosen under slight pressure.

After the soldering iron has been in use for some time, the length of time depending upon the amount of use—once a day, if the iron is left plugged in all the time—the iron will need to be retinned. This should not be neglected; a dirty, pitted iron cannot produce a good solder job.

Most electric soldering irons are designed to heat rapidly; to become hot enough to use in 5 or 10 minutes. If it is found advisable to leave the iron plugged in all the time, in order to prevent the iron from overheating and shortening its life, some provision should be made to reduce the current flow through the iron. Soldering-iron manufacturers make a thermostatically controlled iron stand which will provide overheat protection, or a device may be assembled in the shop which serves the same purpose. If a 100-w lamp bulb is connected in series with the soldering iron, it will limit the current to a safe value, yet the iron will remain warm enough for occasional (not constant) use. The higher the wattage of the series lamp, the hotter the iron will remain.

## Now that you have read this chapter, can you answer these questions?

**1.** How would you use the series test lamp to determine that an appliance is grounded?

**2.** What manner of repair is preferable to splicing the cord on an appliance?

**3.** What is the proper method of removing an appliance cord from the receptacle?

4. If an appliance is to be used where there is a likelihood of a chair leg being set on the cord, which type of cord will last longest?

5. Why is type HPD cord not soldered onto the terminals of the appliance fitted with this type of cord?

6. Why should an appliance be disconnected from its source of power while being serviced with a series test lamp?

7. What type of cord would be suitable for use on a soldering iron? An electric clock? An electric drill?

8. What is a short circuit?

9. What is an open circuit?

10. Would acid core solder be suitable for soldering the attachment cord to the field coils of a universal motor?

11. What type of solder flux is most suitable for electrical appliance work?

*chapter* **4**

# Heating-Element Appliances

The simplest type of appliance is that which contains a single heating element and an attachment cord. Its electric circuit is shown in Figure 4-1.

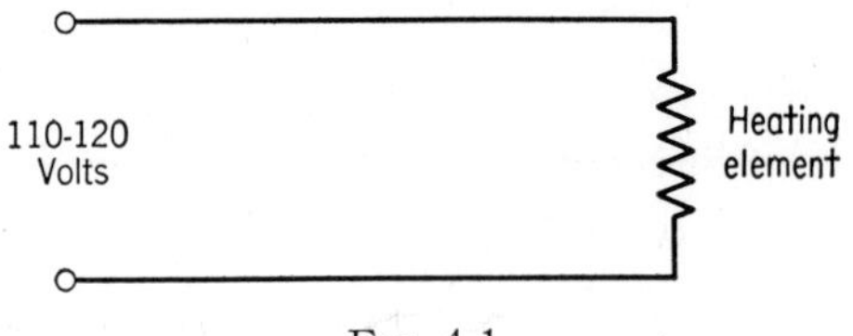


FIG. 4-1.

## IRONS

### 4.1. General Discussion

An example of such an appliance is an electric iron of the style pictured in Figure 4-2. It contains a heating element made of nichrome wire wound on a mica form and connected to the terminal posts extending from the back end of the iron. The electrical condition of this iron can be determined by using the series test lamp. If the heating element is open, the lamp will not burn.

If it is intact, the lamp will glow with slightly reduced brilliance. Similarly, an ohmmeter in a multimeter can be used to check continuity.

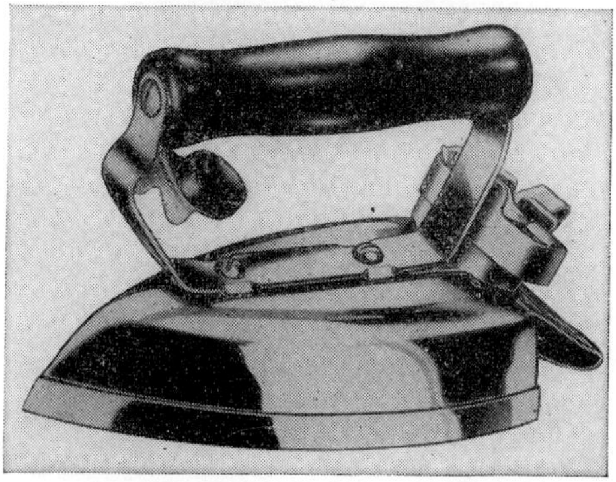

FIG. 4-2.

This iron is disassembled in the following manner:

1. Remove the bolt through the handle.
2. Remove two screws in top housing.
3. Lift off top housing.
4. Remove bolts holding heating element in place.

Bolts that have not been removed for a long period may be quite rusty, and extremely difficult to loosen. If this is the case, it may be found advisable to use penetrating oil, allowing it to soak in for some time. If this treatment is ineffective, it may be necessary to drill out the rusted bolt, rethread the tapped hole, and use a new bolt when reassembling.

The type of iron shown in Figure 4-2 is called a nonautomatic iron. The nonautomatic is an older type of iron; newer styles are equipped with a temperature-control device and are called automatic irons. Many of the nonautomatic irons use an open-type heating element. The construction of this type is shown in Figure 4-3. It consists of nichrome tape wound upon a mica form. When mounted in the iron, this open-type element is sand-

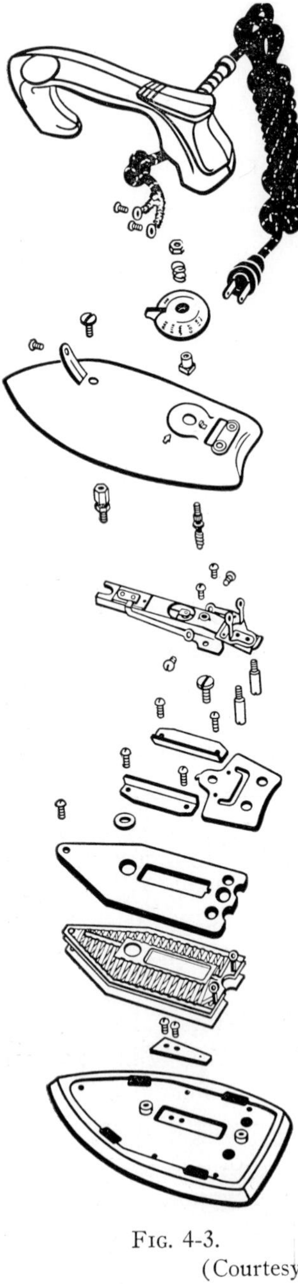

Fig. 4-3.

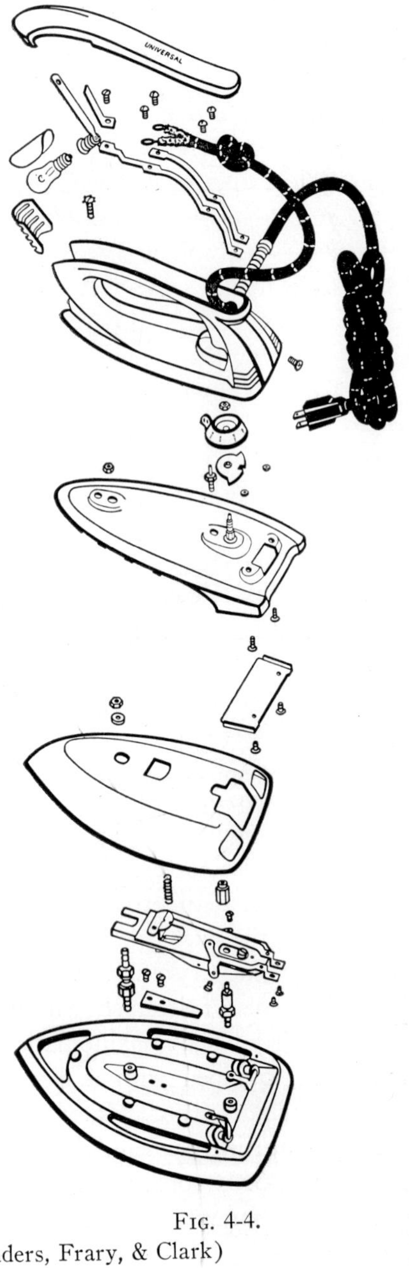


Fig. 4-4.

(Courtesy, Landers, Frary, & Clark)

wiched between a few layers of asbestos or mica which insulate the heating element from the frame of the iron.

In contrast to the open-type heating element is the sealed unit shown in Figure 4-4. The sealed unit contains a nichrome element insulated from its stainless steel sheath by a white powder, magnesium oxide. The entire assembly is hermetically sealed, providing lifetime protection against corrosion of the nichrome element. Some nonautomatic and most automatic irons contain the sealed unit. Because of its construction, repairs to this type of unit should not be attempted in the shop. Instead, a new unit should be obtained from the manufacturer or his dealer.

The open-type element can, of course, be repaired, since all of its parts are accessible. Your parts dealer can supply you with a nichrome sleeve with which a broken element may be patched. The broken ends of the heating element are cleaned with sandpaper and slipped into the sleeve, which is then flattened with a hammer. This manner of repair should be only a temporary expedient; the element should be replaced by a new one as soon as possible. An element which has broken because of age and length of service will very likely develop another break soon after being patched. Replacement is more economical than repair in the long run.

The nonautomatic iron of Figure 4-2 has no switch, and is turned off by disconnecting its plug. This should always be done at the iron plug, *not* the wall plug, since the iron-plug parts are designed to withstand the damaging effect of the arc produced when the heavy current required to operate the iron is interrupted. The current requirement of a 1,000-w iron is about 8.33 amp. Some irons carry the warning on the name plate that the iron is to be plugged into a wall or base receptacle only. Both the wire and the socket of a pendant ceiling fixture are inadequate to handle the iron current.

Many ten-cent stores and hardware stores sell a low-cost extension made with type POSJ wire. Very often this extension is to be found used with an iron, especially in homes lacking a sufficient number of convenience outlets, for appliance owners often have the mistaken idea that since the cord is available on the open market it is suitable for any appliance. This practice results in unsatisfactory iron performance and, worse, is a fire hazard. The over-all length of attachment cord and extension will present too much cord resistance. The wattage dissipated as heat in this cord is equal to $I^2R$ (Chap. 1). The iron will be operating at reduced wattage, and the cord heat will cause the insulation on the POSJ cord to deteriorate rapidly. The hazard is intensified if, as is often done, the extension is stapled to the baseboard. A short circuit could easily start a fire and destroy the building. This applies not only to an iron but to any appliance, particularly to one with a high-wattage consumption.

## 4.2. The Automatic Iron

Most irons of recent manufacture are automatic irons, and are equipped with a sealed element. The automatic feature consists (visibly) of a knob or lever calibrated with the proper ironing temperature for various fabrics. This iron is illustrated in Figure 4-5. The automatic control is made so as to act as an ON-OFF switch at its extreme low-end setting. The iron plug has been eliminated in the modern iron, the cord being attached to terminals inside the iron.

The method of disassembly differs with the various makes, but since all brands follow a somewhat similar pattern of manufacture, one example should be sufficient. One popular make is taken apart in the following manner:

1. Remove the screw holding name plate at base of handle. Remove name plate.

2. Four screws are visible beneath name plate. Remove outer ones, loosen inner ones.

3. Slide handle backward. This releases it and it can be removed. Inside handle are attachment-cord-terminal screws.

4. Remove split washer on control-knob shaft. Remove shaft and control knob. *Important:* Observe, or mark, setting of

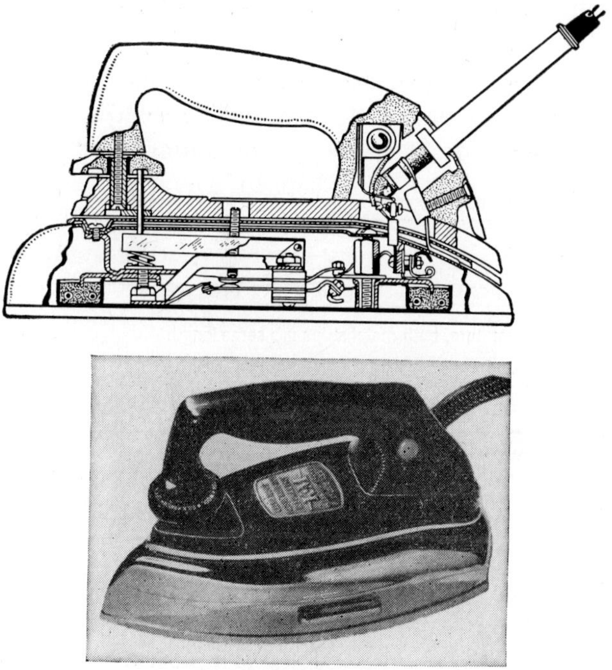

FIG. 4-5. (Courtesy, Knapp-Monarch Co.)

control knob, in order that it may be reassembled without altering adjustment.

5. Remove bolt holding cover assembly. Remove cover assembly.

6. Control mechanism and heating element are now accessible for disassembly and repair or replacement.

## 4.3. The Control Assembly. The Thermostat

The basic purpose of the control mechanism of an automatic iron is to provide a device that will permit the user to adjust the temperature to suit the material being ironed. Before the introduction of the automatic iron, it was necessary to unplug the iron whenever it became too hot. The control on the automatic iron is calibrated not in degrees of temperature, but according to fabric types—that is, the control is turned to "cotton," "wool," or whatever the fabric may be, thus simplifying operation. (The temperatures corresponding to various settings are given in Section 4.5.)

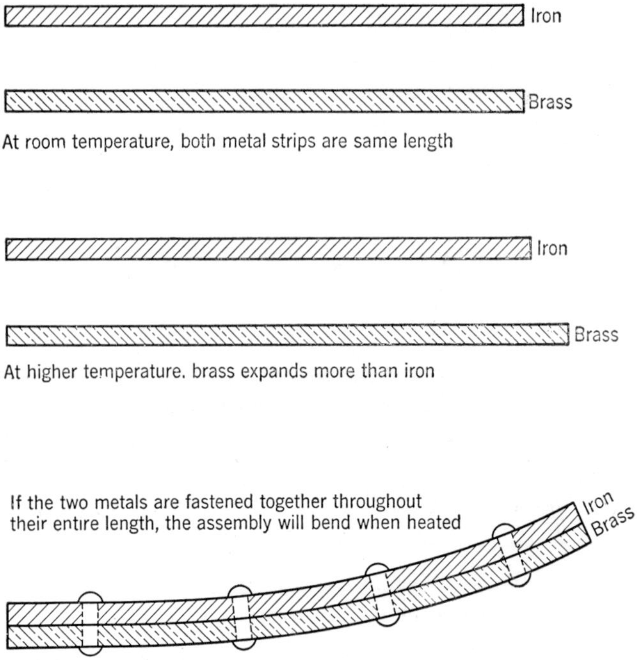


FIG. 4-6A.

The most economical method of temperature control is through the use of a thermostat. The thermostat is a device consisting of two metals bolted, riveted, or fused together. It is shown in Figure 4-6A in its simplest form. As depicted here, the thermostat consists of a strip of brass and one of iron, both the same length, bolted together. Each of these metals will expand when heated, but the expansion of the brass piece is about 50% more than that of the iron. Since the two metal strips are fastened together throughout their entire length, this uneven expansion of the elements of the thermostat will cause a bending or bowing of the assembly. The thermostat is, then, a mechanical device that changes its shape when the temperature changes.

In order that it may control an electrically operated appliance, making it responsive to changes of temperature, the thermostat must become a part of the electric circuit, or in some way affect the electric circuit. If the thermostat (Figure 4-6B) is rigidly fastened to the appliance at one of its ends, a rise and fall of temperature will cause a back-and-forth movement of the free end. If, during its travel, the free end is allowed to touch a metallic surface, the electric circuit can be completed through the thermostat and the metal it is contacting; when this contact is broken it is equivalent to opening a switch in the appliance, thus turning it off. Observe in Figure 4-6C that if the iron faces the contact surface, an increase in temperature causes the electric circuit to close. Conversely, if the brass faces the contact metal, the circuit will close when the thermostat cools. The latter system is used in an electric iron, since it is desired to turn the iron off for a few minutes by means of the thermostat as soon as the iron exceeds a safe temperature for the type of fabric being ironed.

The thermostat may be made adjustable if the contact X in Figure 4-6C is fastened to a screw or lever. It may then be moved closer to (or farther from) the thermostatic element, and the degree of bending and the temperature change necessary to accomplish it will be adjustable. Thus, if contact X in Figure 4-6C is moved upward, the heating element must heat the thermostat to a higher temperature before it will bend sufficiently to open the electric circuit. The thermostat control knob may be used to turn the iron off altogether if its extreme setting is such as to remove the contact from the thermostat range of movement at room temperature.

The thermostat contacts X and Y are made of silver, or silver-plated brass. Silver is the best conductor of electricity known, meaning that it has the lowest resistance of any conducting metal. But more important is its behavior toward the interruption of a heavy current. When a circuit carrying as much

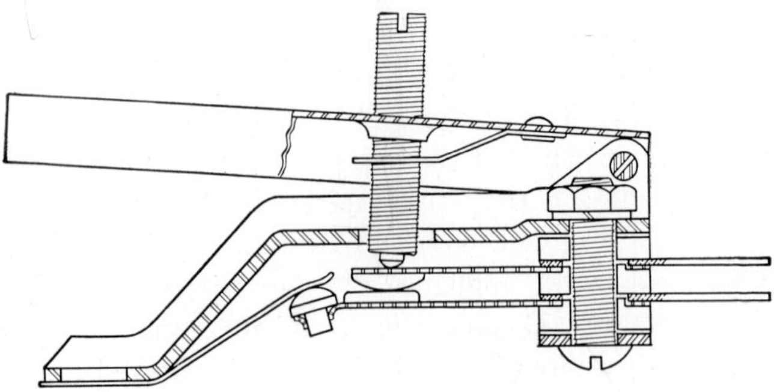

Section through thermostat

Fig. 4-6B.

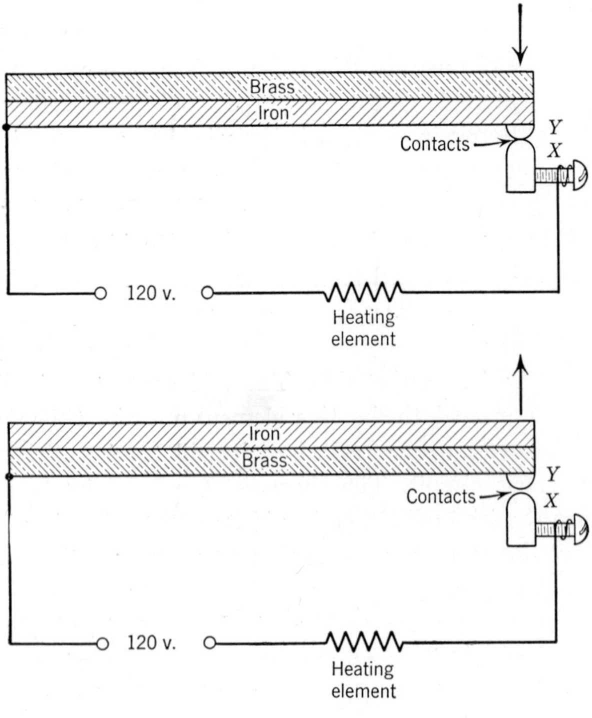


Fig. 4-6C.

current as is required for the operation of an electric iron is opened, an arc will form because the current "jumps" the small air gap resulting from contacts barely separated. This arc causes a melting of the metal, since an intense heat is created momentarily by the arc. At this temperature the contact metal will chemically combine with the air; it is said to "oxidize," or form an oxide coating on the contact surface. This oxide forms on all metals used for contacts, and behaves as a layer of insulation on all metals except silver. The oxide coating on silver is as good a conductor as the silver itself. Silver contacts, therefore, last longer and give better service than any other electric metal.

If the switch moves rapidly from closed to open position (snap action), the arc formed will be of short duration and reduced severity. However, the thermostat is a slow-moving device and encourages the most severe arcing. It serves best when used with alternating current, and many thermostatically equipped appliances bear the notice "for use with alternating current only." While the appliance may operate on direct current, contact life is greatly reduced because of the prolonged arcing caused by d-c operation. The arc may heat the contacts to a temperature at which they will fuse together, making thermostatic action useless.

## 4.4. The Thermostat Used on Alternating Current

Most homes are wired for 60-cycle alternating current. The nature of this current is such that it moves in one direction through its conductors for a short length of time, stops (reduces to zero value), and then travels in the opposite direction for a while. All this is accomplished in 1/60th of a second, or 60 times a second: thus the name 60-cycle a-c. The behavior of alternating voltage and current are shown graphically in Figure 4-7.

With a-c applied, a thermostat may draw an arc at the instant it breaks circuit, but less than 1/60th of a second later the voltage will go through zero and the arc ceases. True, the current then goes to its previous high value (but of opposite direction). However, the disrupted condition of the air, due to the arc which allowed the arc to persist (called ionization) no longer obtains, and the arc will not re-form. By contrast, the only thing that will permit the arc formed by a direct-current circuit to extinguish is the opening of contact so far that the spacing is too great for the current producing the arc to sustain it. This requires quite a length of time in the slow-moving thermostat circuit, and much contact damage can occur while the arc exists.

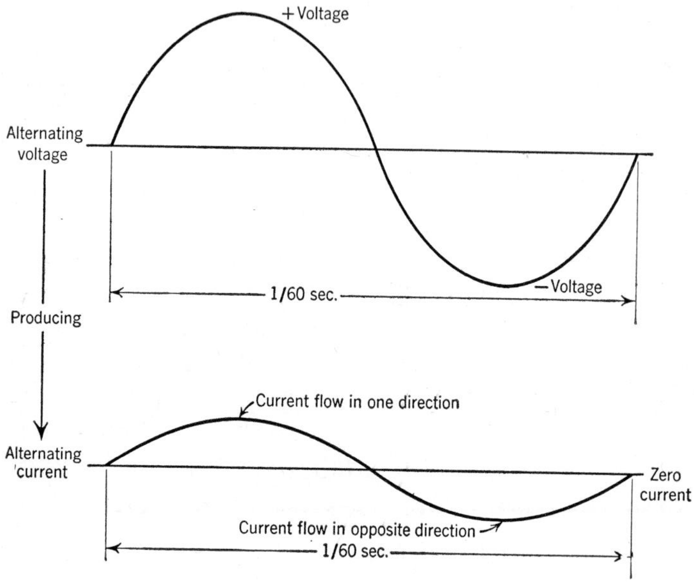


FIG. 4-7.

The heart of the thermostat is the assembly of brass and iron fastened together. This is called a bimetallic strip. Commercially, "invar" metal is used instead of iron, with brass as the other metal. Because of the extensive use of thermostats, bimetallic sheets are manufactured, and the materials are fused, not bolted, together. The sheet is then cut into strips of the proper length for use. In this form, the bimetallic strip looks as if it were but one metal, and its color is that of a piece of iron that has not been polished or finished.

The thermostat need not be a current-carrying part of the

electric circuit. Often the free end of the bimetallic element is attached to an insulated lever which, in turn, operates the electric contacts. In this case it is not necessary to insulate the thermostat from the frame of the appliance in which it is used.

As it goes through its cycle of operation, the thermostat itself uses no current; it merely opens and closes the electric circuit. Its task is temperature control: to cause an appliance to become warmer or cooler at the flip of a lever. Now, the thermostat cannot and does not affect the temperature of the heating element while current is flowing through it. This temperature is determined by the wattage rating of the heating element itself. But if the heating element reaches a temperature of 1,000° F. at its surface and maintains that temperature for one minute, the appliance as a whole will not get as warm as if the heating element had been at 1,000° F. for three minutes. In neither case will the appliance itself be likely to reach the same temperature as its heating element. However, the operating temperature of the appliance will obviously be higher if the appliance is on three minutes and off one minute during each cycle of thermostat operation, than if the current is on one minute and off three. The thermostat accomplishes temperature control by varying the length of the on and off portions of the operating cycle.

## 4.5. Ironing Temperatures

If the thermostat is set to operate at 400° F., the heating element will glow until it has heated the surrounding air and other objects, including the thermostat bimetallic strip, to 400° F., at which time the thermostat will open and the heating element will be open-circuited. If the appliance is an iron, the ironing surface will cool off because of heat radiation into the air and conduction of heat into the material being ironed. The ambient* at the thermostat will remain close to 400° F. for a longer time. The thermostat will not close immediately; there will be a slight time delay before the bimetallic strip loses enough of its heat so

*Surrounding temperature.

that it can begin to bend back. This time delay, and resultant temperature difference, between turn-off and turn-on of current is called the *differential* of the thermostat. An electric iron has a differential of from 30° F. to 150° F. The ironing temperatures for various fabrics is as follows:

| | | |
|---|---|---|
| Rayon | approximately | 225° F. |
| Silk | " | 300° F. |
| Wool | " | 350° F. |
| Cotton | " | 400° F. |
| Linen | " | 525° F. |

## 4.6. Adjusting the Thermostat

An iron may be checked for proper temperature by means of an oven tester or a deep-fat frying thermometer whose scale is as high as 600° F. Place the iron on some insulating material (asbestos or glass wool), place the bulb of the thermometer under the iron, and try two or three settings of the control. It is not necessary to check all the settings of the control knob, since the manufacturer has calibrated his thermostat so that if it is correct at one setting, all others will fall in line.

Obviously, the range of motion of the thermostat bimetal can be altered by bending or twisting the bimetal itself. This method, however, is uncertain, and often destructive. Furthermore, the manufacturer almost invariably builds into his control mechanism a variable factor to allow thermostat adjustment. It is customary to fasten the control knob to a shaft, the other end of which is threaded. Turning the control knob will move the shaft toward or away from the thermostat switch contacts, altering the spacing between them and the time required for the thermostat to bridge the gap. A stop is provided to limit the rotation of the control knob to less than one complete circle.

A small amount of adjustment may be obtained by loosening the knob-setscrew, removing the knob, then putting it back on the shaft with the pointer located at the correct temperature value. If a greater change is required, the stop arm may be removed, the shaft turned 360°, and the stop arm replaced. A combination of the two methods will permit close calibration of the thermostat.

The thermostat in an automatic iron is an assembled unit, and repairs to this unit are not feasible. If the unit is found to be defective, it should be replaced with a new one. The new thermostat may require adjusting as outlined above.

## 4.7. Repairs to Sealed Unit

The majority of modern irons are fitted with the sealed unit heating element (Fig. 4-4). In many cases the lead wires from the plug terminals are welded into place. If these lead wires should become broken, they can be replaced with new ones provided a welding torch or prestolite torch is available. Silver solder or brazing rod should be used with borax as a flux. Heat the metal parts to be welded to a temperature high enough that the silver solder or brazing rod will melt when touched to them. Do not heat the solder directly with the torch. Soft solder should not be used, as the iron temperature will cause it to melt. If the sealed unit is open-circuited (as indicated by the series test lamp or multimeter) it should be replaced with a new one.

## 4.8. The Steam Iron

It is customary to dampen clothes before ironing so that the steam produced by the heat of the iron will soften the fibers in the cloth, allowing the iron to remove wrinkles entirely. Today's housewife is finding it convenient to eliminate the troublesome process of sprinkling by using the steam iron. This newcomer to the appliance field has a built-in water chest from which steam is ejected through a vent in the sole plate directly onto the surface being pressed. (Steam-iron cutaway, Fig. 4-8.)

The steam iron is equipped with a thermostat for automatic operation and has an electric circuit that is identical with that of the regular iron; the main difference lies in the use of gaskets and water-tight fittings which prevent water in the reservoir from seeping down into the heating element, where it might produce a short circuit or ground.

The method of disassembly of most brands is quite similar to that of the regular iron. Some brands of steam irons have a fitting recessed into the sole plate from which the steam is ejected. It is necessary to remove this fitting with a socket wrench in order to remove the top cover from the sole plate.

The steam vent is equipped with a valve which is controlled externally and which will direct the steam downward through the

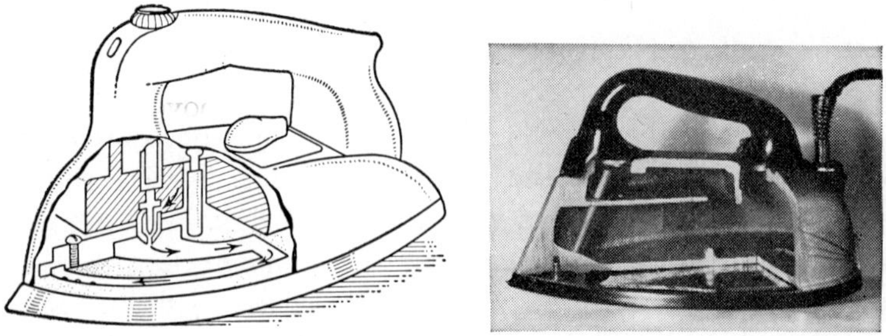

FIG. 4-8. (Courtesy, Steam Electric Mfg. Co., St. Louis)

sole plate or upward through a vent in the handle and then straight out from the handle. This permits dry operation of the iron.

Perhaps the most common trouble experienced with the steam iron is caused by lime deposits from the water in the reservoir. The lime deposits can clog the outlet vent so that steam will not issue from it. Most steam irons are supplied with a blow-out vent which prevents the user from being injured by explosions resulting from high steam pressures built up when lime deposits clog the outlet in the sole plate. These deposits should always be cleaned out whenever a steam iron is serviced.

Lime deposit can be prevented by using only distilled water in the steam iron. One convenient source of distilled water within the home is the electric refrigerator. If, when the refrigerator is defrosted, the drippings from the ice surrounding the freezer compartment are collected, this water can be used in the steam iron. Since ice consists entirely of condensed water vapor, these drippings will necessarily be free from minerals that would clog up the iron.

When new, a steam iron may eject water along with the steam. The condition corrects itself after the first few times the iron is used, or as soon as the surface within the boiler becomes sufficiently "wetted" that drops of water no longer cling to it but fall back into the main body of water instead.

## *Repairing Irons*

### 4.9. Iron Fails to Heat

The cause of failure to heat is either a power failure or an open circuit in the iron. The receptacle and fuse can be indirectly tested by trying another appliance in it. An electric lamp gives the most distinct evidence of the presence of power at the outlet; if the lamp operates, the receptacle and fuse are functioning properly.

In testing the iron circuit, the easiest tests should be made first of all, in the interest of saving time. Examine the cord and plug for a fault. The wires may have loosened from under the attachment screws in the plug cap. If this is the case, merely tightening the screws will put the iron back into service. Quite frequently a break in the cord can be located by flexing and feeling the cord along its length. If it seems to bend too readily at one spot, or has a soft place, or appears burned, blackened, or charred, a broken wire should be suspected. When such a break occurs quite close to the iron or plug cap, the defective portion can be clipped off with a pair of wire cutters, and discarded. The end of the cord is prepared as described in Chapter 3 and reattached. This procedure is not advisable if it materially shortens the cord length; in this event, the cord should be totally replaced.

If neither cord nor plug appears to be faulty, the iron must be dismantled for further tests and repairs. On most newer-type irons the cord is internally connected. Access is obtained to the terminal block to which the connection is made by removing the metal plate at the rear of the iron shoe; the cord is then removed.

Testing across the inside terminal screws with an ohmmeter or series test lamp will give more positive evidence of whether the fault is in the cord or in the iron. If the lamp burns (series test lamp), or if the ohmmeter indicates a resistance value somewhere between 12 and 24 ohms, the thermostat and heating element are satisfactory; the trouble is in the cord. If the ohmmeter reading is at infinity, or if the test lamp fails to burn, the thermostat and heating element should be examined and/or tested. Loosen the screw or setscrew holding the thermostat knob in place; remove the knob. Loosen the screws holding the top iron cover and handle; remove them. The thermostat is now visible and can be examined for defect. This visual test is not necessarily conclusive, for a thermostat may appear to be in good condition and yet fail to function properly. A more satisfactory test consists of disconnecting the thermostat from the circuit and testing for continuity with ohmmeter or series test lamp.

If all the preceding tests have disclosed no defect, the inevitable conclusion is that the heating element has an open circuit. This may be verified by measuring the iron resistance, the value of which is given above. The open-type heating element can be either repaired or replaced, but the sealed unit must be totally replaced; it cannot be opened for repairs without causing irreparable damage. Often the sealed-unit heating element is the most costly part of the iron, making repairs economically unfeasible, as the cost of repairs may approach that of a new iron. Fortunately, the sealed-unit heating element is quite durable, and seldom fails during the normal lifetime of the iron.

A "thermostatic" heating element is occasionally encountered. In such a case the nichrome wire is severed, but the ends are touching, and the circuit appears to be complete until the heat produces sufficient expansion to cause the ends to part, opening the circuit. As the iron cools, the broken ends again touch. This condition may cause the iron either to fail to heat, or to get only moderately warm. Placing an ammeter in the circuit will indicate, by the behavior of the meter needle, whether the heating element is acting in this manner.

## 4.10. Iron Does Not Get Hot Enough

One reason the iron does not get hot enough may be the "thermostatic" heating element described in the preceding paragraph. More common causes are a defective heating element or a defective cord or plug.

The amount of heat produced depends upon the resistance in the circuit; anything which causes an increase in circuit resistance results in less heat. The iron thermostat may be the cause of this condition through failure to make good contact. Deeply pitted, warped, or melted contacts introduce additional circuit resistance, a condition usually obvious from visual examination. Replacement of the thermostat with a new one is the only satisfactory method of repair, for attempts to fix a thermostat are seldom successful.

Poor contact between cord and terminal in plug cap or iron introduces additional circuit resistance, and causes the iron to produce too little heat. At the point of poor contact, some heating will occur, and blackening due to heat provides visual evidence of the site of poor connection. Usually the cord and plug are damaged by the heat and should be replaced.

## 4.11. Iron Gets Too Hot

When an iron gets too hot, this condition is invariably caused by the contact points on the thermostat being stuck or welded together. In this case the iron must be disassembled, and the thermostat removed and replaced with a new one.

## 4.12. Iron Is Noisy

This is a not uncommon complaint about a moderately new iron. A cracking and snapping noise often develops after the iron has been in use for just a few months. This results from the repeated expansion and contraction of the parts of the iron, producing some loosening and resultant shifting. It is not necessarily a defective condition, and usually will be tolerated by the owner after its cause has been explained to her. However, steam produced by the ironing process may cause rusting of the interior of the iron, aggravating the normal amount of noise. Removal of rust, especially in the vicinity of nuts and bolts, along with tightening of the hardware, may reduce the noise.

# TOASTERS

## 4.13. General Discussion

The toaster, like the electric iron, is manufactured in two styles, the automatic and the nonautomatic. The nonautomatic is the simpler mechanically and electrically. Its electric circuit, which is shown diagrammatically in Figure 4-1, is very simple, consisting of a heating element and its connecting wires. The heating element is a thin ribbon wound on a mica form which is mounted vertically inside the toaster. Figure 4-9 shows this type of construction.

FIG. 4-9. (Courtesy, Knapp-Monarch Co.)

On either side of the appliance is a horizontally hinged door. A slice of bread to be toasted is placed on a small ledge inside each door. The user must open the doors from time to time to check on degree of brownness. When one side of the slice of bread is properly browned, it is turned over and the process repeated for the other side.

This is obviously a simple appliance from the standpoint of both operation and repair. The most likely sources of difficulty, if the toaster is inoperative, are the cord set, heating element, or connection terminals. Replacement parts are available, and the series test lamp will indicate the portion of the circuit that is the cause of trouble.

## 4.14. The Automatic Toaster

The nonautomatic toaster requires the close attention of the operator, and many a piece of toast has been burned in this appliance because the owner's attention has strayed. To eliminate this nuisance, many automatic and semiautomatic features have been developed for toasters.

Perhaps the first automatic device to be used was the thermostat. This assembly is found on many toasters today. The toaster in Figure 4-9 has a bimetallic strip of the thermostat located at such a position that the bread touches it while being toasted. When the bread is properly browned, its surface temperature has reached the point at which the thermostat operates and opens the electric circuit.

If the bread is left in too long, however, the thermostat will close, and eventually the toast will burn to a crisp, so an indicating device is used to warn the operator that his toast is ready. The toaster shown in Fig. 4-9 has a small pilot light mounted on top of the toaster. Instead of an ordinary lamp bulb, a small nichrome coil—a part of the heating-element circuit—is located beneath a glass cover. When the toaster is turned on, the heating element will glow, and so will the nichrome coil indicator. The closed doors make the heating element invisible, but the indicating coil glow may be seen through its window. When the surface temperature of the slice of bread activates its thermostat, the glow disappears, indicating to the user that it is time to turn the toast over, or remove it if already toasted on one side.

The glow-lamp indicator is not extremely brilliant, and the fact that it has gone out may often escape notice. A more dynamic type of indicator is that shown in Figure 4-10. Here can be seen mounted beneath a toaster a bell, quite similar to that on an alarm clock. Alongside the bell is an electromagnet, which is connected in parallel with the heating element. Both heating element and electromagnet are controlled by a thermostat. When the thermostat operates, the heating element cools, but at the same time the electromagnet releases its hold on a small steel ball which then drops down onto the bell.

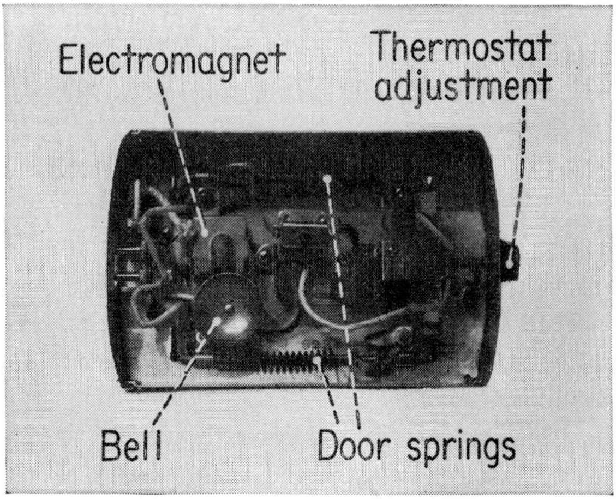


Fig. 4-10.

Not all people are in agreement as to what degree of brownness constitutes a well-done piece of toast. To accommodate these

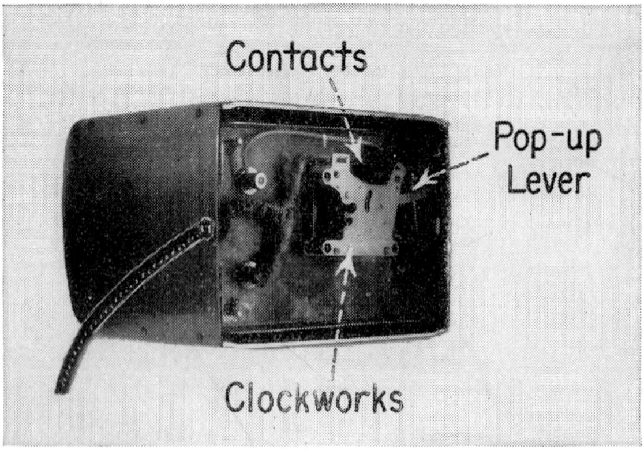


Fig. 4-11.

various tastes, many toasters are equipped with a selector knob. This knob, calibrated for toast color ranging from light to dark, controls the thermostat. When the stationary contact is moved closer to the thermostat, it must bend farther (take more time) to open the circuit, hence the toasting time is increased.

The thermostatically controlled devices thus far discussed do not totally shut off the toaster, and if left to itself the thermostat will continue to cycle, to the detriment of the toast. Figure 4-11 shows a mechanism used on many models to make them more fully automatic. It consists of clockwork similar to that used in an alarm clock. After the bread is placed in the toaster, a lever is depressed. This lever simultaneously turns on a switch in the heating-element circuit and winds the clockwork. The clockwork ticks for the proper length of time required to toast the bread and then turns off the switch, shutting off the toaster altogether.

FIG. 4-12. (Courtesy, Landers, Frary, & Clark)

The toasting time is shortened by use of the oven-type construction. The style of this toaster is shown in Figure 4-12. There are three heating elements in this appliance, one at the center and two located on the outer sides of the space for bread.

Both sides of the two slices can thus be toasted simultaneously and the process timed; the toaster automatically turns itself off when the toast is ready for consumption.

## 4.15. The Pop-up Toaster

The culmination of automatic operation is represented by the fully automatic toaster with the pop-up feature. The toaster in Figure 4-12 does not open up; instead, the two slices of bread are placed in the top openings. The slices thus placed extend above the top of the toaster for about a third of the height of the slice. The handle at the end of the toaster is depressed and as it moves down (against a spring pressure) the bread moves down into the toaster. When it reaches the bottom, the handle latches. When the toast is finished, the timing mechanism releases the latch, allowing the handle—and the toast—to pop up. In the models using clockwork for a timer, the same wheel of the clockwork that turns off the switch also releases the catch which holds down the pop-up mechanism. Note the bar extending from the clockwork in Figure 4-11.

Many newer model toasters employ a thermostat for timing and pop-up. The operation of two popular brands using this system will be described in the following.

## 4.16. The Thermostat as a Timing Device

Observe the circuit of Figure 4-13. The three resistors in parallel are the three heating elements for toasting bread. The fourth resistor, shunted by a thermostatic switch, is a short length of nichrome ribbon, and, as may be seen in Figure 4-14, is wrapped around the bimetallic strip of a thermostat. Figure 4-14 illustrates the mechanism involved in the operation of timing the toasting process by use of a thermostat. The mechanism shown is located at the bottom of the toaster. The behavior is as follows:

The thermostat T is heated by its short length of heating element, and begins to bend. The spring shown in Figure 4-14 prevents the free end of the thermostat from moving easily; however, it is hinged at its captive end, consequently the bimetal will assume a curved shape. The motion thus produced is transmitted to the hinged end of the strip and also to an arm A fastened to the thermostat. Arm A moves until its motion is arrested by bumper B. Further bending of the bimetallic strip will cause its free end to overcome the spring tension and it will move.

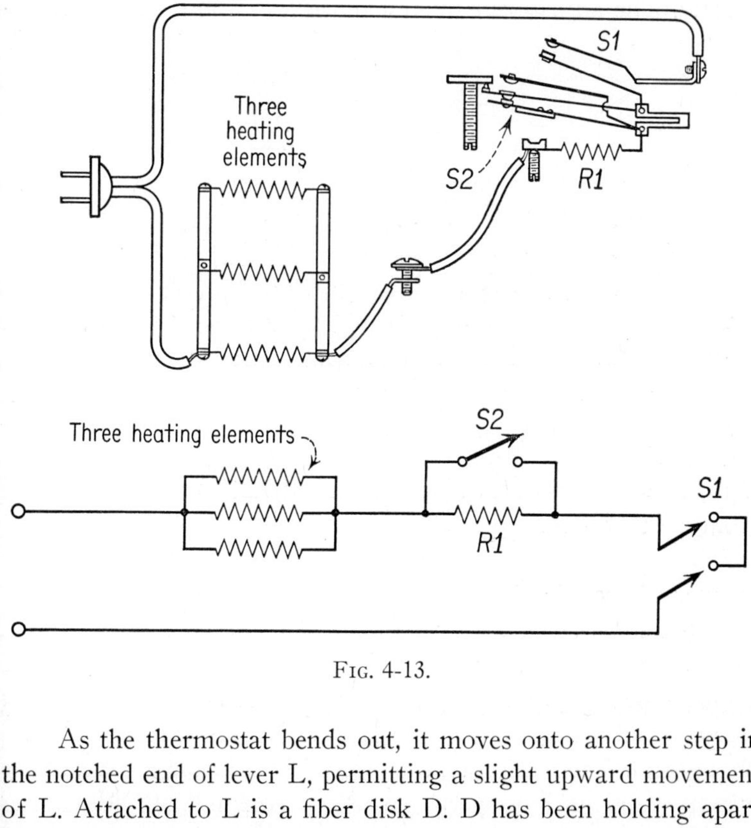


FIG. 4-13.

As the thermostat bends out, it moves onto another step in the notched end of lever L, permitting a slight upward movement of L. Attached to L is a fiber disk D. D has been holding apart the contacts of *S2*, which are now allowed to close as a result of the movement of L.

Closing of *S2* stops the current flow through the thermostat heating element. The thermostat bimetal cools, and retracts. Arm A returns to its original position near the thermostat, and, in so doing, trips a cam (seen under arm A in Figure 4-14), causing the pop-up mechanism to operate, and opening the main switch, *S1*.

Electrical values and component sizes are such as to allow this cycle to occur during approximately the time required to toast a piece of bread properly. Bumper B has a short length of thread machined on its surface, and may be moved to and fro slightly. The adjustment thus obtained will allow enough varia-

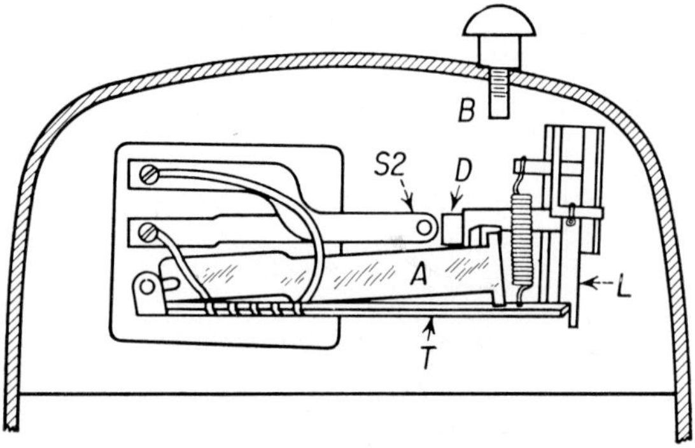


FIG. 4-14.

tion in toasting time so that the control knob can be calibrated from light to dark.

The thermostat as a time-delay device is used in another manner. A popular brand of toaster employs a bimetallic strip mounted so as to be deliberately bowed in the direction opposite to its normal bend when heated. The circuit is practically that of Figure 4-13. The auxiliary heating element is located near the bimetal, and a small adjustable reflector directs heat down onto the bimetal. The tension on the bimetal is adjusted so that at the instant the bread is properly toasted the accumulated heat causes the thermostat to operate. It snaps in the direction of its normal bend and kicks a lever which releases the pop-up mechanism and opens the main switch.

The thermostat must be allowed to cool before the toaster can again be used. Upon cooling, it snaps back, allowing the pop-up mechanism to engage the released lever.

The pop-up mechanism consists essentially of a spring which pulls up the small platforms on which the bread slices are placed, together with a catch which holds down the mechanism against the spring tension and which, when disengaged, allows the spring to pull up the assembly and expose the toasted bread. The spring is a rapidly acting device, and if allowed to operate unchecked would toss the toast into the air clear of the toaster. To prevent such behavior, a small piston and cylinder arrangement is fastened onto the pop-up assembly, and the slow movement of the piston dispelling the air in the cylinder through a small vent deters the rapid action of the pop-up spring.

When servicing a pop-up toaster, it is wise to examine this check valve, making sure that it is well lubricated. A light coating of oil on the cylinder walls assures smooth operation.

## *Repairing Toasters*

### 4.17. Toaster Will Not Heat

If the toaster fails to produce any heat, the probable cause lies in one of the following: power failure, defective cord and/or plug, defective thermostat, or damaged contact points. The possibility that the difficulty is due to all three heating elements in the pop-up type toaster having burned out simultaneously is quite remote. However, the single element of the nonautomatic toaster is frequently found to have burned out—a condition which can readily be determined from visual examination.

The list of probable causes above should be investigated in the order given when servicing a toaster. The receptacle can be tested by substitution servicing; try another appliance in the outlet and see if it will operate. The most likely cause of power failure is a blown fuse. Next in likelihood is a defective or burned-out duplex receptacle. The third possibility is damaged wiring. A blown fuse or defective receptacle can be readily remedied by the appliance service man; repairs to house wiring may or may not be within his capabilities, depending upon his training and experience. Local ordinances may require that repairs to house wiring be done only by a licensed electrician.

The line cord and plug are next in order. Examine for poor connection at cord ends in plug cap. Flex and feel the cord for evidence of a break as indicated by a soft or unusually flexible spot. If such a break occurs close to the end of the cord, the cord can be cut and the small end discarded; otherwise, a new cord set should be installed.

If none of the foregoing is the cause of the failure to heat, it will be necessary to dismantle the appliance.

Most pop-up toasters contain a switch. The mechanism of this switch is operated by the lever which is depressed when lowering the bread into the toaster. The parts of the switch are mounted on the toaster frame (under the outer cover) in such a manner as to be entirely visible when the cover is removed. With the outer shell removed, brace the toaster in such a manner as to allow it to be operated. Depress the starting lever and observe the performance of the switch, with emphasis on the following details:

1. Do the contact points actually touch? Damaged contacts, or broken or bent switch parts, may make the switch inoperative, a condition which will obviously cause the toaster to fail to heat.

2. Are the contact points badly pitted? Badly pitted or burned contacts may touch physically but fail to complete the circuit electrically. If not too badly corroded, the points may be filed to renew electrical contact; otherwise, they must be replaced.

3. Observe the contacts when they separate. Is an arc formed? The production of an arc indicates that a current-carrying circuit has been interrupted. In the toaster which fails to heat, no such arc should occur.

In addition to the contact points associated with the switch, another pair is in the toaster, controlled by the thermostat. (It is often quite possible to position the toaster, with outer shell removed, at such an angle as to allow observation of the thermostat in operation. While the thermostat should fail to go through its operating cycle if the toaster defect is of such a nature as to prevent it from heating, observation under actual operating conditions is a valid servicing procedure in general, as well as a check on satisfactory operation following repairs.)

If the fault is in the thermostat it will be evidenced by such indications as pitted or burned contact points, broken or bent thermostat parts, or a break in the portion of the heating element which applies heat directly to the thermostat. Almost any fault occurring within the thermostat assembly requires replacement, since repair of a thermostat is seldom satisfactory. Furthermore, most supply houses do not carry thermostat parts; the entire assembly only is available.

## 4.18. Toaster Toasts Unevenly

The pop-up toaster contains three heating elements, connected in parallel. If any one of the three should suffer a break, it alone will fail to heat; the others will operate in a normal manner. This trouble will be easy to isolate, since the faulty element will be dark while the others are glowing. It will, of course, be necessary to dismantle the toaster to obtain access to the defective element, replacement of which is more satisfactory and permanent than an attempt to repair by splicing at the break.

The possibility of burning the bread by direct contact with the heating element is avoided by the use of bread guides: bent pieces of wire laid in grooves or slots in between the elements. Careless dismantling of the toaster can cause these guides to spill out in a disconcerting fashion, whereas if the appliance is carefully taken apart, and each guide wire carefully removed, the pattern of their placement will be readily apparent, making reassembly much easier after the defective element has been replaced. It may even be advisable to make a simple sketch of the guide positioning and electrical connections to the heating element.

Another type of uneven heating is that which produces toast

which is too pale, or is burned. The apparatus which controls the timing of the toasting process is either clockwork, or a bimetal strip whose path of bending is arranged so as to require a time interval proportional to the toasting time. With either kind of timing apparatus, the cause of faulty timing can be ascertained by observing the operating cycle with the outer shell removed:

1. The clockwork timer may merely be filled with crumbs, in which event cleaning with carbon tetrachloride and lubricating with clock oil will restore operation. Damaged gears, springs, and so on, require replacement of the timer.

2. The thermostat-type timer is subject to such defects as bent parts, broken heating element, or jamming due to accumulated crumbs. The nature of the damage and its extent will dictate the extent of repair or replacement necessary.

## 4.19. Toaster Fails to Pop Up

Failure to pop up is closely associated with improper heating, for a toaster with a defective pop-up mechanism will cause toast to burn. Customarily the timer controls pop-up operation, releasing, at the end of the timing cycle, a spring which raises the bread platform (page 80). Failure to pop up may result from faulty timer, broken or displaced spring, or jammed platform. Actual operation of the toaster with outer shell removed will enable the service man to determine what the difficulty is.

A part of the pop-up mechanism is a piston-and-cylinder check, the purpose of which is to retard pop-up movement and prevent the toast from being thrown from the toaster. Either the failure of the toaster to pop up, or too rapid pop-up, can occur as a result of a faulty check, the former if the check is jammed, the latter if it has become too loose. Cleaning and lubricating the check will generally improve either condition.

## 4.20. Toaster Has Been Dropped

It is not unusual for the owner of a toaster which has been dropped to bring it to a repair shop without having determined whether it will still operate, fearing that an attempt to operate it may cause further damage. The first test is therefore to plug it in and see whether operation is normal or erratic. If it will not satisfactorily toast bread, the tests and repairs given in the preceding paragraphs should be followed. Even though the performance may appear to be normal it is, nevertheless, advisable to dismantle the appliance, examining it for possible sources of future trouble. Observe especially the following:

1. Bases, handles, knobs, and other appurtenances which are made of plastic or bakelite may have been cracked by the fall. To reduce the chance of these parts collapsing or falling off later on, they should be replaced.

2. The door or drawer at the base of the toaster, intended for crumb removal, may have been sprung or bent so as to make it difficult to open, or may even prevent it from latching closed. With proper shop facilities it may be possible to restore its original shape; otherwise, replacement will be necessary.

3. The outer shell may have been sprung or bent. The metal of the outer shell is thin enough that it is often possible to restore its original shape by hand pressure. This procedure will not, of course, remove dents; but the purpose of restoring shape is to insure adequate clearance for internal moving parts.

4. Run toaster through operating cycle with outer shell removed and observe the performance of the pop-up mechanism, thermostat, and so forth, for any evidence of damage to these parts. (This test and the following one should also be performed with slices of bread actually in the toaster.) Run through operating cycle again with outer shell in place; if all is well, performance should be identical.

## HOTPLATES

### 4.21. The Basic Hotplate

The basic hotplate contains a heating element of nichrome wound on a ceramic form called the brick, and an attachment cord. Its circuit is that of Figure 4-1. Because of its simple circuit, this unit does not present much of a service problem. The troubles that might disable it are: a defective cord set, pitted terminals, an open heating element. It is only rarely that a sealed unit is used on hotplates. Most are the open type, and in the event of a heating element burn-out or damage resulting in an open circuit, the defect is visible and the coil can easily be replaced. Nichrome wire in coiled form and of various wattage ratings is available for such replacement.

In the event that the exact value is not available, use the next *lower* wattage element, removing the necessary length to bring it to the proper value. This length may be determined from the wattage equations in Chapter 1 and by use of the ohmmeter.

For example, an 800-w unit is to be replaced, and the only available replacement is a 550-w. Using the wattage equation watts equal $E^2/R$, and 115 v as the likely voltage, the resistance of the 800-w unit is $115^2/800$, or 16.5 ohms. The replacement unit at 550 w has a resistance of $115^2/550$, or 24 ohms. By use of the ohmmeter the 16.5-ohm point on the new 24-ohm element may be located and the excess removed.

The new element will be tightly coiled and, as such, too short to fit in the length of groove in the ceramic plate. This is as it should be, for if the new element coil is stretched as it is put into place, it will have some spring tension to hold it in place. So, in stretching a new coil, be careful not to overstretch it, or it will not stay in place in the groove.

## 4.22. Double Units

In order to make the hotplate more versatile, it is provided with two bricks, each with two or sometimes three heating elements of different wattage ratings, and a switch for each heating element. This style is shown in Figure 4-15. Figure 4-16 is the circuit diagram of a typical hotplate of this design. As an example of its versatility, this hotplate may be used to make coffee. For percolator coffee, the higher wattage element is turned on and its heat employed to start the coffee percolating. The high-heat element is then turned off and the medium- or low-heat unit turned on to finish the coffee. Other methods of coffee-making, such as drip and filter, may be followed, utilizing the high- and

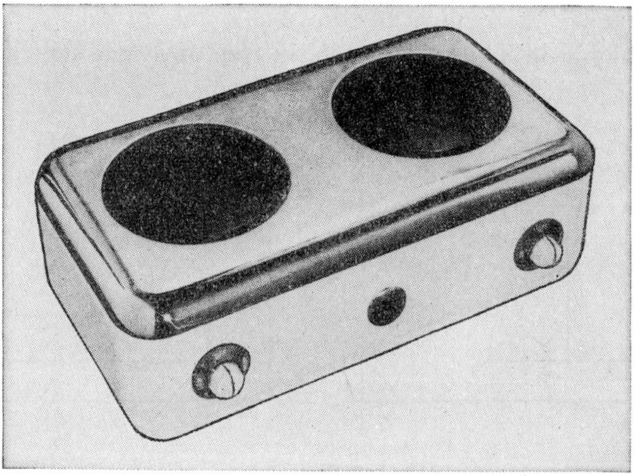

FIG. 4-15. (Courtesy, Knapp-Monarch Co.)

low-heat elements. The same principle will, naturally, apply in the preparation of other foods.

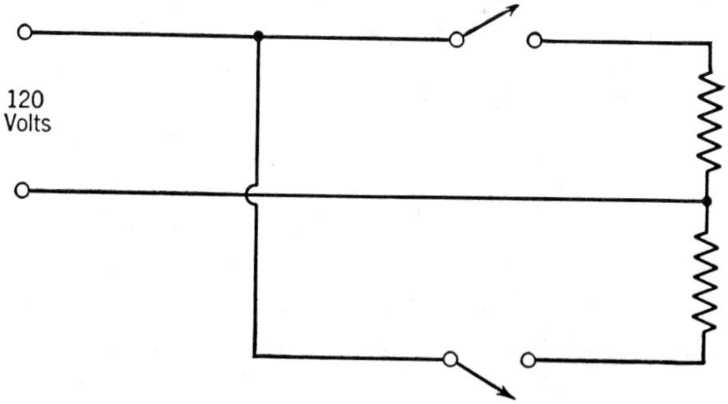


FIG. 4-16.

The dual unit of Figure 4-15 will, of course, be usable if one side is inoperative. Consequently, when a hotplate is received for repair, it often will have something wrong with both plates. In servicing an appliance in this condition, it is necessary to disassemble it completely in order to get to all the points of trouble. It is advisable to make a circuit diagram of the hotplate, as shown in Figure 4-17, to remove any doubt as to the correct wiring when reassembling it. This is particularly true of a unit supplied with

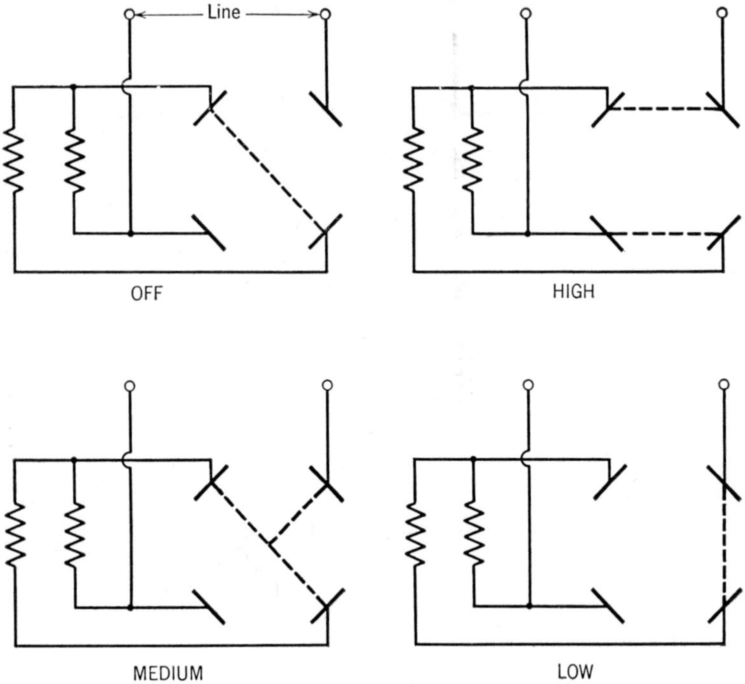


FIG. 4-17.

a four-position heater switch. Figure 4-17 shows the circuit diagram of this switch in its four-heat positions—high, medium, low, and off. Note that two heating elements are used with this switch, but that they need not be of different wattage ratings. In the high-heat position, both elements are at full heat, since they are in parallel across the 120-v line. The medium-heat position places only one of the heating elements across the 120-v line; the other has no voltage applied. In the low-heat-switch setting both

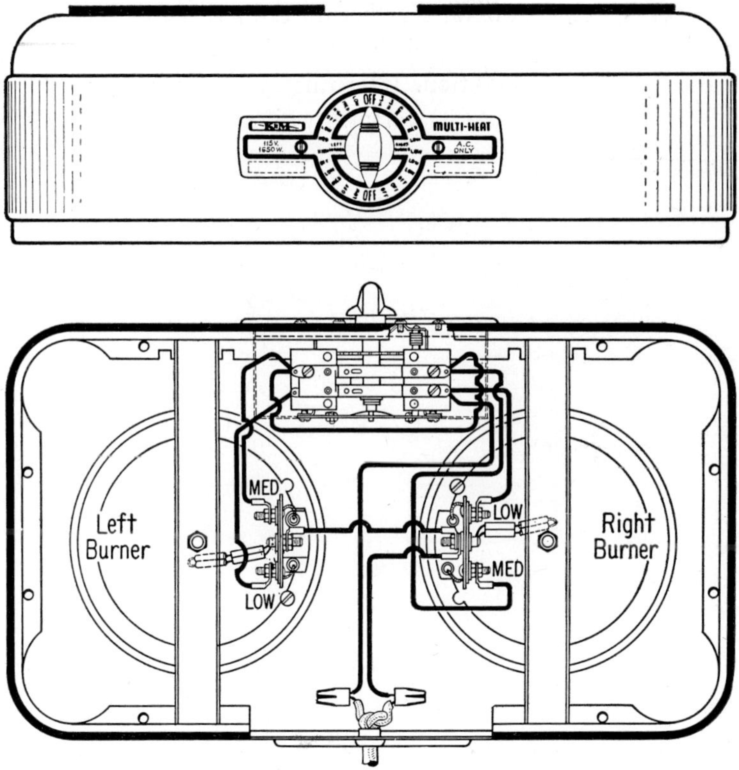


Fig. 4-18. (Courtesy, Knapp-Monarch Co.)

elements are in series across 120-v, and one of the line leads is opened for the OFF setting of the switch.

How will this circuit behave if both elements are the same value of resistance? If each is, for example, a 500-w nichrome coil, the two in parallel will provide 1,000 w for high heat. The one alone on medium heat will produce the heat resultant from 500 w of electrical energy. In the low-heat position two resistors are placed in series. By Ohm's law, doubling the resistance will cut the current flow in half. But wattage is the product of volts times amperes. The voltage is still 120, and the amperage is half that of one heating element; consequently, the wattage is half that of one heating element. Two 500-w elements placed in series will produce only 250 w! Furthermore, in the system just described, the heat of each switch setting is exactly one half that of the next higher position. It is this system of multiple heats which gives the hotplate its versatility; it may easily be used for

FIG. 4-19. (Courtesy, Nesco)

all the cooking processes necessary to prepare a meal, with the exception of baking.

The switch of Figure 4-17 is disassembled by pulling the knob outward and then unscrewing it. The cover slips off next, exposing the switch parts and terminal screws.

Two newer hotplate styles are displayed in Figures 4-18 and 4-19. The principles of operation are the same as in the older types; however, each possesses a feature to attract the prospective user. The hotplate in Figure 4-18 has two burners, each controlled by a common switch—an idea intended to simplify operation. The circuit arrangement, as it appears when the bottom plate is removed, is also shown in the illustration. This particular style of drawing is particularly helpful in assuring proper rewiring when servicing the appliance.

The broiler and grill in Figure 4-19 is presented as an infrared cooker. Actually, infrared or radiant heat is produced by any heating element, a fact which is utilized in the engineering of this appliance, allowing broiling to be done below the heating element. The element itself is an open-style coil, easily accessible for servicing.

## *Repairing Hotplates*

### 4.23. Hotplate Will Not Heat

Possible reasons why a hotplate fails to produce heat are as follows:

Power failure
Defective cord or plug
Defective switch
Poor internal connections
Open-circuited heating element
Low voltage

The procedure for checking receptacle for power and cord and plug for defect are the same as for similar troubles in the electric iron and toaster (Sections 4-9 and 4-17.)

If power is available, and cord and plug are found to be satisfactory, the heating element should be examined for a break. As the heating element on most hotplates is of the open type, this examination can be made without dismantling the hotplate. Quite often the break occurs close to a terminal screw, so it is advisable to examine the portion of the heating element nearest the point where it goes through the brick into the interior of the appliance. A broken or burned-out heating element is best repaired by replacement with a new one, for, although patching is possible, the heating element that burns out once is likely to do so at some other site soon after being spliced. It is customary today to make this type of repair by replacement of the entire heating element and brick assembly, which is more readily available at supply outlets than either component alone, and at a quite reasonable cost.

Poor contact at junction points is a common cause of failure to heat. To obtain access to these points of damage it is necessary to open up the appliance. This is accomplished, on most models, by removing the bottom cover plate (Fig. 4-18), which gives access to the interior of the hotplate. An examination is then made of the points at which cord, connecting wires, and heating-element ends are fastened under screws. Visible indication of defective connection is a discoloration of the screw and/or wire, which may be further verified by manipulation of the wires for evidence of looseness or actual separation. Whether or not poor contact has occurred at a discolored terminal, it remains a potential trouble spot and should be repaired; a new screw and nuts and new wiring should be installed. The screw and nut which have been subjected to sufficient heat to produce discoloration will be tightly welded together, and great care must be exercised in their removal lest the pressure applied by the tools break the porcelain brick. Occasionally removal of the hardware is easier to accomplish with a bolt cutter or hack saw than with screw driver and socket wrench. Choice of a tool depends upon the construction of the appliance, and the extent to which it can be readily dismantled to the point where this repair can be made. When replacing the burned nut and screw, the new ones should be pulled up snug but not too tight, with precautions again being taken against breaking the brick.

The switch as a possible cause of the hotplate's failure to produce heat has been left until last, since it is the least accessible of all the parts of most hotplates. It can be removed and tested (in the ON position) with ohmmeter or series test lamp for continuity, or it can be bypassed with jumper wires, and the cord plugged into the receptacle. If the hotplate now heats, the switch is the obvious cause of trouble. Switches are considered as a sealed unit, which must be replaced rather than repaired when defective.

## 4.24. One Unit Only Will Heat

All except the very simplest hotplate bricks contain two heating-element coils, an arrangement which allows more than one heat value to be obtained by different switch settings, corresponding to various single, series, and parallel connections of the two elements. If one of the pair should fail to function, only one heat value can be obtained from the hotplate. Failure could be due either to a defective switch or to a broken heating element. On all but sealed units, the heating-element break can be found by visual examination. The sealed unit, however, must be disconnected from its circuit wiring and tested with ohmmeter or series test lamp for continuity of its several sections.

If the cause of single-heating-element operation is due to switch trouble, it is a bit more difficult to isolate, especially if the switch is one of the type having a circuit similar to that of Figure 4-17. Testing of this switch is complicated by the many leads to and from the switch. Perhaps the most direct approach to this servicing problem is by voltage measurement, as follows:

Remove the bottom panel, exposing the terminals below the heating elements. This will also make the screw terminals at the switch accessible.

Plug in the appliance and turn the switch to the position in which it is supposed to operate the heating element which fails to glow.

Test across the heating element terminals for line voltage.

Test across the corresponding terminals at the switch.

If voltage is available, the heating element or connecting wires are faulty.

If no voltage is measured, the switch is the defective part, and must be replaced.

If no a-c voltmeter is available, the above test can be made using a 120-v lamp in a pigtail socket, full brilliance of the lamp corresponding to a voltmeter reading equal to line voltage.

## 4.25. Hotplate Blows Fuses

One of the first tests which should be made in routine servicing of appliances is to plug it into the tester shown in Figure 2-2, the operation of which is explained in the accompanying text on page 35. This tester gives instant indication as to whether or not the appliance has an internal short. If it does not, the blown fuse is caused by an overloaded circuit. If the hotplate has an internal short, it may be due to a defective cord or to internal wiring. To determine which of the two is the cause, disconnect one terminal of the cord connection to the appliance and, with an ohmmeter, test separately the cord and the remainder of the appliance. Zero ohms on the meter indicates a short. A shorted cord should be discarded and replaced. Shorted internal wiring can be located by careful examination, especially at points where wires cross. Replace the defective wire with a new piece of the same type.

## ROASTERS

### 4.26. The Roaster Oven

The roaster oven (Fig. 4-20) is an appliance that was developed for the purpose of cooking a substantial meal. It consists of an inner enameled lining surrounded by an asbestos-encased heating element. The heat is kept from dissipating into the surrounding air by a layer of glass wool or rock wool; an outside cover completes the assembly. The heating element is in two parts, one section of which fits snugly around the sides of the inner lining, the other part against the bottom. The two parts are usually connected in series and the entire unit is rated at around 1,300 w.

Supplied with the appliance is a set of pans which, when nested together, fit snugly into the roaster, making it possible for the main dishes of a meal to be cooked simultaneously.

The roaster is frequently thermostatically controlled. The control knob is located at the front center; the thermostat is behind it underneath the outside cover. It is calibrated in degrees of temperature of the inner compartment. This thermostat calibration is adjustable so that corrections may be made.

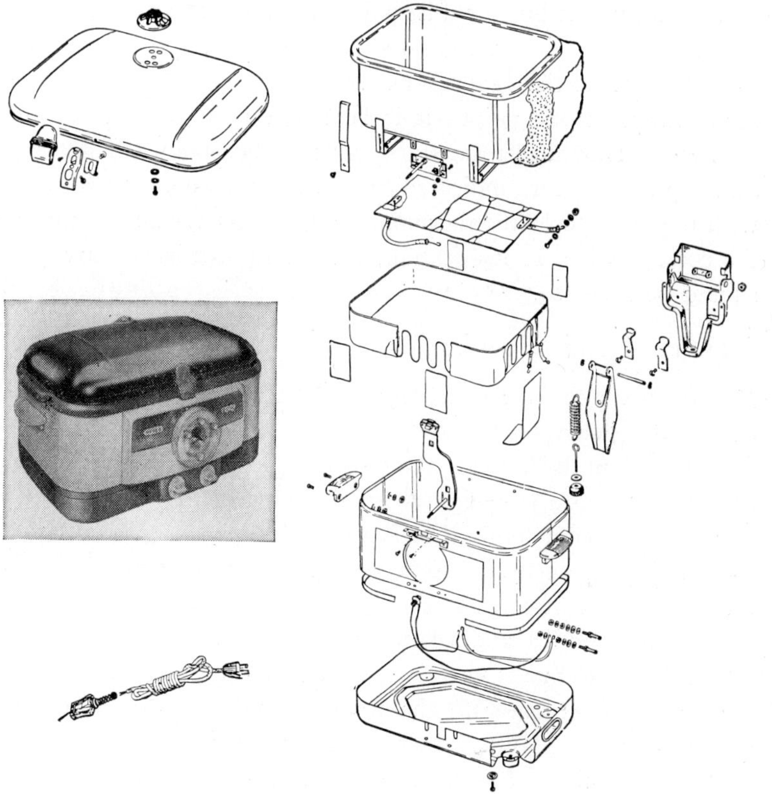

FIG. 4-20. (Courtesy, Nesco)

## 4.27. Temperature Adjustment

The temperature of the roaster oven may be checked with an oven thermometer. The thermometer is placed on the lifting rack supplied with the oven, and the cover closed. The thermostat should be allowed to open and close three times before a reading is taken from the thermometer. The thermostat will overshoot on its first cycle; it may also on the second. By the third cycle it has settled down to its normal operation. The thermometer should be read when the thermostat opens and again when it closes. The average of these two readings should agree with the calibration on the thermostat knob and its pointer. If there is a disagreement, the setscrew holding the knob should be loosened and the knob reset to correct the calibration. When the thermostat has been recalibrated at one point—it is best to do this at a mid-point setting—it should test satisfactorily at other points. That is to say, the temperature indicated by the control knob should agree with the average of the thermometer readings for any setting of the control knob. If it does not, the thermostat is defective and should be replaced.

## 4.28. Pilot and Glow Lamps

At this point the question might be raised: How can it be determined whether the thermostat is open-circuit or closed-circuit without dismantling the roaster to look at it? On the front of the roaster is a pilot light or glow light which glows when the thermostat is completing the electrical circuit and goes out when the thermostat opens. Look at the circuit of Figure 4-21. Here is shown a circuit consisting of three resistors and a thermostat (switch marked T) and a lamp. *R1* and *R2* are the bottom and side heating elements. *R3* is a short length of nichrome wire whose resistance ratio to the total resistance of the circuit is such as to cause 2.5 v (of the total 120 v) to appear across it. If a pilot-lamp bulb rated at 2.5 v is put in parallel with *R3*, the bulb will have the proper voltage applied to its terminals and will glow. When the thermostat opens, the entire circuit, including the lamp, will be turned off. When the pilot lamp blinks on and off, it indicates to the user of the appliance that the roaster has come up to full temperature as indicated by the control knob.

The circuit of Figure 4-21B is similar to that of Figure 4-21A except that there is no lamp paralleling *R3*. *R3*, in this case, is a coil of nichrome placed behind the pilot-lamp window, and the glow of this coil when current is going through it indicates that the circuit is in operation. The lamp of Figure 4-21A can burn out without detriment to the operation of the roaster; however, if the glow-coil indicator burns out, the entire circuit is opened and the roaster is disabled.

Another arrangement that is sometimes used is shown in Figure 4-21C. *R3* is still the glow lamp, but it is shorted out while the heating elements are at top heat. When the thermostat opens, the glow lamp turns on, but the added resistance in the circuit lowers the wattage of the entire circuit and a reduced heat

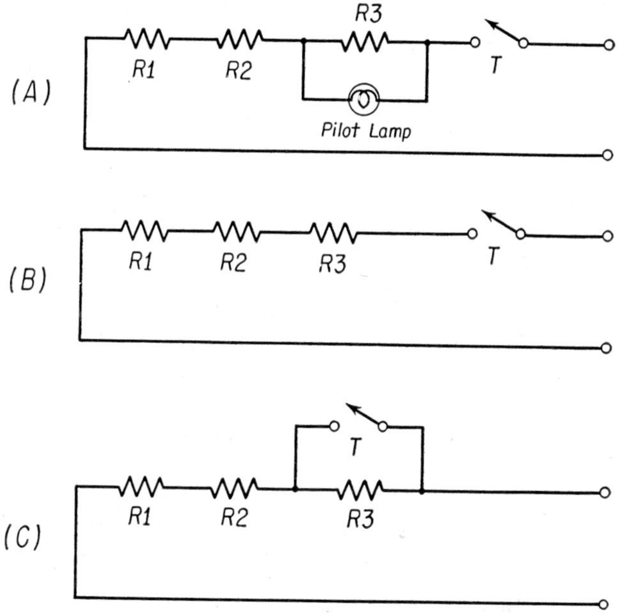


FIG. 4-21.

causes the thermostat cycling to begin. Note that the OFF and ON conditions of the thermostat are the exact opposite of the arrangement shown in Figure 4-21B. In the event there is no pilot indicator on the roaster, an ammeter (Fig. 2-4) will reveal whether the thermostat is opened or closed.

## 4.29. Timers

One other device will complete the modern roaster. Figure 4-20 shows a clock mounted on the front of the roaster. Also shown are set-on and set-off knobs. The clock on some models is an electric one, and may, if desired, be left on continuously for the purpose of providing a kitchen timepiece. Built into the clock mechanism is a switch which may be used to turn on and off the

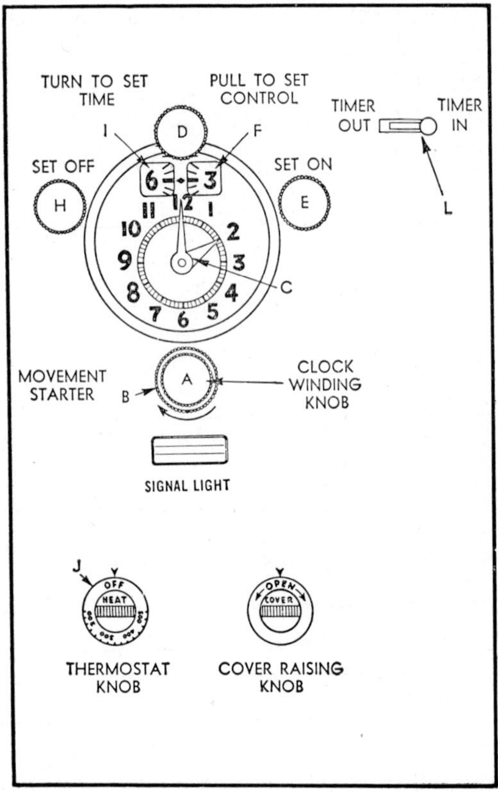


1. Be sure Timer switch "L" is snapped to the right to "IN" position.
2. Wind the clock by turning Clock Winding Knob "A" clockwise until fully wound. Make sure Time Clock has started by turning Movement Starter "B" clockwise until stopped; then release.
3. Set the hands "C" to the correct time of day by turning knob "D" clockwise.
4. Turn the right hand knob "E" marked "SET ON" clockwise until dial "F" shows the time you want the roaster to start cooking.
5. Turn the left hand knob "H" marked "SET OFF" clockwise until dial "I" shows the time you want the roaster to stop cooking.
6. Pull out knob "D" which you used to set the clock hands, until the switch clicks. The automatic Time Clock is now in operation.
7. Set Thermostat Knob "J" at desired cooking temperature as given in recipes.
8. Plug Roaster Cord securely into roaster and convenient outlet.

FIG. 4-22. (Courtesy, Nesco)

heating element. Moreover, the clockwork is designed so as to turn on the switch at whatever hour the set-on pointer indicates, and turn it off at the time indicated by the set-off pointer. Mrs. Housewife may place the main course of her meal in the roaster in the morning, set it to cook from three p.m. to five p.m., leave the house for the day, and return to find it ready to eat. The appearance and operation of a timer is shown in Figure 4-22.

The repair of a clockwork mechanism is a job for a watchmaker and, in general, should not be attempted in the appliance repair shop. Realizing this, most manufacturers do not make available parts for clock mechanism repairs; it is their policy, instead, to supply the complete unit for replacement. An exception to this is a brand of electric clock which has a sealed unit with reduction gears contained in the sealed-in part. This assembly is available for replacement through dealers who handle this brand of timepiece. This brand of clock and its sealed unit are shown in Figure 10-9.

The manufacturers of the roaster oven also make a smaller appliance of a similar pattern. In Figure 4-23 is a round casserole which is a simplified version of the roaster just discussed. Notice that this appliance has no thermostat, no pilot lamp, no timer. In some models there is a double heating element providing two heats—low and high. At the rear of the unit is a recessed place where the attachment-cord plug is plugged in. There are, however, three, instead of two, prongs for this plug. The plug will fit only two prongs. A sliding panel exposes only two of these prongs at a time. The center prong is attached to both heating elements, and the outer prongs each to one of the elements. One position of the sliding panel permits the plug to be fitted onto the prongs for the high-wattage element, and the other sliding-panel position permits use of the low-heat element. Another arrangement allowing two heats with a simple shifting of the plug has three prongs set in a triangular shape. Attaching the plug to the top and left prongs connects one heating element to the source of power; fitting the plug onto the upper and right prongs provides another heat by putting the other heating element into the circuit.

## 4.30. Disassembly

Any one of the roaster ovens is easy to disassemble for repair. The bottom cover is removed by loosening the two or four screws which hold it in place. This exposes the bottom layer of insulating glass or rock wool, which may be lifted out of place. If the appliance has a bottom heating element, thermostat, pilot lamp, or clock, these parts are now visible and, with the exception of the clock, may be removed for repair. The outer cover

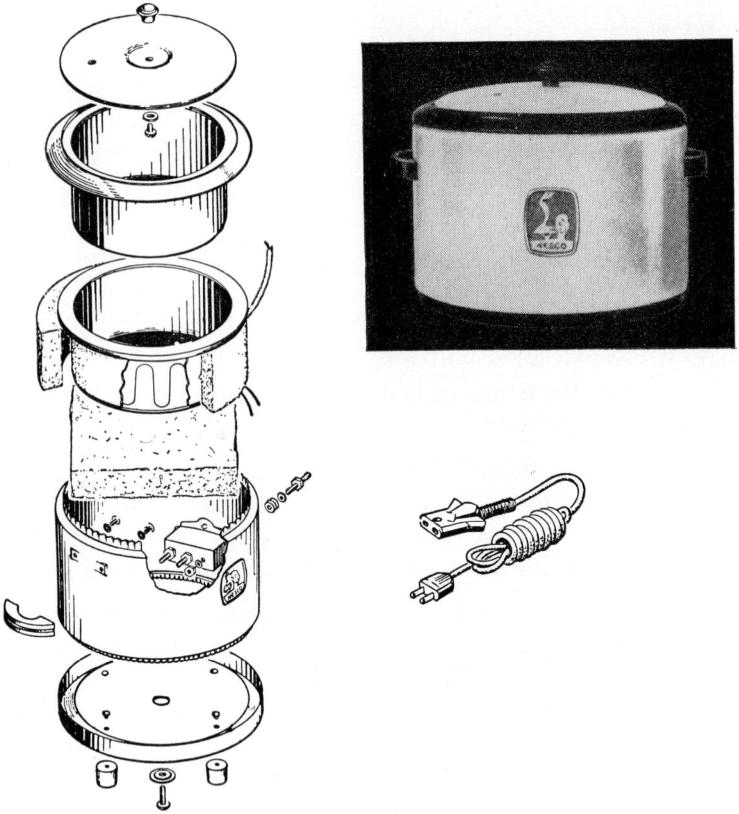

(Fig. 4-23. (Courtesy, Nesco)

may be slipped off, and side insulation removed; these parts are not bolted down but merely held in place by the bottom cover. This exposes the side heating element. Care should be exercised in handling glass wool, because this material causes an annoying itching when it comes in contact with the skin. The use of talcum powder to cover the hands and arms while handling glass wool will reduce the tendency to cling, and to a large degree eliminate the itching produced by it.

## *Repairing Roasters*

### 4.31. Roaster Fails to Heat

Failure to heat will be due to one or more of the following:

Power failure
Defective cord set
Defective thermostat
Broken heating element
Poor internal connection

Power failure may be due to these conditions:

Blown fuse
Defective receptacle
Defective wiring

Testing for power failure by substitution is explained in Section 4-9.

The cord set on a roaster is a separate unit consisting of a 6-foot length of HPD wire with plug cap and heater plug attached. It can be tested for an open circuit as follows:

1. Connect a jumper across the prongs of the plug cap.

2. Test across the terminals of the heater plug (at the end of the cord opposite from the plug cap) with ohmmeter or series test lamp. Zero ohms, or failure of the lamp to burn, indicates a defect in the cord set. Replace all or part of the set.

3. Make an identical test across the terminals at the roaster with the thermostat advanced to an ON position. If a timer is built into the roaster, it should also be turned on. Zero on the ohmmeter, or failure of the test lamp to burn, indicates that the defect is within the appliance, which must then be dismantled for further testing.

The insulating material in the roaster is glass wool, and must be carefully handled. See Section 4-30 for recommendations in this regard.

After the roaster has been opened, the control devices are the next parts to be tested. These consist of any or all of the following:

OFF-ON switch
Thermostat
Timer

All of these are usually located at the same electrical position in the circuit (Fig. 4-21). To determine whether the cause of failure to heat lies in the heating element or the control devices, place a jumper wire around the controls, thus completing the heating-element circuit around them, and once again test for continuity at the terminals to which the plug attaches. Indication of a complete circuit is evidence that the controls are faulty and should be separately tested.

The thermostat is a form of switch and can be tested as such: that is, for continuity in the ON position. The same test is used on the OFF-ON switch if one is present. Neither the switch nor the thermostat is so built as to allow of repairs; consequently, a new one must be installed.

The timer consists of a clock mechanism, which may be either electrical or mechanical (similar to the works of an alarm clock). Repairs to the clock portion of the timer is of the same nature as that described in Chapter 10 for electric clocks. The timer also contains a set of contacts operated by the clockwork. Damage to the contact points can result in failure to heat. If the manner of assembly of the timer is such as to allow dismantling, the mechanism and contact can be examined and, if need be, replaced; otherwise it is tested as a single pole switch, and if found defective must be replaced.

If all controls are found to be satisfactory, the terminals at which connections are made should be examined for evidence of a condition which might cause current interruption. These are the indications:

Burned or charred insulation on wires
Discolored bolts or screws

Manipulation of the wires leading to the terminals will help to locate defective connections. (Whether a cause of trouble or not, any damaged wires or discolored terminal hardware should be replaced.)

If all other parts appear satisfactory, the conclusion to be drawn is that failure to produce heat is due to the heating element(s). The nichrome wire used in roasters is of a rather large gauge sandwiched between sheets of asbestos. While the assembly can be opened for examination, a test with an ohmmeter or series test lamp will show if the nichrome is broken. Replacement assemblies for both bottom and side elements are available.

## 4.32. Roaster Does Not Get Hot Enough

Too little heat is due to three factors:

Cord and plug
Thermostat
Poor internal connection

Cord and plug can cause reduced heating through poor connection where cord is fastened to plug. This is apparent by the discoloration which the heat produces at the point of poor contact. Whether to repair or replace the cord set depends upon its general condition and the extent of heat damage. If in doubt, replace it; a new cord set is, in any event, insurance against immediate trouble from this assembly.

If the thermostat has got out of adjustment, it can cause either too low or too high temperatures. If operation is not too far off normal, some correction can be obtained by moving the thermostat nearer to or farther from the heating element, as required. Because of mounting limitations, however, the thermostat cannot be moved too far, so if the temperature is greatly at variance with normal the thermostat should be replaced. See Section 4-27 for comparison of roaster temperature with thermostat calibration temperature.

Procedure for repairs of poor internal connections is the same as given at beginning of this section.

## 4.33. Roaster Shocks User

The obvious cause of shock is an unintentional ground—that is, the internal wiring is touching the frame of the appliance at some spot. This might occur in the roaster at four places:

Plug terminal
Control device (thermostat, timer, OFF-ON switch)
Pilot lamp
Heating element

Isolating the ground requires that the roaster be disassembled. As each of the components is disconnected from the remainder of the circuit, it is tested for continuity to the roaster frame. Either an ohmmeter or a series test lamp can be used for this test, one terminal of the tester being placed on the frame of the roaster, the other on the electrical terminal screws of the various parts of the roaster—pilot lamp, thermostat timer, and so on—until the part causing the trouble is located. The part being tested must be disconnected from the remainder of the electric circuit lest it appear defective due to being electrically continuous with the part which actually is grounded.

If the ground occurs at the heating element or wiring, it is possible to eliminate it by placing a sheet of asbestos between the wire and the frame, being sure to fasten it in place securely. If, however, the ground is within some part which is bolted onto the frame, this part must be replaced.

Occasionally, the ground is of a nature known as intermittent, meaning that it occurs and then disappears at random. Such a ground is more difficult to locate. Often its site will be disclosed when the parts of the roaster are moved to and fro while being tested. Examination of the appliance for worn or broken insulation is another scheme for locating an intermittent ground.

## 4.34. Pilot or Glow Lamp Burned Out

If a glow lamp is used in the roaster, it will consist of a short coiled length of nichrome wire located behind a small window through which its glow is visible. Some or all of the current for the roaster goes through this coil, and its glow is evidence that the roaster is operating. If the glow lamp fails to burn, either it is burned out (as can be observed when the appliance is disassembled to the point where this part is visible) or some other part in the roaster is preventing current flow, and repair or replacement of the defective part, as indicated above, will restore glow-lamp operation. If the glow coil itself is defective, a replacement with a coil of identical gauge and resistance is essential; if data is not available as to gauge and resistance, a replacement part can be obtained from either a parts supplier or the manufacturer.

When a pilot lamp is used, it will be a low-voltage lamp because of space limitation. The voltage divider principle (Sec. -40) is used to supply the required low voltage, the various sections of the heating element acting as the voltage divider. Thus, the roaster current is 10 amp, a length of wire having 0.15 hms resistance will produce a voltage drop of 1.5 v, a value suitable as a source of voltage for a pilot lamp of that rating. Such a calculation, based on a knowledge of the appliance current and the pilot-lamp voltage, will enable the service man to determine the proper value of the voltage drop wire. The drop wire is necessarily located close to the pilot lamp, and is often connected the thermostat. If, when the thermostat is serviced, this wire is connected to the wrong end of the thermostat, the pilot lamp will burn out the first time the roaster is operated; the repair man should be careful to avoid this error.

If the pilot lamp is burned out, there is usually a break to be seen in the filament. It may be tested with an ohmmeter, or by dry cell of the proper voltage; but not with the series test lamp. The current required to operate the test lamp will burn out a pilot lamp.

## 4.35. Lid Will Not Remain Closed

Two types of lids are to be found on roasters. One is merel lifted on and off the roaster; the other is hinged to the roaste and held closed by a latch at the top front. The fit of hinge an clamp on the latter type may have become too tight or too loose or hinges may have become bent, any of which might cause fail ure of the lid to close. Adjustments on both hinge and clamp ar provided to allow for such an occurrence. Loosening the scre holding the hinge in place allows the hinge to be moved a shor distance. The screw holding the clamp fits into a slotted hole loosening the screw permits up and down adjustment of th clamp. One other lid adjustment is available: the spring whic causes the lid to rise when the latch knob is operated can b adjusted for greater or less tension by a screw to which th spring is fastened. The setting of this screw is secured by a loc nut, which must be loosened to allow the spring to be adjuste (Fig. 4-20).

# HOTPADS

## 4.36. General Discussion

Pictured in Figure 4-24 is the electric heating pad, an appl ance which has provided untold relief to sufferers from su ailments as can be alleviated by the application of heat. The us of this appliance is warned by the manufacturer to take care prevent blistering from too prolonged use, particularly if a hea cover is used over it.

This appliance is provided with a heating element of ve fine nichrome wire in order to obtain the high resistance nece sary to provide a very low wattage, and consequently low he dissipation. The average temperature of a hotpad ranges fro 115° F. to 175° F. The hair-fine nichrome wire used is coil around a length of asbestos string, and this string is sewed or a piece of cloth inside the hotpad. The outer cover, in manufa ture, is seamed on three sides, then turned inside out. T lectrical parts are inserted and the opening top-seamed. When he hotpad is disassembled for repair, the top-seamed end should e opened. After repairs have been made it will, perhaps, be dvisable for the repair man to enlist the aid of wife or mother o resew the outer cover.

FIG. 4-24. (Courtesy, Landers, Frary, & Clark)

The switch with which the hotpad is fitted has four posi- ons—high, medium, and low heats, and off. Two circuits are own by which this is accomplished. Figure 4-25A is the dia- am of a circuit of a tapped heating element; varying heats are tained by varying the resistance in the circuit. The bottom sition of the switch (in the diagram) provides high heat, and other positions are for progressively lower temperatures. A ore elaborate hookup employing four thermostats is that of gure 4-25B. The thermostats are labeled *T1, T2, T3, T4*. The ttom position of the switch is high heat, and the circuit consists of *T2,* the heating element, and *T1*. Both thermostats are set fo the same temperature—about 175° F. *T1* is an emergency ther mostat. It will prevent overheating in the event of failure of *T* (or any of the other thermostats when in use). Moving the switc up one notch—to the medium-heat position—puts *T3* in th

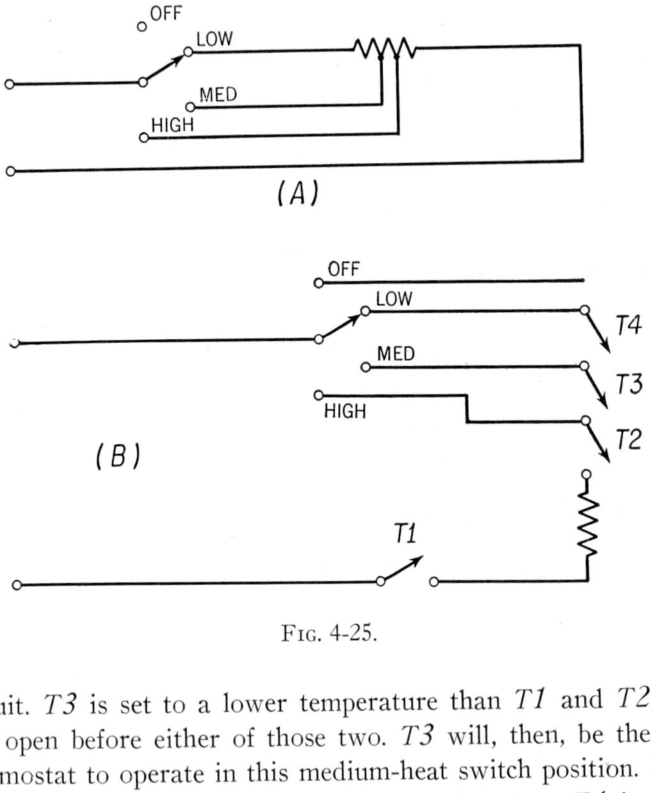


FIG. 4-25.

circuit. *T3* is set to a lower temperature than *T1* and *T2,* a will open before either of those two. *T3* will, then, be the on thermostat to operate in this medium-heat switch position. Mo ing the switch up to the next-to-last notch brings *T4* into t circuit in series with the heating element and the other therm stats. *T4* is set to the lowest heat of all and now controls t average temperature of the hotpad. This system of having mo than one thermostat in the heating element circuit is a wort while safety precaution. If any of the thermostats should f and refuse to open, the user will still be protected against ov ıeating of the pad, since the other thermostats in the circuit at he same time will provide protection.

When servicing a heating pad it is advisable to isolate the ause of trouble with as little dismantling as possible. All parts re sewed into place, and any stitching which is ripped out will equire some time to replace. Switch terminals, places where ttachment cord connects to heating element, and thermostat erminals are good check points. By progressively checking for ontinuity, using the series test lamp from point to point, the efective element, wire, or thermostat may be definitely located nd replaced without disturbing the other circuit components.

## *Repairing Hotpads*

### .37. Pad Fails to Heat

Failure of the hotpad to heat can be caused by the following:

Power failure (Sec. 4-9)
Defective cord or plug
Defective switch
Defective thermostat
Open-circuited heating element

The cord on a hotpad cannot readily be disconnected from ıe appliance, and thus cannot be tested for an open circuit with- ıt ripping apart the hotpad. However, the switch and the plug ın quite easily be checked as the cause of failure to heat. The vitch is mounted on the cord somewhere near the center of its ngth, making the former accessible for servicing while the plug in its conventional location. Proceed as follows:

1. Examine the plug cap terminals for evidence of poor connection to cord. Repair if necessary.

2. Open the switch by removing the two screws which hold its covers in place. Examine for signs of breakage, bent contacts, or discoloration due to heat. Complete the cord circuit by jumpering around the switch. Plug in hotpad and

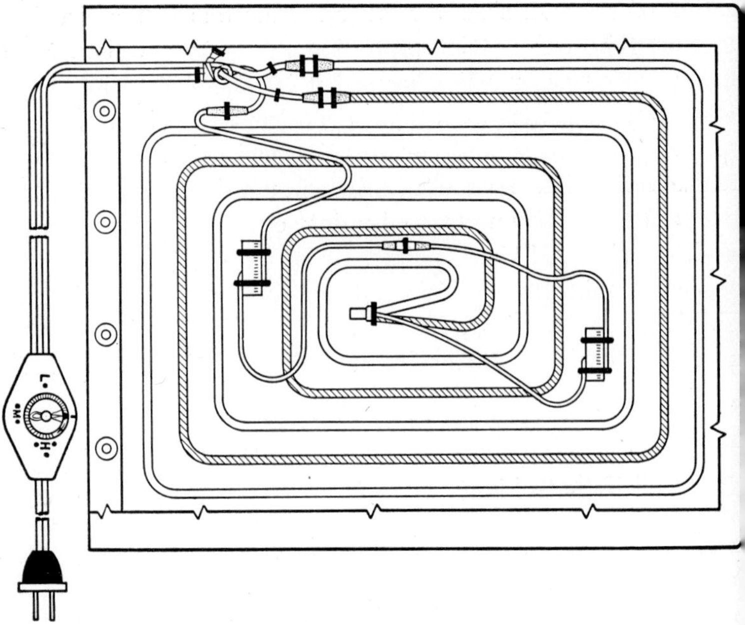

FIG. 4-26.

see if it now heats. If it does, the fault is in the switcl Replace the defective switch with a new one.

3. If necessary to test further, cut the threads at the sean of the hotpad, exposing the interior.

4. Locate the connections of the cord to the heating elemen Disconnect the cord and test its conductors with ohmmet or series test lamp for continuity. If the cord is in part three-conductor cable (Fig. 4-26), the color of the insula tion, or the color of a tracer thread covering the insulatio will help to identify corresponding ends of wires whi making the continuity test. Discard damaged cord; repla with new one.

5. Test each thermostat. This is done by disconnecting o end of it from the circuit and applying the continuity test to the thermostat terminals. At room temperature, the

should be practically zero ohm continuity through each thermostat. A defective one will have a measurable amount of resistance or show as an open circuit.

6. Test the heating element with an ohmmeter. A high (by comparison with other appliances) resistance reading is normal. A defect in the heating element is indicated by a reading of infinity on the ohmmeter.

Replacement of the heating element is somewhat difficult, ince it must be sewed into the hotpad: a craft which is not rdinarily considered as a part of the appliance repairman's trade. )n the other hand, inasmuch as the heating element will not e visible when the hotpad is reassembled, electrical security is nore important than the quality of the tailoring.

The heating element assembly—nichrome wire wrapped round an asbestos cord—is sold from spools, and the proper ength to use must be calculated from the wattage rating of the otpad. This calculation supplies the necessary electrical resist- nce value. Resistance is measured along the new heating element o determine the correct place to cut it. The new heating element 1 the circuit should not be connected by soldering; instead, ne of the clamp-type connectors should be used.

## .38. Hotpad Gets Too Hot (or Not Hot Enough)

The hotpad temperature will be abnormal if the thermostat defective. Following are the usual temperature values when peration is normal:

| | |
|---|---|
| High | 175° F. |
| Medium | 150° F. |
| Low | 115° F. |

The actual temperature of the hotpad can be determined by rapping it around a thermometer, giving the hotpad time nough to heat, and then reading the temperature. If a labora- ry-type thermometer is used, the bulb and lower stem only eed be wrapped in the hotpad, and continuous observation of the behavior of the heating element and thermostat(s) may thus be obtained.

The thermostats used on some hotpads are adjustable. External to the thermostat, at one end, are located a small screw and lock nut. The screw adjusts the position to the stationary contact in the thermostat. Tightening the screw increases the cutout temperature of the thermostat, while loosening it lowers the temperature. The hotpad should be wrapped around the thermometer while this adjustment is being made, the thermometer indicating when a correct adjustment has been obtained.

Observe the circuit shown in Figure 4-25B. Four thermostats are used here, one for each of the three temperatures of the hotpad, and the fourth as a safety feature; its cutout temperature is slightly above the highest heat of the hotpad, and it is located where it will break the circuit regardless of switch position, in the event of failure of one of the other thermostats to operate. The fourth, or safety thermostat, should be adjusted first of all, the others afterward, when working on this hotpad.

Another form of erratic operation is the behavior of hotpad which may heat one day, yet refuse to do so the next. This is due to a broken heating element which behaves normally when the hotpad is folded or positioned so as to cause the broken end of the heating element to touch, yet in another position will be open-circuited and produce no heat. Testing the heating element with an ohmmeter while flexing the hotpad will verify this condition. It is necessary to replace the heating element to restore normal operation.

## 4.39. Hotpad Blows Fuses

Examine the portion of the cord adjacent to and within the hotpad. This section of the cord is subjected to an unusual amount of bending and flexing, and there is a possibility that the insulation may have parted, allowing the conductors in the cord to touch, blowing a fuse. Repair or replace cord.

# COFFEE MAKERS (PERCOLATORS)

## 4.40. General Discussion

As in the other appliances that produce heat electrically, the electric percolator—shown in Figure 4-27—is fitted with a nichrome-wire heating element. This will either be a sealed unit,

FIG. 4-27. (Courtesy, Landers, Frary, & Clark)

or will be found enclosed in a shell which opens at the bottom. The sealed unit or element container is pressed into the bottom of the percolator and fastened into place with a nut, under which is a gasket. All precautions are taken to make the fitting watertight so that coffee cannot get out of the pot and seep into the electrical parts below. The nut that holds the heating-element assembly in place is located inside the pot, and is not easily accessible with conventional shop tools. It may be found necessary to fashion a special wrench for this purpose; or, if the repair shop is specializing in the repair of some one brand, the manufacturer will supply, at a small cost, the special tools required to repair his appliances. The heating-element assembly is removed by pressing it out at the bottom of the coffeepot. This will require some force, so care should be taken that any damage due to hammering is directed to the heating-element assembly, which will be replaced, rather than to the coffeepot itself. A new gasket should be used when reassembling to prevent leakage.

A protective device is built into the coffeepot. In some cases this is a "fuse" (Sec. 4.41). This fuse consists of a piece of alloy metal with a low melting point. The fuse completes the electric circuit and, in the event of overheating, will melt and open the circuit. The fuse is not self-healing, but must be replaced with a new one after it has melted. To prevent the fuse from melting unnecessarily, the appliance owner is instructed (by the booklet enclosed with the new appliance) not to operate the coffeepot without water in it.

Protection from overheating, and consequent discoloration and possible damage to the coffeepot, is achieved in some makes of percolator by use of a thermostat. This thermostat is designed to open after the length of time required to make the coffee. Because tastes vary as to the length of time the coffee should "perc," an adjustment for the thermostat, with an external control knob, is provided. In a circuit such as that shown in Figure 4-28, a pilot lamp may be used to indicate the coffee is ready. *R1* is the heating element and *T* is the thermostat. The pilot lamp *P* is in a portion of the circuit of a tapped resistor, *R2*. The tap is located at such a point as to provide approximately 5 v between the tap and nearest end of the resistor, to operate the pilot lamp. *R2* and the pilot lamp are both shorted out by the closed thermostat until the coffee is finished. The thermostat then opens, allowing current to flow through the pilot lamp, and its glow indicates that the coffee is ready. Also, the opening of the thermostat puts *R2* in series with *R1*, reducing the current flow through the heating element and causing operation at a reduced wattage and at a temperature which serves merely to keep the coffee hot.

Occasionally a percolator is received for repair because moisture in the electric parts has caused shorts or grounds. The

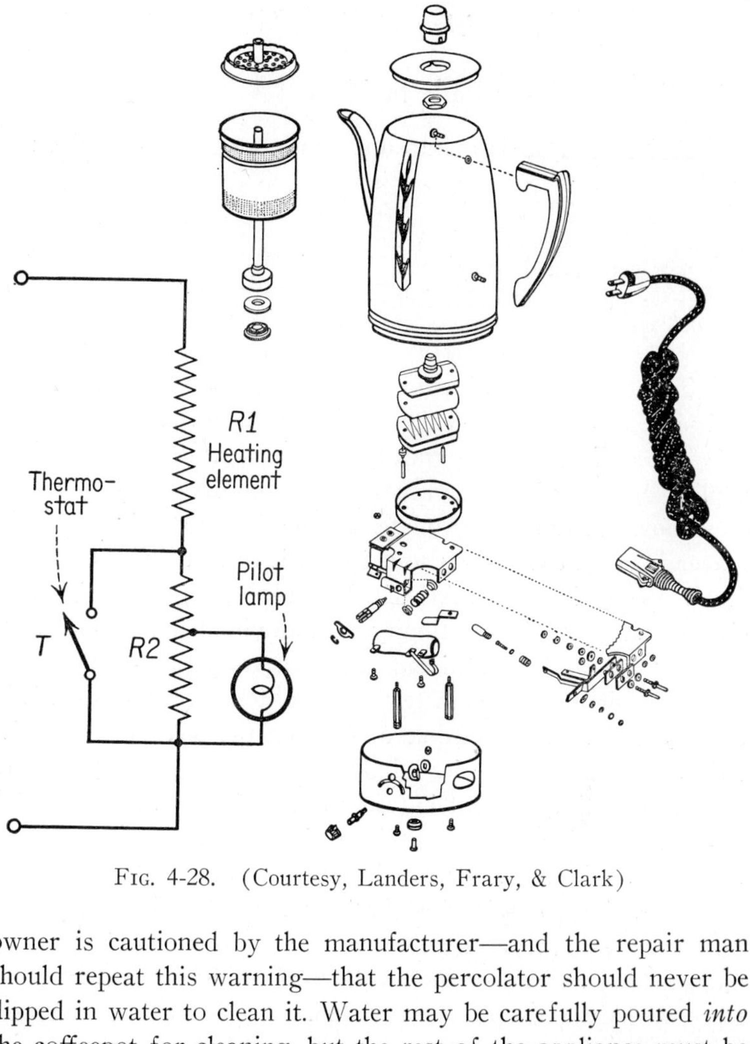


FIG. 4-28. (Courtesy, Landers, Frary, & Clark)

owner is cautioned by the manufacturer—and the repair man should repeat this warning—that the percolator should never be dipped in water to clean it. Water may be carefully poured *into* the coffeepot for cleaning, but the rest of the appliance must be kept dry. Pure water is an insulator, but tap water contains dissolved minerals which make it a conductor, and the conducting paths which water produces in the electrical part of the appliance cause short circuits, grounds, insulation deterioration, and a host of other electrical troubles.

## *Repairing Coffee Makers*

### 4.41. Coffee Maker Fails to Heat

Failure to heat is due to one or more of the following:

Power failure (Sec. 4.9)
Defective cord and/or plug (Sec. 4.9)
Defective thermostat
Open-circuited heating element
Blown-out fuse

The test and repairs for power failure and defective cord and plug are discussed in the section indicated.

The coffee maker thermostat is located in the bottom of the appliance. It can be made accessible for observation and testing by removal of the bottom plate. As the thermostat in the coffee maker is not a covered or sealed unit, it can easily be examined for evidence of damage. Also, it should be disconnected from the circuit and tested for continuity with an ohmmeter or series test lamp. As a thermostat is merely a heat-operated single pole switch, it should, at room temperature, test as a closed switch; that is, it should measure zero ohms on the ohmmeter, or give full brilliance on the series test lamp.

The heating element is tested in like manner. Disconnect it from the circuit and measure its resistance. Compare the measured value with that calculated from the known wattage of the appliance. An open-circuited heating element is indicated by a resistance measure of infinity, or by failure of the series test lamp to glow. If either thermostat or heating element is found to be defective, it should be replaced.

The coffee maker shown in Figure 4-28 has the heating element located below the coffeepot, where it is easily accessible; in some other makes, however, the heating element is placed in a cylinder which extends up into the coffeepot and is held in place by a gasketed nut. Removal of the heating-element assembly for replacement requires that this nut be removed—a task which may require special tools, and extreme caution lest the appliance be damaged (Sec. 4.40).

The fuse in a coffee maker consists of a piece of low-melting-point alloy which either completes the electrical circuit or holds it closed by the pressure it exerts on a contactor. Unlike an ordinary fuse—which melts because of its own heat—the coffee-maker fuse melts because of the heat of the appliance. The primary purpose of the fuse is to prevent damage resulting from dry operation of the coffee maker. The metal parts of the coffee maker will actually get hotter if the appliance is operated dry than it will with water in it, since the highest temperature to which the coffee maker can rise with water in the pot is the temperature of boiling water, 212° F. No such temperature limitation occurs with dry operation; thus, the protection offered by the fuse is against damage caused by dry operation. The fuse should, of course, be checked as a possible cause of failure to heat, especially if it is known, or has been reported, that the coffee maker has been operated without water in the pot.

## 4.42. Coffee Maker Fails to Turn Off

The automatic action of a coffee maker is intended not so much for heat control as for time control. The thermostat is heated in such a manner, and at such a time rate, as to cause it to act rather slowly—so slowly, in fact, that it does not operate until the coffee is finished. When the thermostat opens, two things occur: the pilot lamp turns on, and a resistance is placed in series with the heating element (circuit of Fig. 4-28) which lowers the temperature of the heating element to where it will just keep the contents hot. The thermostat is slow to close, too, generally not closing again until the appliance is disconnected. If, then, the thermostat is stuck, or its points welded together, the pilot lamp will not turn on, and full heat will be supplied to the contents of the coffee maker long after the contents are ready. Hence, a complaint that the coffee maker gets "too hot" can be attributed to a defective thermostat, which can be either repaired or replaced, as necessary.

## 4.43. Pilot Lamp Will Not Burn

Failure of the pilot lamp to glow may be due to one or more of three causes:

Burned-out lamp
Lamp loose in socket
Open circuit to lamp

The lamp can be tested by connecting it across a dry cell or battery of voltage equal to the lamp rating. If a battery is not available, an ohmmeter can be used for this test, provided the batteries inside the ohmmeter do not exceed the voltage rating of the lamp. If it does, the ohmmeter may burn out a good lamp. A low-resistance reading on the ohmmeter indicates a good lamp; infinity, a burned-out lamp. Do not use the series test lamp; it will burn out a perfectly good pilot lamp.

If the lamp is loose in its socket, or if the metal parts of the socket have become corroded, causing poor contact, this condition is usually evidenced by moving the lamp in its socket with the appliance plugged in and the thermostat contacts held apart with a piece of insulating material—fiber board, for example. If the lamp has been making poor contact, it will flicker occasionally when moved in its socket. It may be possible to clean and tighten the socket; otherwise, it must be replaced.

Consider the circuit of Figure 4-28. Notice the resistor placed in series with the heating element when the thermostat is open. Observe that this resistor is tapped to supply pilot-lamp voltage (voltage-divider principle). If the portion of the resistor between pilot lamp and heating element becomes open-circuited, the pilot lamp will receive no current—will fail to glow. If the portion of the resistor across which the pilot lamp is connected should become open-circuited, the pilot lamp will be burned out. In either case, the keep-hot feature will fail to operate. So, the combination of pilot-lamp failure and cooling of the coffee maker immediately after the coffee is made indicates that the resistor has become open-circuited. The obvious repair is replacement of the resistor.

## 4.44. Coffee Maker Blows Fuses

Having eliminated an overloaded circuit as the cause of fuses blowing, the coffee maker should be checked for an internal short. Proceed as follows, using an ohmmeter.

1. Disconnect the heating element and test for resistance value. Zero ohms indicates a short. A shorted heating element is usually due to deterioration of insulation by moisture. If the heating element is shorted, this source of trouble (moisture) should be checked, and the leaky condition repaired, along with replacement of the heating element.

2. Quite often, bare copper strips are used as the conductors from terminals to heating element. These strips are insulated from other parts by their own rigidity, which positions them so as not to touch other conducting parts. Observe if these are touching one another or the frame. If so, bend them so as to allow adequate clearance for good insulation.

3. Test the terminal screws to which the plug attaches. These screws are insulated from the frame by mica washers, and the mica may have slipped, broken, or become deteriorated, allowing the short to occur. The screws should be tightened, and the mica washers replaced if necessary.

# WAFFLE IRONS AND SANDWICH GRILLS

## 4.45. General Discussion

The waffle iron and the sandwich grill are essentially the same appliance, the only difference being in the type of grid employed. The sandwich grill is provided with a flat, smooth grid, while the grid of the waffle iron is a pattern which is the inverse of the familiar waffle design. More than one manufacturer has made a device that is a combination of the two by supplying both types of removable grids with his appliance. The unit is equipped with a heating element rated at around 750 w. This heating element is separated into halves; one is mounted below the bottom grid, and the other above the top grid. The two parts are connected (most frequently) in series, and are joined electrically by wires running through a length of flexible tubing at the rear of the appliance.

To obtain satisfactory service from the waffle iron, it is essential that the two halves of the heating element be of correct value. If the resistance is not properly divided when this appliance is repaired, there will be an uneven distribution of heat, resulting in uneven cooking.

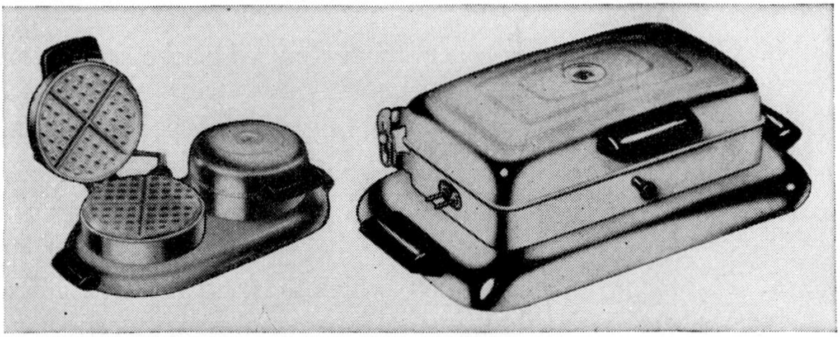

FIG. 4-29. (Courtesy, Knapp-Monarch Co.)

This type of appliance is used with foodstuffs which are to be rapidly cooked—actually, only the surface is cooked thoroughly; therefore there is no need to use a control device, so you are not likely to find a thermostat on the waffle iron or sandwich grill. Some are, however, fitted with an indicator which shows the progress of the cooking or grilling process. The usual construction of this device is a bimetallic strip in the form of a spiral coil. One end of the coil is fastened to the appliance, and the free end has a pointer attached which is visible through a small window in the top. Fastened below the pointer is a scale. As the temperature of the appliance and the cooking food increases, the bending action of the bimetallic strip causes the pointer to move across the scale. The pointer has been calibrated to show exactly when the grilling is completed and food is ready to be removed.

As has been previously pointed out, uneven heating is one of the troubles that may occur in this appliance. Another is no heat at all, resulting from an open heating element or a defect somewhere else in the electric circuit. These troubles are relatively easy to remedy. There is, however, another class of troubles which beset this type of appliance because of improper use. Manufacturers specify that a new waffle or sandwich grid must be greased before being put into use. The grease is applied the first time the iron is used, and the appliance heated until the grease smokes. The first waffle made after this absorbs the excess grease and should be discarded. The grease which remains in the grid prevents subsequent waffles from sticking. If the appliance should at any time be overheated, the oil will be boiled out of the pores of the metal, and any waffles baked thereafter will stick to the grid. The food particles which are stuck to the grid bake on, and removal is impossible by ordinary cleaning methods. Sandblasting is required to put the grid in satisfactory operating condition again.

It is important that the grid be at the proper temperature before pouring on the batter. If it is not hot enough, the waffle will stick, again leaving particles which cannot be easily removed and which will contribute to sticking of subsequent waffles. The proper temperature may be determined by pouring a few drops of water onto the heated grid. If the water forms little balls which dance around, the temperature is just right.

These considerations should be borne in mind when a waffle iron or sandwich grill is brought into the shop with the complaint that food sticks. Although this is not a mechanical or electrical difficulty, the owner will appreciate advice as to how to get the best results from his appliance.

## *Repairing Waffle Irons and Grills*

### 4.46. When Appliance Is Not Worth Repairing

The waffle iron or sandwich grill has an extremely simple construction from an electrical standpoint. It consists merely of a cord and heating element. Since such control devices as thermostat and OFF-ON switch are seldom found on this appliance, the cause of failure to operate is easy to locate.

The main servicing problem encountered is the difficulty in repairing the inexpensive appliances frequently given as prizes or premiums in sales promotions, which are manufactured in such a manner as to preclude repairs. Often the appliance bears no manufacturer's name, so that parts replacement is impossible. As such an appliance was obviously not intended to be repaired, and has slight value, the service man should waste no time in the attempt.

This is not true, of course, of waffle irons and grills offered by the well-known manufacturers, which are dependable appliances with many years of service built into them. Often a simple repair will greatly prolong their period of useful operation. The service man can immediately recognize the difference in craftsmanship between the poorly made and the well-made appliance once the grid is removed, exposing the inner works.

Possible troubles are listed in subsequent sections.

## 4.47. Failure to Heat

Failure to heat may be due to the following:

Power failure (Sec. 4.9)
Defective cord and plug (Sec. 4.9)
Poor internal connection
Open-circuited heating element

Having eliminated the receptacle and cord set as causes of failure to heat, the next step is to open the appliance and examine the interior. An open-circuited heating element will be apparent from the break in the nichrome wire. Poor internal connection is evidenced by a discoloration or corrosion of a terminal connector. If neither of these faults is evident, the wires connecting upper and lower heating element sections should be checked. This wiring is flexed each time a waffle iron is opened or closed, and the bending can cause the conductors to part. A test for continuity

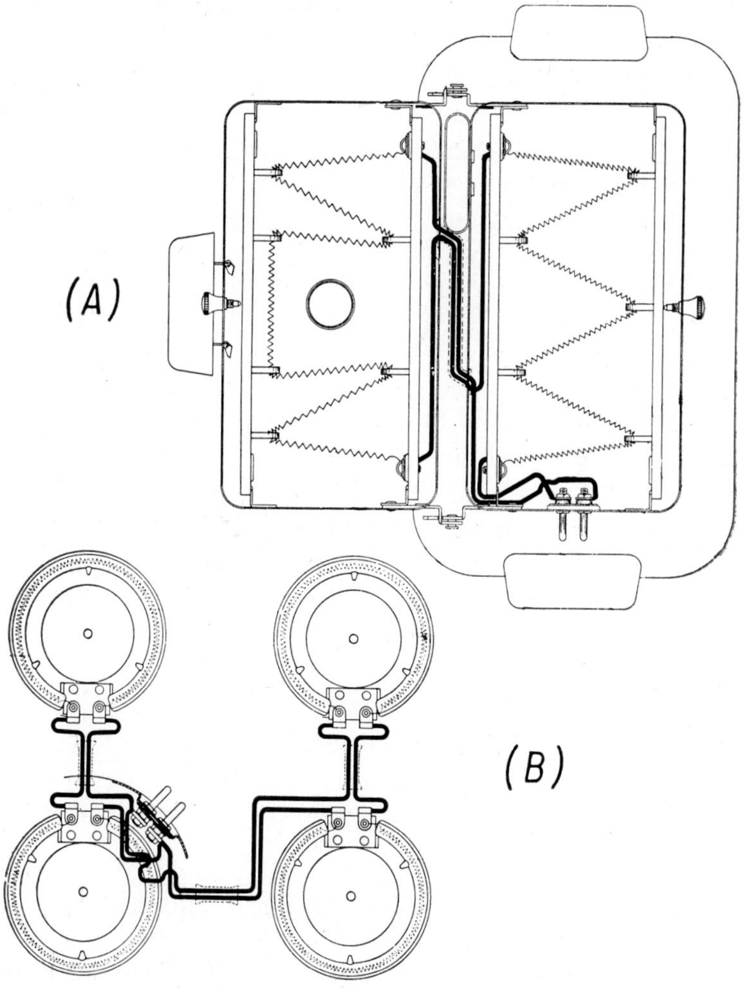


FIG. 4-30. (Courtesy, Knapp-Monarch Co.)

with ohmmeter or series test lamp will show if the wires are damaged. When any of the wiring within the waffle iron is replaced, asbestos-covered wire should be used.

With the waffle iron opened for inspection, the mica and porcelain insulating braces and spacers for the heating element should be examined, and defective ones replaced (Fig. 4-30A and B).

When replacing a defective heating element, it should be borne in mind that the two sections do not have the same resistance value. For even heating, the upper element should produce more heat than the lower, to compensate for heat rising. A greater heat loss into the air occurs from the upper grill than from the lower.

> If the heating element sections are series-connected, the upper element will have a few more ohms than the lower section;
>
> If the heating element sections are parallel-connected, the lower element will have a few more ohms than the lower section.

This is true if we assume that the nichrome wire size is the same for both elements. In any event, the resistance of the old heating element should be measured as closely as possible, and replacement made with the measured value.

## 4.48. Uneven Heating

A waffle iron which heats unevenly has an improper distribution of resistance between upper and lower heating elements, due either to deterioration of the heating element or to improper repair. In either case it may be impossible to find out just what the original resistance arrangement was. Here is an example of how it might be calculated and distributed with fair accuracy.

> Assuming the rating on the name plate is 750 w, 120 v, the correct resistance for the entire appliance is
>
> $$\frac{E^2}{P} = \frac{120^2}{750} = \frac{14400}{750} = 19.2 \text{ ohms.}$$
>
> Cut the heating element into two pieces, one of 10 ohms, the other 9.2 ohms. Place the 10-ohm length in the upper, the 9.2 ohm in the lower, section of the appliance, and test it by actually baking a waffle in it.

## 4.49. Waffle Iron or Grill Blows Fuses

Having eliminated an overloaded circuit as a possible cause of blown fuses, the following should be checked:

1. The cord and plug. Connect the cord set, by itself, into the appliance tester (Fig. 2-2). A shorted cord set should be replaced.

2. The appliance terminals to which the cord connects. Examine and test for looseness and for damaged mica washers. Tighten and replace bad insulators.

3. Worn insulation on internal wiring. If the insulation is damaged so as to allow wires to touch together or touch the frame of the appliance, it can blow fuses. The obvious repair is to replace the damaged wire.

Replacement heating elements for waffle irons and sandwich grills are tightly coiled when purchased, and must be stretched to the proper length for installation. Care should be exercised in stretching the coil lest it be pulled too far and the element sag when put into place. In fact, the element when in position should be under tension from its own springiness. The heat it produces in operation will cause it to expand, and if the element fits too loosely to begin with, it may sag in operation until it touches the appliance frame, causing shorts, hot spots, and discoloration of the finish. The new element when stretched out should measure about two inches shorter than the old element it replaces.

# OTHER HEATING-ELEMENT APPLIANCES

## 4.50. General Discussion. Wattage Value for Various Appliances

There are numerous other heating-element appliances on the market, some of which are discussed in later chapters. Those appliances which are not included herein, such as the curling iron, radiant heater, and so on, are based on the principles already discussed, and a knowledge of these principles will make servicing easy. The basis of all heating-element behavior is Ohm's law; the repair man who keeps this in mind should experience no difficulty in analyzing the electric circuit and making repairs.

The complaint is often heard that an appliance causes fuses to blow, but when the appliance is tested it is found to be perfectly normal. A very common cause of such a situation is an overloaded circuit. Heating-element appliances in particular consume a large amount of current, and two or three such appliances in one circuit will invariably cause the fuse to blow.

| APPLIANCE | WATTS |
|---|---|
| Electric clocks | 1 to 3 |
| Lamp bulbs | 7.5 to 300 |
| Fans | 25 to 100 |
| Sewing machines | 40 to 75 |
| Radios | 50 to 150 |
| Mixers | 150 to 250 |
| Vacuum cleaners | 150 to 400 |
| Refrigerators | 200 to 275 |
| Waffle irons | 500 to 660 |
| Hotplates | 500 to 1,000 |
| Irons and toasters | 600 to 1,000 |
| Sun lamps | 550 to 1,000 |
| Glow heaters | 600 to 1,000 |
| Roasters | 600 to 1,500 |
| Ironers | 1,000 to 1,500 |
| Ranges | 4,500 to 12,500 (Max.) |
| Motors, 1/4 hp | 250 to 300 |
| Motors, 1/4 hp | 450 to 500 |

In homes that have old wiring, the circuits are fused at 15 amp and are often overworked. Newer homes are supplied with a special circuit for appliances fused at 20 amp. Since there is sufficient information stamped upon the appliance name plate to determine its current demands, it is possible to check any circuit to see if the appliances used in that circuit are causing an overload. A 15-amp circuit will safely carry up to 1,800 w; a 20-amp circuit will handle 2,400 w total. The above table shows the typical wattage value for various appliances.

## 4.51. Trouble-Shooting Chart: Heating-Element Appliances

| SYMPTOM | CAUSE | TEST | REMEDY |
|---|---|---|---|
| Will not heat. | Open heating element | Series test lamp or ohmmeter. If more than one element is used, disconnect the several sections and test individually. | 1. Replace with new one.<br>2. Wind new element from spool of nichrome wire. |
| | Defective thermostat | Dismantle to point where thermostat is accessible. Examine for fault which would prevent contact from being made, such as<br>1. broken parts,<br>2. badly pitted contacts,<br>3. broken control rod. | Replace with new thermostat and/or control assembly. |
| | Defective line cord or plug | Remove cord and plug assembly. Twist wires of cord together. Test for continuity with ohmmeter or series test lamp. | If test shows discontinuity, replace with new cord set. |
| | Defective switch | Dismantle appliance and remove switch. Test for continuity in ON position. | Replace with new switch. |
| | Defective receptacle or blown fuse | Try appliance in different outlet and/or try another appliance in suspected outlet. | Replace fuse or receptacle as necessary. |
| | Burned-out fuse in coffee maker | Remove bottom plate and examine fuse—alloy metal will have melted if fuse is out. | Replace with new fuse. |

| SYMPTOM | CAUSE | TEST | REMEDY |
| --- | --- | --- | --- |
| Uneven heating (toaster, waffle iron, sandwich grill). | Open heating element or partially shorted heating element | Test separate heating elements with ohmmeter. All parallel elements should have approximately same resistance value. (Some waffle irons are arranged to produce more heat from top than from lower element to allow for heat losses into air from upper element.) | Replace defective element(s). |
| Appliance gets too hot. | Defective thermostat | Dismantle to point where thermostat is accessible. Examine for welded contacts or broken control assembly. | Replace thermostat and/or control assembly. |
| Will not pop up (toaster). | Defective pop-up mechanism | Remove outer cover of toaster. Plug in, and observe action of pop-up mechanism for defective performance. Observe especially<br>1. spring on clockwork,<br>2. element on thermostat type,<br>3. broken pop-up spring. | Replace defective parts or assemblies. |
| Pilot or glow lamp will not glow. | Burned-out pilot or glow lamp | Test with ohmmeter. (Resistance is quite low normally.) | Replace with new lamp or glow coil. |

| SYMPTOM | CAUSE | TEST | REMEDY |
|---|---|---|---|
| Timer does not operate. | Defective timer | The timer is essentially a switch and is to be tested as such. Make continuity test with timer in ON position. Resistance should be close to zero ohms. | Replace. It is not practical to attempt to repair a timer. |
| Appliance shocks owner. | Internal wiring grounded to frame of appliance | Test with ohmmeter or series test lamp from line cord terminals to frame of appliance. Continuity indicates ground. | Dismantle the appliance, testing for ground at each step. When ground disappears, defective component is indicated. |
| Appliance blows fuses. | Shorted cord, capacitor, or heating element | Check each with ohmmeter. Very low or zero ohms indicates short. | Replace offending component. |
| | Overloaded circuit | Observation. How many appliances are used on the same circuit? Is one of these a motor (which draws a rather large starting current, and in so doing may blow a fuse)? Calculate total wattage and compare with maximum allowable for circuit. | Install additional circuits in home, or rearrange use of existing circuits. |
| Appliance does not get hot enough. | Low voltage, probably due to defective cord, plug, or too much cord length | Voltmeter. | Reduce cord length. Repair offending component. |

## Now that you have read this chapter, can you answer these questions?

**1.** In general, an automatic iron has a higher wattage rating than a nonautomatic iron. Why?

**2.** Explain the operation of a thermostat.

**3.** The heating element of a hotplate has been accidentally broken a short distance from one end. The short length is discarded, and the remainder used as the heating element. Does this increase or decrease the wattage of the appliance?

**4.** The heating element of a waffle iron measures 24 ohms. Of this total, 10 ohms is in the top, and 14 ohms in the bottom of the iron. What effect will this have on the quality of a waffle prepared in this appliance?

**5.** A length of copper wire measures 1.04 ohms. A nichrome wire of identical dimensions has 60 ohms. Why does nichrome make a better heating element material than copper?

**6.** Why is silver employed as a contact material?

**7.** A 1,300-w ironer is to be used in a basement. The only receptacle is at a far end of the basement. Is there any objection to the use of a couple of extension cords to supply power to the ironer? Explain.

**8.** Why do manufacturers stamp on the name plate of some appliances "For use in base or wall receptacle only"?

**9.** Describe the behavior of a thermostatic switch in interrupting a direct current. An alternating current.

**10.** What is the advantage of using a thermostat rather than a variable resistor (rheostat) to control the temperature of an appliance?

**11.** What is meant by "differential" and "cycling" as pertaining to a thermostat?

**12.** On the toaster described in connection with Figure 4-13 the contacts of *S2* have become so badly pitted that the switch will not complete its circuit. What are the symptoms of trouble when this appliance is brought into the shop for repair?

**13.** Describe the method of adjusting the thermostat on a roaster oven.

**14.** A roaster oven is equipped with a 6- to 8-v pilot lamp, receiving its voltage from the drop across a portion of the length of heating element. If the total resistance of the element is 24 ohms, what is the approximate value of the portion across which the pilot lamp is connected?

**15.** It is suspected that the contacts of the thermostat of an automatic iron are welded together. How can it be determined that this is the case without disassembling the iron?

**16.** Why should an electric percolator never be operated dry?

**17.** What damage will result from water getting into the electric parts of an appliance?

**18.** An electric iron is brought into the repair shop with the complaint that it causes fuses (15 amp) to blow. Upon testing, however, it is discovered that the iron draws only 8 amp. What is the trouble?

**19.** Where should a thermostat be mounted with respect to the heating element?

**20.** In Figure 4-17, explain the difference in the circuit between the medium and high heat positions.

**21.** In what respect is an electric heating appliance similar to a lamp bulb? In what respect may it differ?

**22.** What are the possible causes of a steam iron's shocking the user?

**23.** What is the nature of the glow light which takes the place of the pilot-light bulb in some roaster models?

**24.** Why is a fuse used in an electric percolator?

*chapter* **5**

# Electric Ranges

From the standpoint of the fundamental principle of operation, the electric range is merely an elaboration of the hotplate. The range consists of a number of heating elements, controlled by switches and thermostats, and arranged for maximum convenience to the user (Fig. 5-1).

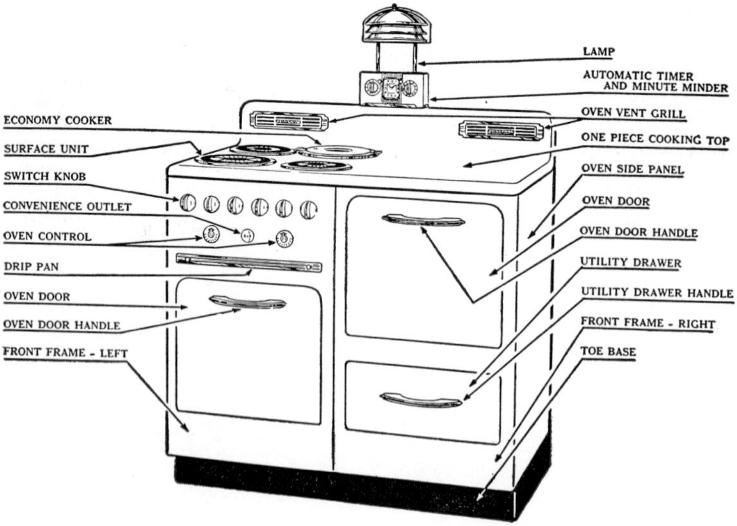


FIG. 5-1. (Courtesy, Landers, Frary, & Clark)

## 5.1. Surface Units

Mounted flush with the top surface of the range are four heating-element units. Each unit consists of two nichrome elements of the hermetically sealed type. A common connection is employed for each heating element; thus, three wires lead from each surface unit to its switch (Fig. 5-2).

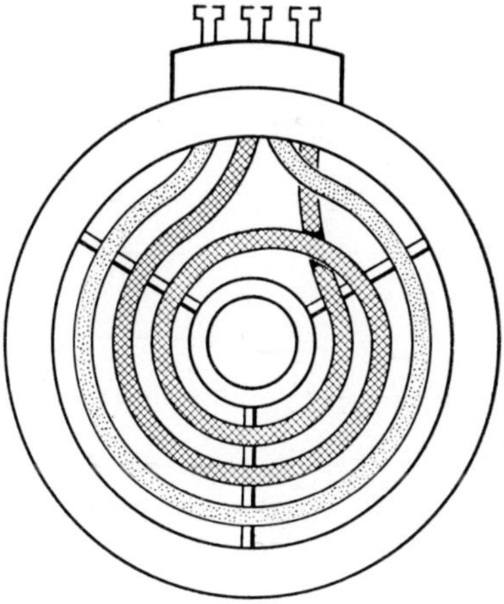

Fig. 5-2.

The hermetically sealed unit consists of a nichrome wire coil placed in a stainless steel sheath. A white powder, magnesium oxide, is packed into the sheath and serves to insulate the heating element from the outer container. In addition to its insulating qualities, the magnesium oxide is not affected by the heat.

The air is expelled from the sheath, and the ends are sealed. The removal of air (and water vapor) from the unit eliminates the corrosive effects of these elements, thus materially increasing the life of the sealed unit over that of an open coil.

The range switch commonly has six positions; five for different heat gradations, and the off position. To obtain this number of heats with only two heating elements, it is necessary to employ the three-wire system.

## 5.2. The Three-Wire System

Briefly, the three-wire system may be considered as having for its source two 110-v generators, connected in series, and a center wire coming from the junction of the two. Being in series, the generated voltages add, providing 220 v between the outer wires of the system, and 110 v from either outer wire to the center wire. In practice, the dual voltage is obtained from a center-tapped transformer (Fig. 5-3).

It can be shown that, if the same current flows through each heating element (load) across the two 110-v circuits, no current will flow in the center wire. This will effect a saving, since a

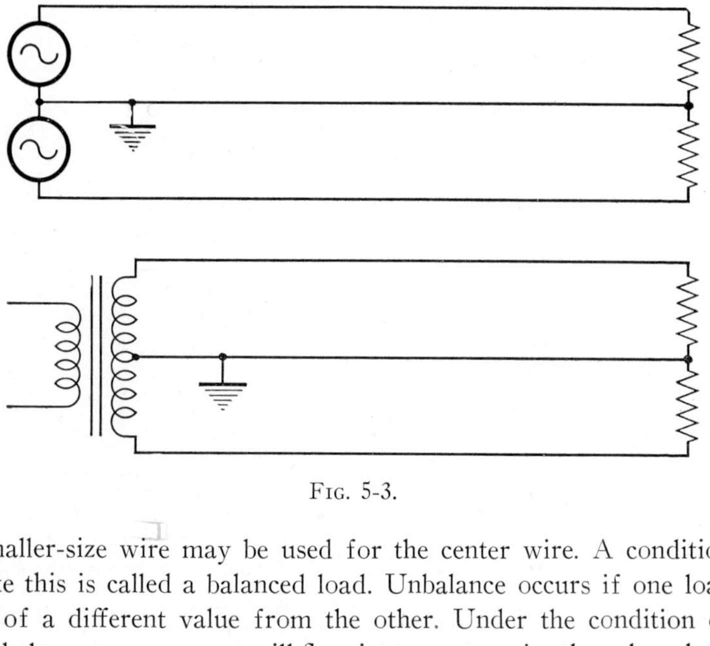

FIG. 5-3.

smaller-size wire may be used for the center wire. A condition like this is called a balanced load. Unbalance occurs if one load is of a different value from the other. Under the condition of unbalance more current will flow in one outer wire than the other; the center wire will carry the difference between the two current values. The entire range circuit is designed on the basis of maintaining a balanced load insofar as is possible.

The center wire of the three-wire system is referred to as the neutral, as this wire is grounded. It is easily identified, being the white or gray wire in the attachment cord supplied with the range. At the terminal post to which the cord is attached, the bolt for the neutral wire is plated so as to have a white or silvery appearance; the bolts for the other two wires are brass. The neutral-wire connection is customarily connected to the frame of the range by a jumper.

## 5.3. The Surface-Unit Circuit

Figure 5-4 is a typical range switch circuit. To obtain the highest heat, the two heating elements are connected (by means of the internal contacts of the switch) in parallel across the high-voltage 220-volt line.

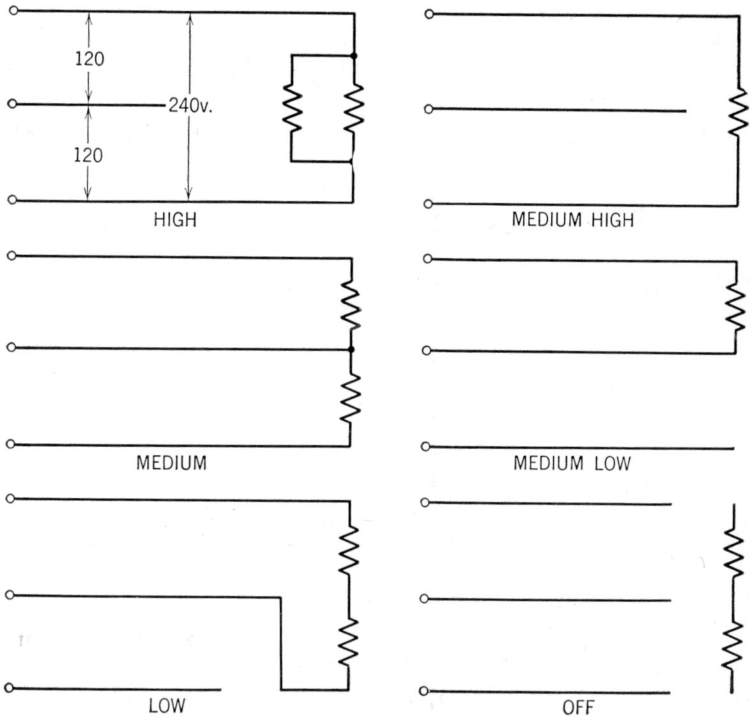


Fig. 5-4.

The next switch position, medium-high, removes one heating element from the circuit, leaving only the other across the 220-v line.

The medium position of the switch has internal connections such as to put each heating element across 110 v. Note that the two elements, being identical, provide less heat in series across the 220-v line than one by itself across 220 v. In this switch position the neutral wire may or may not be connected to the junction of the heating elements. As the neutral wire carries no current, disconnecting it will in no way influence the behavior of the heating elements.

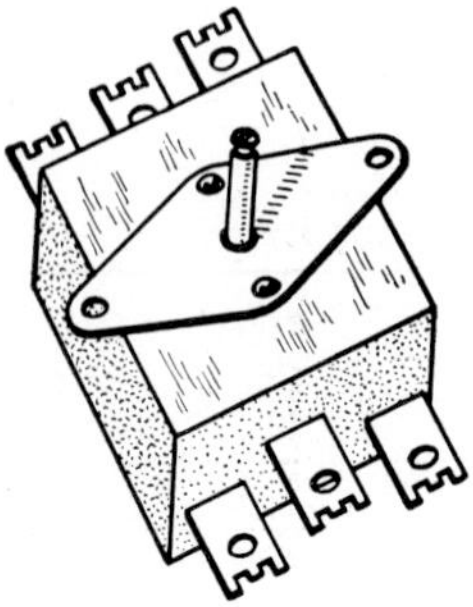

FIG. 5-5.

The fourth, or medium-low-heat, position of the switch does not present a balanced load to the line, since one heating element only is connected across a pair of wires supplying 110 v.

Finally, the low-heat position places the two heating elements in series across a 110-v circuit.

A switch of the type shown in Figure 5-5 is used to change the circuit arrangement so as to obtain five heat gradations. The three top terminals connect to the heating unit, and the three line wires are connected to the bottom switch terminals. The neutral wire connects to the white terminal screw, and is made continuous to the junction of the two elements in the surface unit by the same color code.

Figure 5-6 shows the entire circuit of the four surface units and their switches. The manufacturer will have made some provision for tracing the circuit from the terminal block at the rear of the range through the switches in front to the units on top: the wires may have characteristic color designations (red or black for "hot" wires, white for neutral), or each wire may be identified by small metal strips clamped onto both ends, bearing identical letters or numbers. (In the event such metallic tags have been defaced or removed, the series test lamp will provide a continuity test.) *Disconnect the range when tracing through the circuits,* and disconnect one end of a wire when using the series test lamp to follow it through to eliminate the possibility of an indication of continuity through a parallel path.

The switches may be checked with a series test lamp or ohmmeter to determine whether the internal parts are contacting properly. It is necessary to remove the switch from its circuit and test through the switch in each heat position, remembering that for certain conditions of heat one of the three connections may be open-circuited (Fig. 5-4).

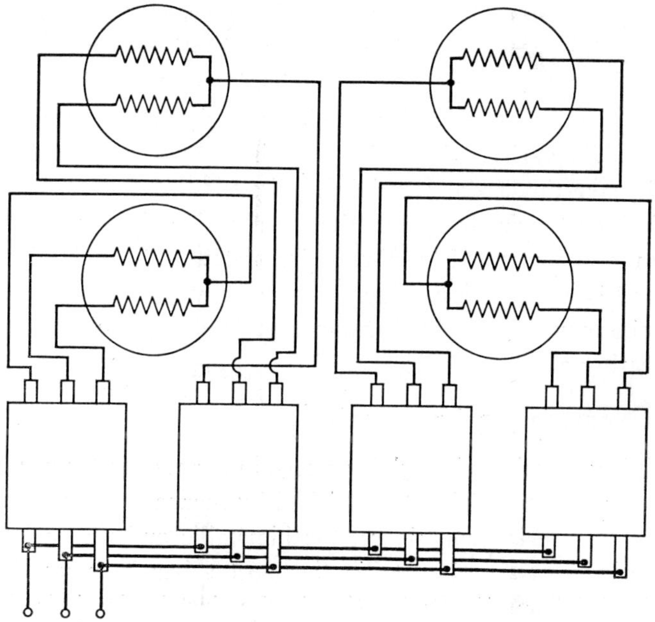

Fig. 5-6.

## 5.4. The Oven

To the housewife, the oven of a range is just as important as the surface unit. Here, too, it is necessary to have a wide variety of temperatures available. However, unlike the surface unit, the oven temperature is controlled by a thermostat, which allows much greater precision in determining the degree of heat than does a switch.

The oven is expected to perform two cooking processes: broiling and baking (roasting is actually a form of baking). In broiling, heat from the top of the oven is directed down onto the foodstuff being prepared, whereas in baking the heat comes from below. Hence, the oven is fitted with heating elements at both the top and the bottom, and provision is made to switch in one or the other unit—or, for quick preheating, both units simultaneously. A four-position switch is used: OFF, PRE-HEAT, BAKE, BROIL. A switch with internal connections such as shown in Figure 5-5 will control these heating elements. Other switches have two layers of "wafers" of contacts, each insulated from the other; each wafer handles the circuit of one heating element. The variety of switches used is too multitudinous to list, but all have the same essential functions.

It is customary to operate the oven heating elements at 220 v, using the outer legs of the three-wire system, thus maintaining a balanced-load condition. Open-type coils are used, the bottom coil being covered by a baffle to prevent food from splashing onto the heating element.

## 5.5. Oven-Temperature Control

Often a recipe will call for a certain exact oven temperature. Temperature control is accomplished by means of a thermostat. Two types are in general use, the bimetallic and the hydraulic. The operation of a bimetallic thermostat has been previously explained (Chap. 4). Its location in the electric circuit is shown in Figure 5-7 (switch marked T). Physically, the bimetallic thermostat must be located within the oven so as to be controlled by oven heat, and its control knob must, consequently, be located atop the oven, or on the oven door.

The modern trend in range design is a flat-top appliance, with all controls except surface-unit switches located on a back panel. The bimetallic type of thermostat does not fit in with this design, since its control knob would be located too far from the bimetallic strip. For this reason another type of thermostatic control is more frequently used in newer ranges, called the hydraulic thermostat.

## 5.6. The Hydraulic Thermostat

Just as the bimetallic thermostat depends upon the expansion of a metal when heated, the hydraulic thermostat operates upon the principle of the uniform expansion of a fluid with increase

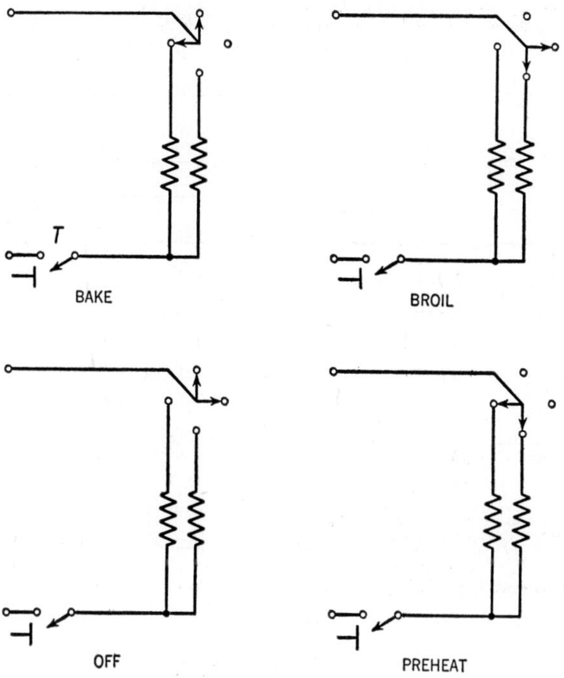


FIG. 5-7.

of temperature. Figure 5-8 reveals the structure of this unit: a slender (capillary) tube which terminates in a bulb containing the fluid. As the bulb is heated, the fluid expands, applying pressure to a diaphragm or bellows. Movement of the bellows or diaphragm is transmitted by a lever or series of levers to the contacts of a switch, causing them to open or close as desired. Externally adjustable spring pressure exerted against the movement of the bellows determines the temperature at which the thermostat will cycle. This unit lends itself admirably to use with the back-panel-control method of installation. The bulb containing fluid is placed in the oven chamber; the attached tube is sufficiently long and flexible to allow the remainder of the unit to be conveniently mounted behind the control panel, through which the knob shaft extends.

The hydraulic unit should be handled with care, since excessive bending of the slender tube may cause it to constrict or may produce a fracture which will allow the fluid to escape. Either condition will render the hydraulic thermostat inoperative.

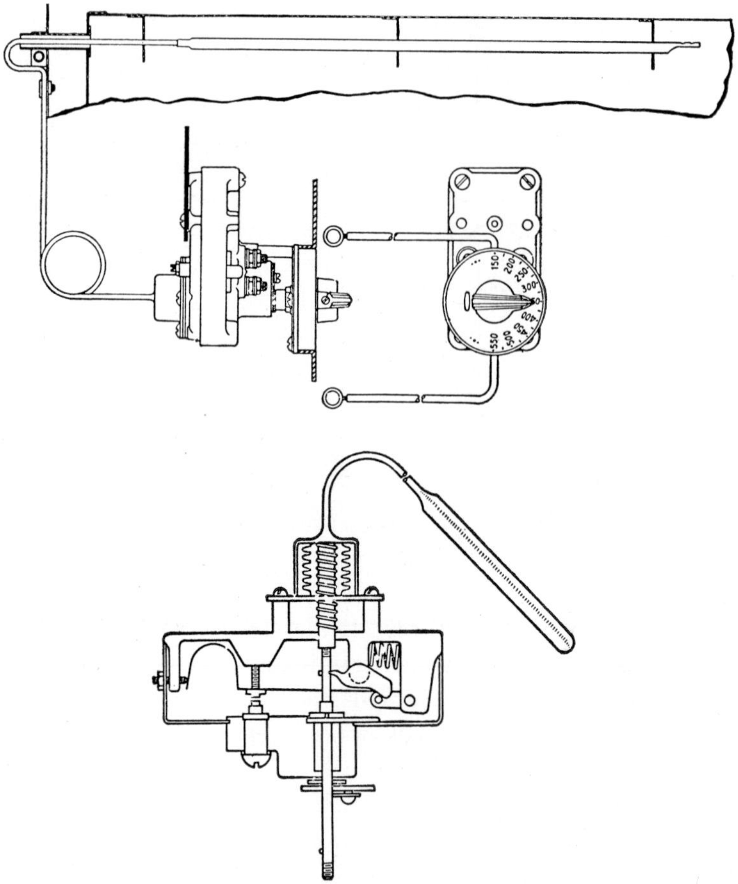


FIG. 5-8. (*Top:* Courtesy, Landers, Frary, & Clark)

Both bimetallic and hydraulic thermostats are provided with a device to allow adjustment of the control-knob calibration so that the oven temperature can be made to agree with the control-knob setting. This usually consists of a screw adjustment exposed to view when the control knob is removed from its shaft. The procedure for adjusting the temperature is given in Chapter 4.

## 5.7. The Relay

Some early models of ranges are equipped with an oven thermometer of the dial type, mounted on the oven door or beside the oven, the thermometer needle serving as a temperature-control device (Fig. 5-9). In addition to the moving pointer of the regular thermometer, a second pointer is placed in front of the

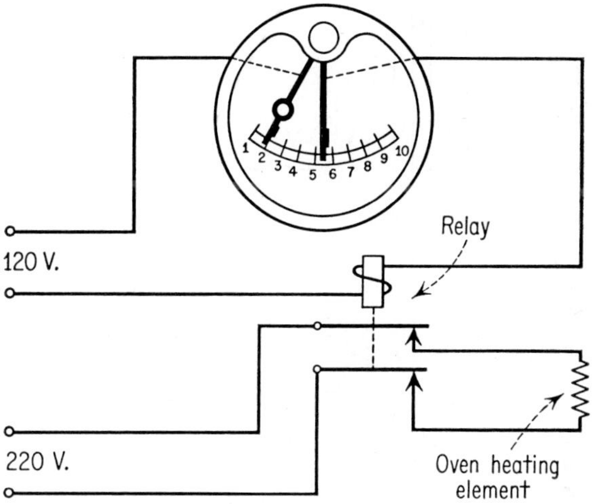


Fig. 5-9.

dial, controlled by an external knob. The two pointers are electrically insulated from each other until the increasing temperature of the oven causes the thermometer needle to move across the dial and touch the second pointer, thus completing an electric circuit in the same manner as the closing of a switch.

The purpose of this device is to control the oven temperature. Although the thermometer is, in a sense, itself a switch, its parts are much too small and fragile to carry the heavy current required for the operation of the oven-heating elements. Instead, it is used in a 120-v circuit, and operates a relay, requiring only a very small amount of current.

A relay, as may be seen from the diagram, is merely a switch opened and closed by the tractive action of an electromagnet. In Figure 5-9 the thermometer is seen to be in series with the coil

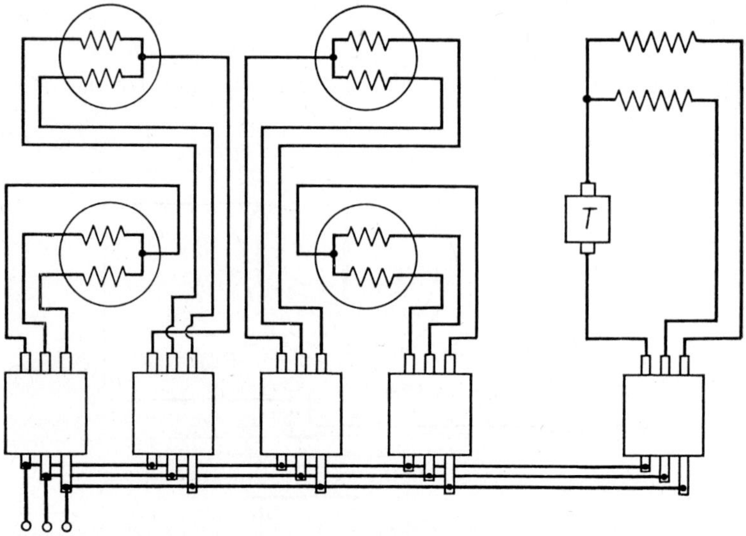


Fig. 5-10.

forming the electromagnet. Many turns of fine wire will provide a powerful magnet at a very low current.

. When the thermometer completes the electromagnetic circuit, the relay contacts are drawn open by the magnetic action and are seen to break the oven circuit. As the oven heating element cools, the thermometer pointers separate, the electromagnet releases its hold on its contacts, a spring pulls the contacts closed, and the heating element again begins to glow.

Figure 5-7 shows the circuit of the surface units of the range. When the oven circuit is added to this, the combination appears as shown in Figure 5-10. Oven and surface units are all that is required to make up a complete range. However, electric range manufacturers make their products more attractive by the inclusion of such extras as a timer, a working light, a lamp inside the oven, a drawer warmer, and an appliance receptacle.

## 5.8. The Timer

The most complex of these devices is the timer. It consists of a clock, which may be either mechanical or electrical, and a set of contacts operated by clockwork (Fig. 5-11). The convenience of this device may be fully appreciated when it is realized that the owner may place the food to be cooked for a meal in the oven, set the controls to the proper times for it to turn on and off, and then leave for the day. The timer will turn on the oven at the predetermined hour, allow it to operate the required length

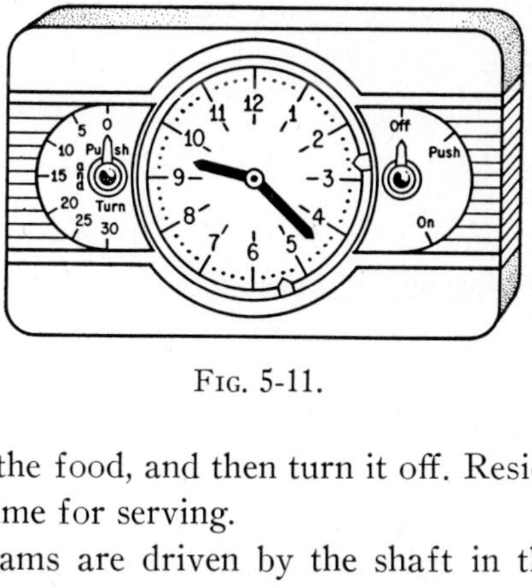


Fig. 5-11.

of time to cook the food, and then turn it off. Residual heat keeps food hot until time for serving.

A set of cams are driven by the shaft in the clock which operates the hour hand. The initial positions of these cams are set by adjusting the timer controls. When the necessary time has elapsed, the cams will have moved sufficiently to operate the switch. As it is not desired that the timer automatically operate the oven every twelve hours, an on-off control is a part of the timer assembly. It should be in the OFF position until or unless the timer is to be used. (The accuracy of the timer switching action is to within ten or twenty minutes of the pre-set time, and should not be used when a recipe calls for critical cooking time.)

The timer may be used to control other parts of the range. Some manufacturers have included in the timer circuit a selector switch so that the appliance receptacle or one of the surface units may be switched into the timer circuit. Figure 5-12 shows the timer as a part of the range circuit.

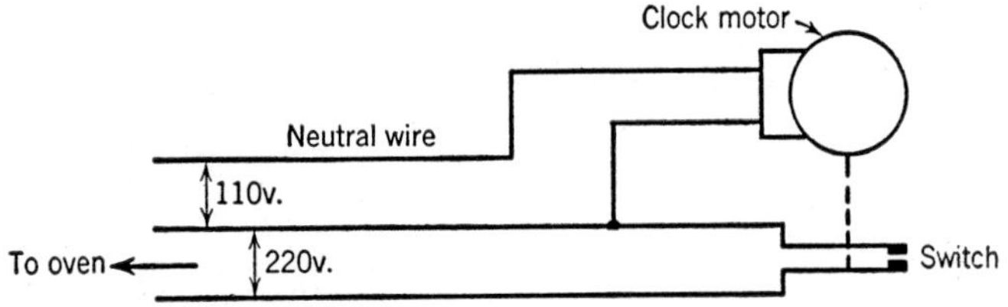


Fig. 5-12.

Repairs to a timer is a job for a watchmaker rather than for an appliance repair man. Perhaps the best solution to timer servicing problems is replacement of the entire defective timer unit.

## 5.9. Mark-Time Meter

The mark-time meter is another type of timer found on some ranges. However, it does not control any circuit, but is only a mechanical clockwork which operates an alarm bell. The dial is calibrated in minutes up to 55 minutes. A pointer knob on the face, when turned from zero, winds the spring which operates the works. As it unwinds, the pointer slowly moves backward toward zero, and at about zero causes a bell to ring. The mark-time meter is convenient for timing projects requiring less than one hour's cooking time. It cannot be used for a period of less than five minutes, for the set knob must be turned past the five-minute mark (at least) to reset the bell clapper.

The servicing of a mark-time meter is, like the timer mechanisms, a job for a watchmaker; unless the appliance repair man is experienced in this type of repair, it is better to replace the defective unit with a new one. Perhaps the most common trouble causing the clockwork mechanism to become inoperative is a broken mainspring.

The use of the mark-time meter is not limited to ranges; at least one manufacturer of washing machines uses this mechanism to operate a motor switch, thus enabling the housewife to time the washing of various types of fabrics. Furthermore, the meter by itself (with bell) is available for timing any other household task.

## 5.10. Other Range Circuits

The remainder of the range circuits are quite simple. They are

1. The oven pilot lamp, located within the oven and turned on by a switch operated by opening the oven door. The majority of ranges have a 120-v bulb, supplied from the neutral wire and one of the "hot" wires. It is not uncommon, however, to find in use a lower-voltage bulb, operating from a voltage divider—that is, it is tied into two points in the oven-heating-element circuit, between which two points there is a voltage difference of the right value to operate the bulb. The exact nature of the oven-lamp circuit may be determined from the range-circuit diagram.

2. An appliance receptacle, mounted at a convenient spot on the top or back panel of the range. The appliance receptacle makes possible the use of a clock, mixer, electric percolator, fan, or other small appliances which, placed on or near the range, offers an added convenience. In its circuit is a 15-amp fuse, and it receives its power from the neutral wire and one "hot" wire. Very often the receptacle becomes inoperative because an overload or short circuit blows the fuse. It may be necessary to move the range away from the wall and trace through the receptacle circuit to locate the fuse. The fuse location is different for each of the many makes of ranges, and may even vary on different models of the same brand.

3. The range lamp, located above the range, is convenient for illuminating the top of the range. It is connected in parallel with the appliance receptacle, and therefore has the

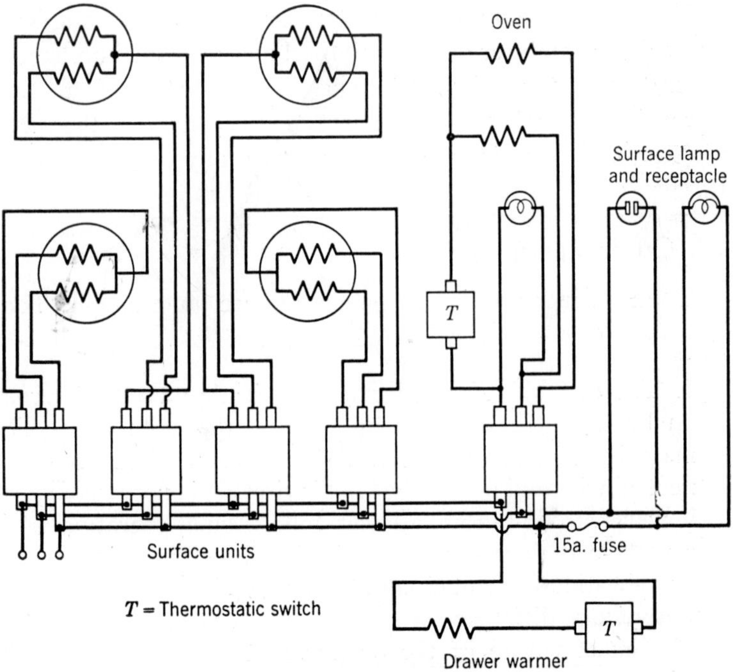


FIG. 5-13.

protection of the same 15-amp fuse. Its pull chain-socket is generally supplied with a 40-w bulb.

4. The warmer. The modern range is designed for the utmost efficiency. Whereas the old-fashioned range with a high side-opening oven had much vacant space below it, today's range utilizes the entire space down to the floor. It often has, in addition to the oven, one, two, or three drawers for storage of utensils. If the range has a warmer, it is located below one of these drawers, and consists of a thermostatically controlled heating element. This thermostat is adjusted so as to open at a comparatively low temperature, since the purpose of this circuit is merely to keep hot bread or other hot food at an appetizing temperature between the times of preparation and serving.

Depending upon the manufacturer's design, the heating element of the warmer may be operated from either 110 or 220 v. This may be determined by consulting the circuit diagram, or by tracing the circuit back to its source.

Figure 5-13, which is an extension of Figure 5-10, shows the inclusion of the additional range circuits.

The circuit (Fig. 5-14) includes the typical circuits found in ranges. Each manufacturer supplies with his piece of equip-

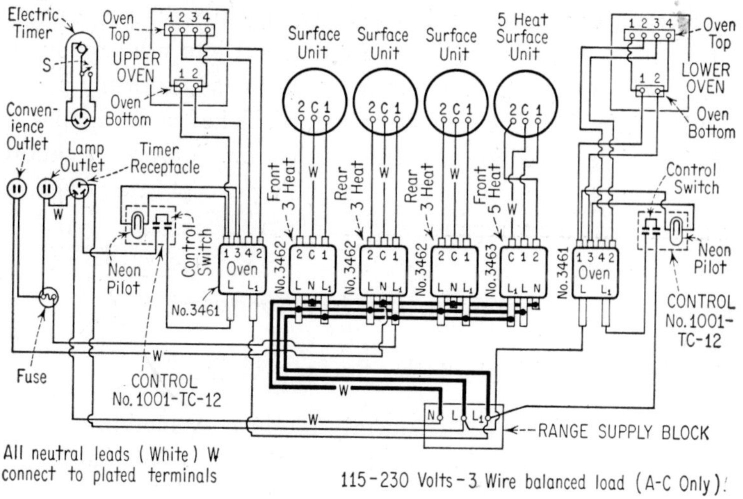


Fig. 5-14. (Courtesy, Landers, Frary, & Clark)

ment a diagram of the circuit. It may or may not be similar to 5-14, since a wide variety of combinations of circuits is in use. The diagram is customarily pasted onto the back panel of the range. At first glance this may seem to be highly complex; however, if instead of attempting to comprehend the entire circuit as a unit, just one circuit at a time is approached, there will be no difficulty in using the diagram as a servicing aid. Figure 5-13 is moderately complex in its entirety, yet it has been developed by combining a number of much simpler circuits. The color code employed in the range itself is often marked on the circuit diagram. Intelligent use of this information will simplify servicing, particularly when the wiring passes through a panel, or from front to rear of the range.

Because of the use of sealed units and standard assemblies, little actual repair can be made to the modern electric range. Servicing consists mainly of locating the defective part, or parts, and replacing them with new ones. It may sometimes be possible to restore service temporarily by a substitution until a replacement part can be obtained. Suppose, for example, that a range has a defective thermostat. There is a possibility that the thermostat from another brand of range can be put into use temporarily (barring insurmountable mounting difficulties), until the correct brand of replacement can be obtained. The same applies to switches, timers, heating elements, and so on. A word of caution in this respect: it is unwise to use anything except *exact duplicate parts* for permanent repairs.

## *Servicing Electric Ranges*

### 5.11. Improper Heat at the Surface Unit

Surface-unit heat is frequently too low—sometimes on one, sometimes on all positions of the heat switch. The causes are as follows:

Defective heating element
Defective switch
Defective wiring

The heating element in the surface unit is in two parts—not necessarily equal—with a common connection (Fig. 9-1). If either of the halves of the unit is open-circuited, the heat obtained will be solely that of the other half, which is, in some switch positions, inadequate for cooking. The continuity of the heating element can be tested with a series test lamp or an ohmmeter. It is necessary to disconnect the wiring from the element when making this test to avoid an erroneous indication caused by a "sneak" circuit. If the wattage rating of the heating element is known, the resistance required to produce this wattage can be calculated and this value compared with the measured value. In any event, the resistance value should lie in the 5-ohm-to-25-ohm range; any value exceptionally greater than this indicates a defective or open-circuited heating element. As most modern ranges employ the sealed heating element in the surface unit, repairs are not possible, and the entire unit must be replaced.

A second cause of failure to heat is a defective switch. The typical range switch is a multiposition switch containing many terminals and contacts. Some are so made as to discourage disassembly for examination, being either welded or riveted together. The easiest way to detect this fault is to measure the voltage at the switch terminals to which the heating element is attached. If a measurement of no voltage is obtained, the switch is faulty and must be replaced.

Finally, the wiring itself may be defective. This is usually noticeable in the form of discolored wires and terminals or a wire actually broken loose from its terminal, unless the fault lies in a section of the wiring which is hidden from view. Tracing voltage with a voltmeter is helpful in locating a defective wire. If voltage is measured at the line terminals but not at the switch, the wiring in between is likely at fault. If voltage is measured at the switch but not at the heating element, the wiring connecting these two is likely at fault. Do not forget that voltage is always measured between two points in a circuit, and the voltmeter indication of faulty wiring includes two wires, both of which must be removed and examined to determine which of the two is defective.

### *Oven Will Not Heat*

The same sequence of servicing procedure as used with the surface unit applies to servicing the oven unit: that is, tests for defective element, defective switch, defective wiring. Less meter servicing and more direct observation is possible here; the oven element is not a sealed unit, so any heating-element defect is easy to find. Furthermore, many ranges are built so that the oven unit plugs into a receptacle at the rear of the oven compartment, and can be removed merely by pulling out.

The oven is thermostatically controlled (Secs. 5.5, 5.6). In addition to the above-mentioned faults, a defective thermostat will result in improper heating or failure to heat. If the defect is failure to heat, the thermostat can be tested indirectly by jumpering around it and observing if the element then heats. If the trouble is too-high heat, the thermostat can be tested by placing an ammeter in the thermostat-heating-element circuit, at the same time placing an oven thermometer in the oven and observing whether the ammeter drops to zero when the oven temperature reaches that indicated by the thermostat setting. If it does not, and the temperature within the oven continues to rise, the thermostat is not opening. Either fault in the thermostat requires its replacement.

An oven timer may be included as part of the range equipment. The timer, as has been noted (Sec. 5.8), is merely a clockwork-operated switch, and it is tested like any other switch. A continuity test should show zero ohms when the timer switch is ON, and infinity when OFF. The timer switch terminals should, of course, be disconnected from the remainder of the circuit while this test is being made.

## 5.12. Range Blows Fuses

An extremely low resistance condition, or a short circuit, will cause the range to blow fuses. Usually this will occur in connection with one particular switch position or a certain combination of switch positions. When this is the case, the repair man can usually deduce which portion of the range is faulty and make the necessary repair or replacement. If, however, the range blows fuses whenever plugged into its receptacle, the fault must be traced through the wiring. Test first across the plug terminals with an ohmmeter, trying pairs of terminals until the pair showing zero ohms is located. Leave the ohmmeter connected to this pair, and individually disconnect the various parts of the range: cord, heating elements, thermostat, timer, and so on. As each in turn is disconnected from the remainder of the circuit, look at the ohmmeter and then reconnect that part before going on to the next. If at any step the ohmmeter goes off zero, then the portion of the range circuit disconnected at that step contains the short. By this system the short circuit can thus be isolated to a single component, which can be either repaired or replaced, as necessary.

## 5.13. Inoperative Timer

The failure of the timer to act as an OFF-ON switch has been discussed above in connection with improper oven heating. The timer, however, may fail to operate with regard to its timing action: that is, fail to turn off and on the controlled circuit at the set time. This may be caused either by a broken wire in the timer motor circuit, or by a defective timer motor. To test the timer, remove it from the range. The timer is usually built so that it can be opened to observe its operation; a broken wire will then be visible. If the wiring is satisfactory, plug in the clock motor and observe its operation. If it fails to turn it may be either burned out or gummed up. For instructions on electric clock servicing, see Chapter 10. If repairs are not possible, the range timer must be replaced with a new one.

## 5.14. Oven Lamp Inoperative

An obvious reason why the oven lamp does not turn on is that the lamp is burned out; equally obvious is the repair procedure of replacement with an identical-type bulb.

The switch which operates the lamp is mounted in the oven framework in such a position that opening and closing the oven door causes the switch lever to operate. If a switch defect accounts for the lamp's failure to burn, the switch must be replaced. While this in itself is a simple repair, it may be somewhat awkward because of the inaccessible site of the switch. To save time, it may be advisable to postpone this repair until a new switch has been obtained, so that the range need be dismantled only once.

## 5.15. Trouble-Shooting Chart: Electric Ranges

| SYMPTOM | CAUSE | TEST | REMEDY |
|---|---|---|---|
| Surface unit will not heat, or will not get hot enough. | Open heating element | The surface unit usually contains two heating elements with a common neutral connection. Disconnect each of the three wires and test heating elements with ohmmeter. Resistance to be expected may be calculated from wattage rating of unit. | New element may be put in open-style unit. Complete replacement necessary if unit is sealed. |
| | Defective switch | Clip voltmeter test leads across wires at surface unit terminals. Operate switch and compare voltage readings with what might be expected from various heat positions (Fig. 5-4). | Replace switch. Repairs not practical. |
| | Defective wiring | Test same as above made at switch ends of wires. Full voltage at switch, not at element, indicates bad wires. | Rewire defective portion (asbestos-covered wire). |
| Oven will not heat. | Same causes as for surface units | Tests same as for surface units. | Repairs are the same as for surface units. |
| Control does not vary oven heat. | Defective thermostat | Voltmeter test across heating element. Use oven thermometer to determine when thermostat should open. | Replace thermostat. |

| SYMPTOM | CAUSE | TEST | REMEDY |
|---|---|---|---|
| Blows fuses. | Shorted wiring. Shorted heating element | Unplug range. Test all pairs of terminals at plug (three tests) with ohmmeter. Operate switches. Zero ohms reading will appear when defective unit is turned on. Suspected unit may be disconnected and tested individually to confirm test. | Replace or repair offending component. |
| Receptacle is inoperative. | Blown fuse | Examine range for location of receptacle fuses. Examine for blowout. | Replace fuse. |
| | Defective receptacle | Make voltage test at receptacle terminal screws. | Replace receptacle. |
| Timer is inoperative. | Probably due to defective motor in electric timer; broken spring in wind-up timer | Dismantle timer until moving parts are visible. Wind or apply rated voltage to motor and observe operation. | Replace timer or timer motor. |
| | Broken wire leading to timer | Check continuity of wiring with series test lamp (range disconnected, one end of each wire disconnected while being tested). | Replace bad wiring. |
| Oven lamp is inoperative. | Burned-out lamp | Test and repair consist of replacement. | (See opposite, column 3.) |

| SYMPTOM | CAUSE | TEST | REMEDY |
|---|---|---|---|
| | Defective switch | Switch located in frame and operates by door (sometimes not easily accessible). Trace through wiring and place jumper around switch. If lamp now burns, switch is defective. | Replace switch. |

## Now that you have read this chapter, can you answer these questions?

**1.** Why is the three-wire system employed to operate an electric range?

**2.** What is meant by a "balanced load"? Why does it represent an ideal condition?

**3.** It is customary to fuse the outer wires of a three-wire system, but not the neutral. What would occur if the neutral wire were fused and the fuse should blow out?

**4.** Why is the sealed-unit heating element the preferred type for use on a range surface unit?

**5.** Describe the hydraulic thermostat.

**6.** Why might a range employ a hydraulic thermostat rather than the bimetallic type?

**7.** What is a relay? How is it used?

**8.** Describe the method of circuit tracing using a series test lamp.

**9.** How is the neutral wire of the three-wire system identified?

**10.** Is the frame of the range grounded? Why?

**11.** Why is the center wire grounded instead of one or the other of the outside wires of a three-wire system?

**12.** How are different temperatures obtained from a surface unit by use of a 110–220-v circuit?

**13.** Why is a fast-action switch used?

**14.** What is the purpose of mounting a receptacle on the range?
**15.** What is used as the insulator for the heating element of a sealed unit?
**16.** What is the manner of repairing a sealed unit?
**17.** What is the purpose of using colored wires?
**18.** Why are switches used, rather than thermostats, for surface-unit heat control?

*chapter* **6**

# Appliance Motors

The simplest form of electric motor is shown in Figure 6-1. It consists of a single coil of current-carrying wire in a magnetic field. (Compare this motor with the generator of Figure 1-14.) Current is introduced into the coil by means of a split-ring commutator supplied with brushes. Imagine this coil as being mounted on a shaft so supported as to allow the coil to rotate past the curved faces of the magnets.

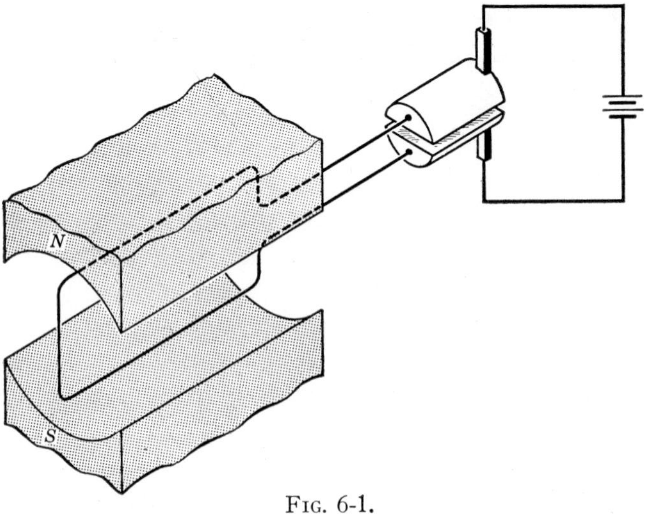


FIG. 6-1.

## 6.1. Motor Action

Figure 6-2 shows a cross section of the coil and magnet poles. The flux from the magnets is seen to travel from north to south poles, while the magnetic fields generated by the current

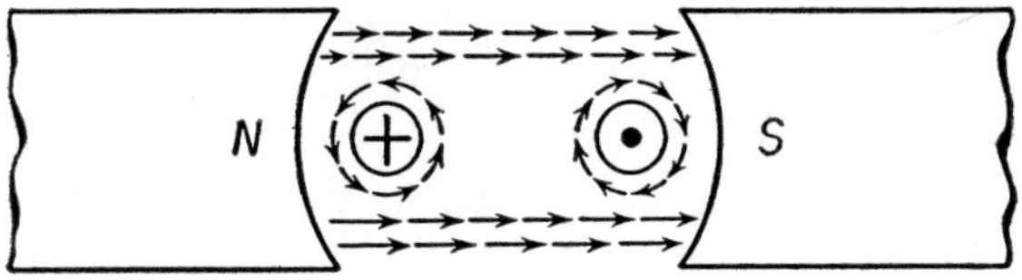


Fig. 6-2.

in the coil are shown in the proper direction as determined by the left-hand rule. Observe the coil half to the left. Current is traveling *into* this wire; its magnetic field's direction is counter-

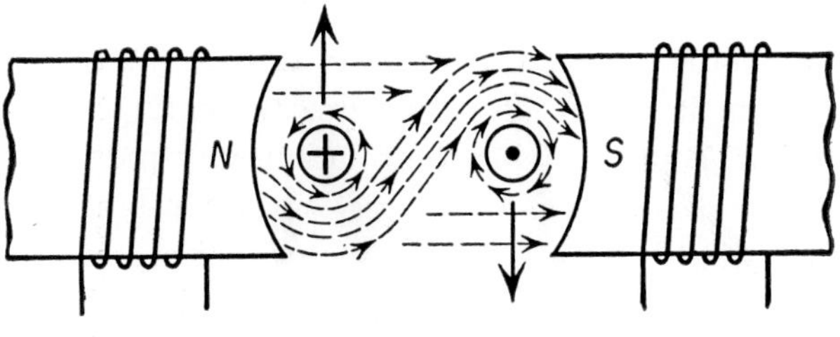


Fig. 6-3.

clockwise. Below this wire, its field is aiding and adding to that of the magnet, while above the wire the fields are opposing, and some cancellation is effected. Meanwhile, below the wire to the right there is a cancellation of the magnetic fields, resulting in a thinning out of the net magnetic field; and above the same wire there is a concentration of magnetic flux. The over-all result, as shown in Figure 6-3, is a warped or distorted magnetic field in the motor proper. The lines of flux will try to straighten, and in the process the wire to the left will be pushed upward, the wire to the right pushed downward. This is called *motor action.*

Obviously, this same principle will apply to a motor with a rotating member consisting of many coils instead of just one; when the coil shown in Figure 6-3 has been moved by the warped magnetic field, another coil or group of coils will have moved into a position where they may be influenced by the magnetic field. The result is a constant rotation of the coil-bearing assembly, which is called the *armature.*

In the example given, the magnetic field was produced by two poles of permanent magnets. The more common practice is to produce the motor *field* by coils around the soft iron projections of the motor frame.

## 6.2. The Universal Motor

As may be seen in Figure 6-3, if the direction of current flow through the motor loop and field coils (the electromagnets) is reversed, this does not effect a change of direction of rotation. It is the same as pulling out the motor cord plug, turning it around, and plugging it in the socket the opposite way—which, of course, will not cause the motor to turn in the reverse direction. If, then, it is possible to reverse the current direction in this motor without reversing the rotation, it is possible to apply to the motor a current whose direction is constantly reversing —an alternating current—and the motor will operate. This type of motor, depicted in Figure 6-4, is used extensively in appliances. The vacuum cleaner, sewing machine, mixer, desk fan, and electric razor are examples of its application. It has been indicated that the motor will operate on either alternating current or direct current, and when designed to do so with approximately the same speed on either it is called the *universal* motor. (This is not a brand name, but refers to the motor *type.*) By comparison with other a-c motors, the universal motor has a higher speed (desirable for vacuum-cleaner use) and its speed may be easily controlled and varied (desirable for mixer or sewing-machine use). The speed of this motor depends upon the current through it, which in turn is dependent upon the voltage across it. If a resistance is placed in series with the universal motor, a lower voltage and current will be applied to the motor, and its speed will decrease. Application of this principle is explained in Chapter 8, Food Mixers.

The universal motor rotates because of interaction of the field magnets and the magnetism produced by the armature

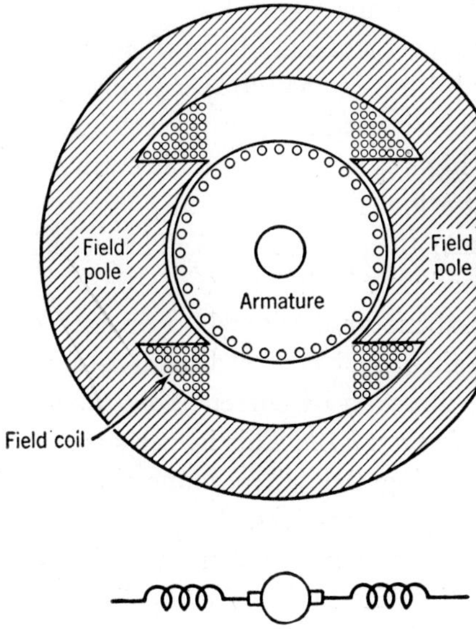


FIG. 6-4.

current. As the armature rotates, its conductors are cutting through the flux of the field poles. This action generates a current in the armature coils, and application of the left-hand rule indicates that this generated current will flow in a direction opposite to that from the source. The generated voltage, called the counter emf, cancels out an equal amount of the applied voltage, and the net voltage at which the motor operates is the difference between the two. As an example, if 120 v is used to operate the motor and its speed is such that 100 v is the generated counter emf, the motor will actually be operating on 120 minus 100, or 20 v.

The magnitude of the counter emf depends upon the speed of the motor. This is because the amount of voltage generated is proportional to the speed a conductor cuts through lines of force. At standstill, there is no counter emf. As the motor accelerates, the counter emf increases in value. Thus, the universal motor operates at a higher voltage when under a heavy load, since this load reduces the speed, lowering the counter emf. The torque (turning power) of the universal motor is greatest at its lowest speed, and decreases as the speed increases. The universal motor, for example, is used to operate electric drills. It will rotate a small bit at a high speed; a larger bit cutting into more metal will be turned at a lower speed, and at an increase of torque, as required to handle the heavier load. The speed of a universal motor with no load may be in excess of 10,000 rpm.

The universal motor, designed to operate either on a-c or on d-c, or on both, may have its direction of rotation reversed by reversing the direction of current flow through the armature or the field coils, *but not both.* This is, perhaps, most conveniently done by interchanging the wires connecting the field-coil ends to the brushes. Some few universal motors have a type of winding which gives optimum performance with a predetermined direction of rotation. Reversing the brush leads in this type of motor will reverse its direction of rotation, but with a severe reduction of speed. To obtain satisfactory reverse operation with this style of universal motor, it must be rewound.

The universal motor requires brushes for its operation. Brushes are noisy; there is a constant whirring sound from this motor. Also, there is a spark at the point where the brushes contact the commutator, and unless filtering devices are used, this spark will cause annoying radio interference.

## 6.3. The Shaded-Pole Motor

The only appliance motor which can operate on both a-c and d-c is the universal motor. Two other types find their greatest use in appliances. They are the shaded-pole motor and the split-phase motor. Both are a-c motors operating on the induction principle, and are called *induction motors*. The smaller as well as the simpler of the two is the shaded-pole motor (Fig. 6-5).

The field of this motor appears at first glance to be the same as that of a universal motor. However, closer examination reveals that the field pole has a slot, about one third of the distance in

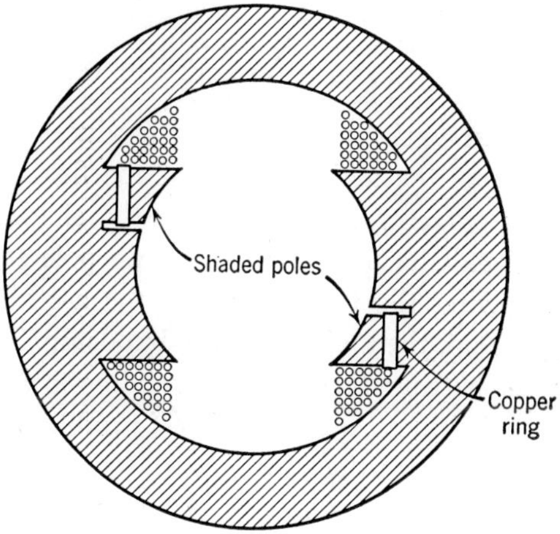


FIG. 6-5.

from the end; and a continuous loop of heavy, uninsulated copper wire or bus bar is placed in the slot and surrounds the smaller portion of the field pole. This is the shading coil, and the portion of the field embraced by this coil is called the shaded pole.

The revolving part of the motor is called the rotor. It has no commutator; this motor does not require brushes for its operation. The conductors of the rotor are heavy, uninsulated copper bars running the length of the rotor and welded or riveted into place. A brass ring at each end of the rotor short-circuits all these bars together. Construction of this type is called a squirrel-cage rotor. There is no electrical connection between the line and the conductors of the rotor; they obtain their current by induction.

The operation of the shaded-pole motor is as follows. Consider the alternating current cycle shown in Figure 6-6. Each half cycle (alternation) may be thought of as having three stages. First is the upward part of the curve, which represents current increasing from standstill. Next is a brief period, at the top of the curve, wherein current is undergoing only slight change. Finally the curve slopes downward toward zero, depicting a stoppage of the current flow preceding reversal.

These current variations are applied to the field coils of the shaded-pole motor. The magnetic flux produced by the coils follows the current variations and thus produces an alternating flux. The field from the main portion of the field pole varies as does the applied current. The flux from the shaded portion of the pole lags behind the flux from the main pole segment.

Again following the three parts of the a-c alternation: as the current builds up, the main-pole flux builds up. The flux from the shaded pole, cutting through the shading coil, generates a current in that coil. The coil current itself produces a flux *opposing* the shaded-pole flux; therefore, most of the field magnetism emanates from the main pole.

As the a-c cycle reaches its peak, there is no *change of current,* and the flux produced will be constant, not in motion. No current is generated in the shading coil, and a field of uniform intensity emanates from both main pole and shaded pole.

The flux is again in motion on the downward part of the alternation. The motion is of such a direction, however, that the current generated in the shading coil produces a flux *aiding* the flux from the main coil. Thus, a greater field strength is obtained from the shading pole than the dying field strength of the main pole.

In effect, this sequence of flux variations produces a rotating magnetic field within the motor (Fig. 6-6). The rotating magnetic field cuts through the conductors of the stator, inducing in them a current flow which is quite large, because of their low resistance. As the rotor wires are short-circuited, the induced current flow is in a circular path, forming an electromagnet with the rotor iron. The principle of repulsion, wherein like poles repel, causes the motor to turn. Its direction of rotation will be from main pole to shaded pole of the same magnetic polarity.

To reverse the direction of rotation of this motor, it is necessary to disassemble it and turn the field structure around so that

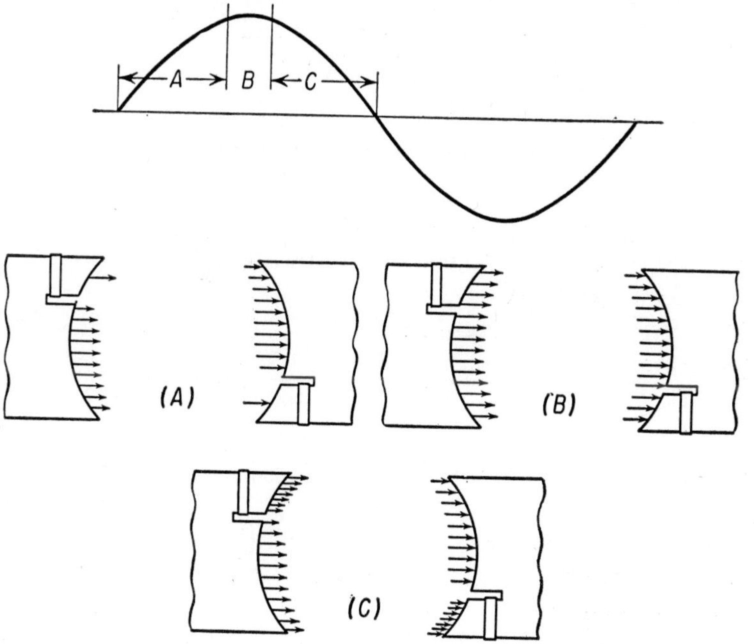


FIG. 6-6.

the direction from a main pole to shaded pole will be reversed. The principal use of this motor is on small desk fans. Its design is such that it will operate indefinitely with a locked rotor at no damage to the motor.

## 6.4. The Split-Phase Motor

The largest of the motors used on appliances is the split-phase motor. Most commonly employed in the 1/4-hp size, this motor is the one found on washing machines and ironers. It is strictly an a-c motor, and any attempt to operate it on direct current will damage the windings.

The rotor of the split-phase motor is an enlarged version of the squirrel-cage rotor of the shaded-pole motor. The field, or stator, differs considerably from that of other appliance motors. In both the universal motor and the shaded-pole motor the field is formed by a coil slipped over a piece of magnetic iron. The coil may be formed external to the motor and put into place after

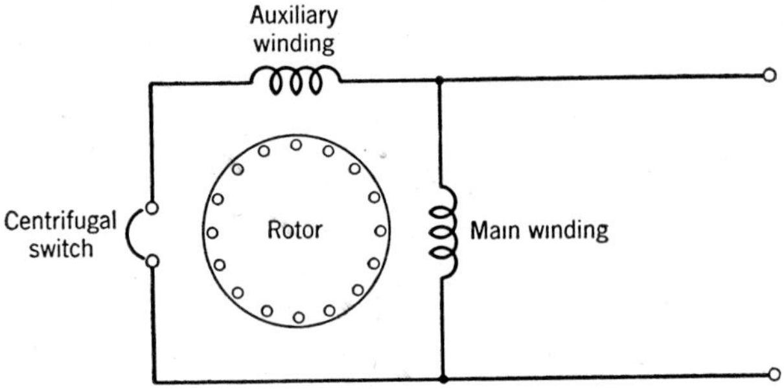


FIG. 6-7.

being completed. This is known as a *concentrated* winding. In the field of the split-phase motor is a series of slots, and the field coils are wound into these slots, much in the same manner as the conductors of an armature. This type of construction is a *distributed* winding. Its use allows the various coils used to overlap.

The split-phase motor field contains two windings, the *main* or *running* winding and the *auxiliary* or *starting* winding. As its name implies, the auxiliary winding is used only while the motor is starting, and is disconnected when the motor approaches full speed. A centrifugal switch, one which operates because of weighted levers thrown outward by rotor speed, is attached to the rotor shaft, and at about 80 per cent of full speed this switch disconnects the starting winding from the line. The motor then runs on the main winding only.

The main winding is placed in the bottom of the slots so as to embrace as much of the field-pole iron as possible. It has the greater number of turns of a relatively heavier wire. These two factors combine to cause the main winding to possess a high inductance. It has been stated (Chap. 1) that one of the properties of an inductance is to cause the current to lag behind the voltage in an a-c circuit.

The starting winding is designed so as to have as little inductance as possible. It consists of a smaller-size wire, and, being wound in the top of the slot, surrounds a smaller quantity of iron. Hence it is considered to be resistive rather than inductive in nature. The current does not lag the voltage in a purely resistive circuit.

The split-phase motor for appliance use is a four-pole motor. The main winding may be one continuous wire. The coils for one pole are wound in adjacent slots spanning one fourth of the field structure. The next pole is wound in an equal number of slots, but the coils are wound in the opposite direction; thus, with current applied, adjacent poles will be of opposite magnetic polarity. The winding continues in this manner until four poles have been formed, each of which is wound in a direction opposite to that of its neighbors.

The starting winding is wound in exactly the same manner as the running winding, forming four poles. It is, however, started in such a manner that its pole centers are located midway between the centers of two main winding poles. The use of slots rather than solid field poles allows this to be done. Such a positioning of the two windings is called a 90° electrical displacement.

The two windings are connected in parallel across a 120-v a-c line. Since a parallel circuit is a constant-voltage circuit, both windings have the same voltage impressed; the currents through the two windings are dependent upon their resistance and inductance. The main winding is more inductive than the auxiliary; therefore, the main-winding-current maximum and minimum occur later than do those of the starting winding. The time difference between the fluxes produced by the two currents causes the equivalent of a rotating field, which the iron rotor follows.

The starting winding does not have enough turns of wire to withstand continuously the current resultant from 120 v. The starting switch opens the starting winding circuit at almost full speed, protecting this winding from burn-out. After the starting switch has opened, the displaced magnetic field producing initial rotation no longer exists, yet the motor continues to run. Having been started by some auxiliary means, the split-phase motor will continue to rotate in the direction started, even though the auxiliary device is removed. If the starting winding in a split-phase motor is inoperative, the rotor of the motor can be given a fast spin, and the running winding will continue to turn it in the direction started.

When the rotor is turning it is moving through the magnetic field of the main poles. The bars through the rotor have a current induced (generated) which makes of the rotor an electromagnet. The interaction between the rotor as a four-pole electromagnet and the field poles produces sustained rotation.

Since the split-phase motor will run in the direction started, it is the relationship between the direction of the currents in the starting and running windings which determines the initial direction. To reverse the motor, either the starting or the running winding connection to the line must be reversed, but not both. The direction of rotation is from auxiliary to main pole of the same magnetic polarity.

Two factors, lower speed and the auxiliary winding being in the circuit, cause the split-phase motor to draw more than 15 amp when starting. At full speed the current is much less, generally 4 or 5 amp. Motor protection in the form of time-lag fuses or circuit breakers will prevent the high starting current of this motor from blowing fuses when actually the overload is only of brief duration.

The rotating magnetic field is produced by an alternating current. The speed of the rotating field depends upon the speed (in cycles per second) of the changing alternating current. Thus, the rpm of the motor is determined by the rpm of the alternator supplying it. To produce a 60-cycle a-c, a four-pole generator must rotate 1,800 rpm. A four-pole split-phase motor tries to rotate at the same speed, 1,800 rpm. If the rotor were rotating at exactly the same speed as the magnetic field, there would be no current generated in the copper bars of the rotor; hence, it would not be an electromagnet. If the rotor turns at a slower speed there will be a relative motion between rotor bars and field flux, and a generated current will flow through the rotor bars. Its direction will be such as to sustain the rotation generating it. The speed of the rotating field is called the synchronous speed (1,800 rpm for a four-pole motor). The difference between the synchronous speed and the actual speed is the *slip*. The most common rating of appliance split-phase motors is 1,725 rpm. The slip is 75 rpm. Increasing the motor load or decreasing the applied voltage will cause a slight increase in slip, but not enough to make it practical to use either of these methods to vary the motor speed. The split-phase motor cannot be used where a wide range of speeds is desired. At best, an induction motor can operate at only two or three different speeds, and to accomplish this, multiple windings are required. Some large circulating fans are equipped with a split-phase motor with two sets of windings. A switch allows a change from one winding to the other, producing high and low speeds.

The principle of a magnetic flux cutting through a conductor and generating a current therein applies not only to the copper wires in a motor, but also to the iron field and armature or rotor parts as well. Although iron is a poorer conductor than copper, the mass of the iron parts results in a very low resistance value. Ohm's law,

$$I = \frac{E}{R},$$

indicates that the low resistance of the iron will result in a very heavy generated current flowing through the iron parts of an a-c machine. The value of these *eddy* currents, as they are called, can be lowered by increasing the resistance of the iron. To accomplish this, the iron parts are made of many thin strips, or *laminations,* fastened together. The direction of stacking is such that the eddy currents must flow through the stack. An insulating coating on each piece of iron—varnish, paper, or oxide coating—acting as an insulator, increases the resistance to the flow of eddy currents, and results in cooler operation of the a-c machine.

## 6.5. The Capacitor-Start Motor

The split-phase motor starts to turn because of the rotating magnetic field effect produced by making one winding resistive, the other inductive, in nature. This causes a slight time difference between maximum and minimum field flux conditions in auxiliary

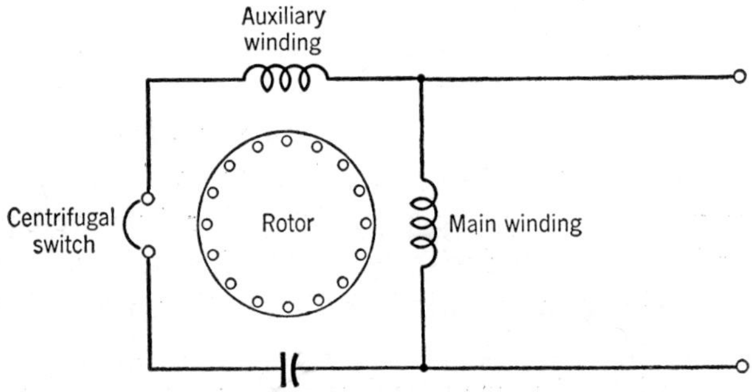


FIG. 6-8.

and main windings. If this time difference could be increased to an optimum of one fourth cycle, then the motor would be smoother and more powerful: that is, more starting torque would be developed. A closer approach to this ideal is obtained when a capacitor (Sec. 1.16) is placed in the starting winding circuit (Fig. 6-8).

Whereas the inductance of the main winding causes the current to lag, the capacitor in the auxiliary winding circuit will cause the exact opposite; the current will lead the voltage. If the proper value of capacitor is used, this motor—called the capacitor-start motor—has a time (or phase) difference between starting and running winding fluxes of almost 1/4 cycle and possesses very high starting torque.

The capacitor-start motor is used on some large fans, and

is just about the only kind found on electric refrigerators, where a high starting torque is needed. The starting torque of the split-phase motor is adequate for washing-machine and ironer use; consequently, the more expensive capacitor-start motor is not used on these appliances. After the starting period has ended, both type of motors run in exactly the same manner—governed by the same electrical principles. The difference between split-phase and capacitor-start motors exists only during the starting period.

While it is possible to convert a split-phase motor into a capacitor-start motor by inserting the proper value of capacitor in the starting winding circuit, this procedure is not recommended, mainly because the proper value of capacitor is determined only by a trial-and-error process. Furthermore, the increase in torque thus obtained is less than that obtained by using a capacitor-start motor manufactured as such. Also, if the wrong-size capacitor is used, the starting torque may be less than the motor originally possessed.

As the principle of capacitor starting does not involve the use of a resistive winding, the capacitor-start motor does not contain as small a size wire in the auxiliary winding as a split-phase motor does. Thus, if the capacitor in a capacitor-start motor should develop a fault (open circuit or short) the motor will not continue to operate as a split-phase motor; instead, it will just hum and refuse to turn. When this condition is encountered, one of the things to suspect and test is the capacitor. Capacitor tests are given in Section 7.4.

## 6.6. Dual-Voltage Motors

The split-phase and capacitor-start motors used on appliances are all four-pole motors. The usual scheme of manufacture is to wind all four poles of each winding continuously, using only one length of wire for each. Some of these motors, however, are wound of two lengths of wire, the wire being severed between poles 2 and 3 of each winding. Such a motor is designed so that the number of turns of wire used allows the motor to be operated on 220-v a-c when all four poles are connected in series. Connecting poles 1 and 2 in parallel with poles 3 and 4 cuts in half the total turns across the line; thus, the motor can be now used on 110-v a-c. A motor of this kind is called a dual-voltage motor. All eight coil-end wires are brought outside the motor, and are numbered or otherwise identified. A diagram of connections for these eight wires is placed on the motor housing, and by following this diagram the motor can be adapted for use on either 110 or 220 v.

## Now that you have read this chapter, can you answer these questions?

**1.** What is meant by a "fractional horsepower" motor?
**2.** What is an induction motor?
**3.** What action in a motor is used as a basis for its type name?
**4.** Why is the universal motor so named?
**5.** Why is a commutator needed on a universal motor?
**6.** Which has the greater resistance, the starting or the running winding of a split-phase motor? Of a shaded-pole motor?
**7.** Which winding is put into a split-phase motor first? Why?
**8.** How would you reverse the direction of rotation of a washing-machine motor?
**9.** What is meant by counter electromotive force? Does it occur in a universal motor only?
**10.** With no load, which has the higher speed, a universal or a shaded-pole motor?
**11.** How would you reverse a universal motor? A shaded-pole motor?
**12.** If there is a capacitor mounted across the brush terminals of a universal motor, what is its purpose?
**13.** Describe the construction of a squirrel-cage rotor. Why is it laminated?
**14.** How can the direction of rotation of a shaded-pole motor be determined without actually running the motor?
**15.** What is a concentrated winding? A distributed winding?

16. Describe the action of a centrifugal switch.

17. The starting current of a split-phase motor is quite high, but is reduced to a lower value when running. Why is this so?

18. What is meant by synchronous speed?

19. What is the "slip" of a motor?

20. What are eddy currents? How may they be minimized?

*chapter* **7**

# Vacuum Cleaners and Fans

As has been previously stated, an electric current perform one or both of two functions in an electric appliance. It eithe produces heat, or turns a motor; or both. The production of hea electrically has been considered in the foregoing chapter, and w are now ready to consider the appliance which requires the us of a motor. Such an appliance is the vacuum cleaner.

## VACUUM CLEANERS

### 7.1. The Two General Types

In general, there are two designs for vacuum cleaners: th tank type, and the upright (Fig. 7-1). The function and princip of operation are the same for both; the two designs are merel a matter of styling and customer accommodation. The princip of operation is simple—a motor-driven fan produces a suctio which draws dirt from carpet or upholstery.

### 7.2. The Upright Vacuum Cleaner

The motor in the upright vacuum cleaner is located close t the floor and may be in either a vertical or horizontal positio

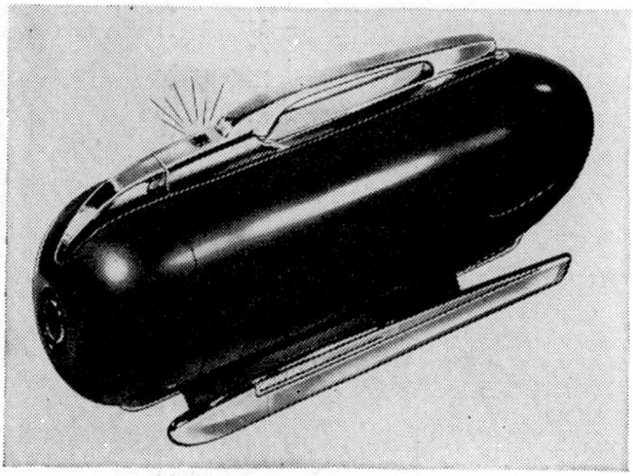

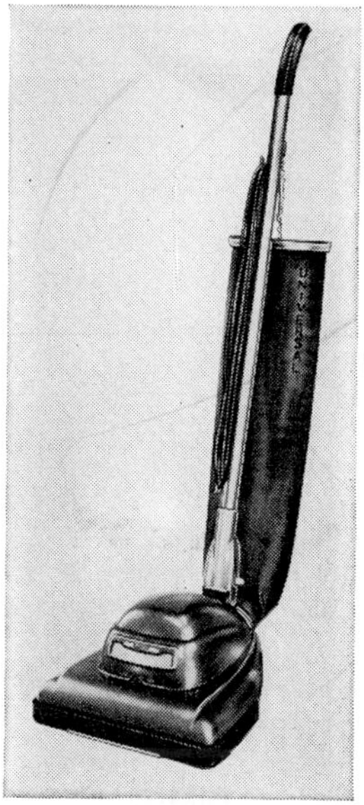

FIG. 7-1.
Three Types of
Universal
Vacuum Cleaners.
(Courtesy, Landers,
Frary, & Clark)

epending on the brand and model. At the end of the motor shaft ; the driven fan blade. Below the blade is a flanged opening ırough which the dirt is drawn. As is shown in Figure 7-2, the lade draws the dirt past the motor and through a vent to which ; attached the dirt bag. Observe that the motor is sealed from ıe compartment in which the blade is located, so that dust cannot et into the motor and do damage. The motor shaft extends past ıe fan blades, and there may be a belt attached which drives a oller brush located at the bottom opening. This brush loosens ıe lint from the carpet as it rotates, allowing the vacuum cleaner ) do a better cleaning job.

The brush rotates at a rather high speed, for it is driven—

with very little reduction due to pulley size—by a high-speed motor. At each end of the brush, where it is mounted on the machine, a bearing is located. Because of the surrounding dust, it is difficult to keep these bearings properly lubricated; the dust

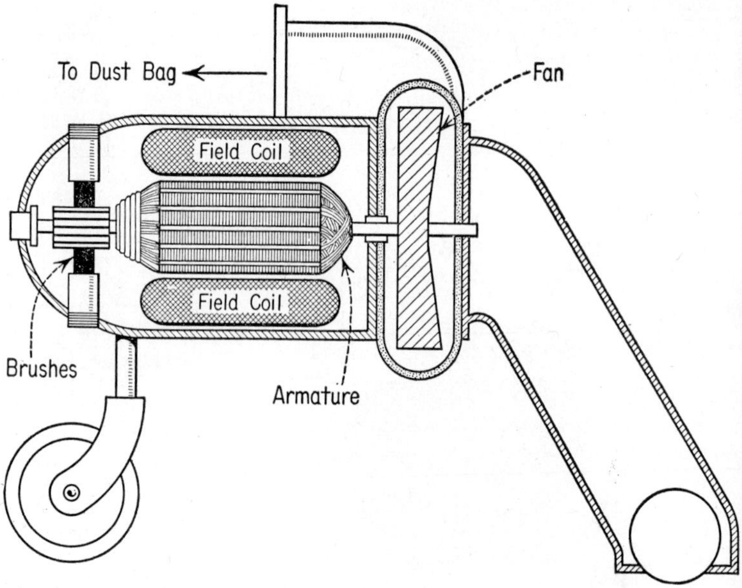


FIG. 7-2.

soaks up the oil and gets inside, causing wear. This will, of course make the vacuum cleaner noisy, and cause the brush belt to wear out prematurely. Regardless of other complaints, every vacuum cleaner of the upright type received for repair should be checked for defective or worn brush bearings. The customer will appreciate this servicing, which will cause a marked improvement in the cleaner's performance. The brush, if adjustable, should be set so as to extend 1/32 inch below the nozzle.

The bag into which the dust is drawn is made of a porous cloth with mesh of such size as to allow air to escape, but not dust. After the bag has been in service for some time the pores in the cloth become clogged with dust particles so that the flow of air is impeded. When air in the bag cannot escape, the fan i unable to draw more air up into the bag, and the suction of the vacuum cleaner is very poor. Hence, any bag which shows by its condition that it has been on the machine for a long time should be replaced.

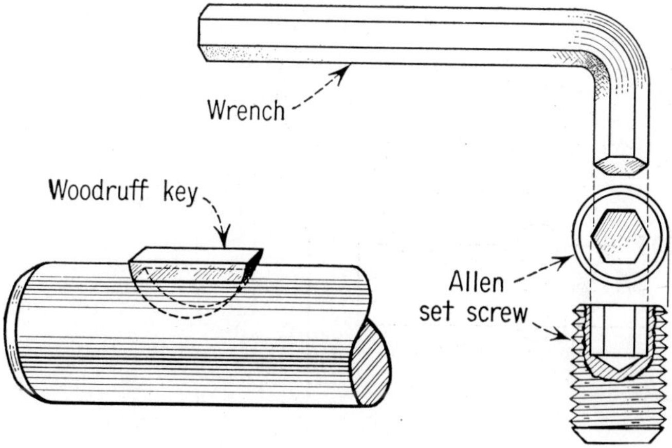


FIG. 7-3.

A number of different systems for attaching the fan blade to the motor shaft are in use. One method is to thread the shaft and the fan-blade bore, the blade being screwed onto the shaft. To remove this type of attachment, the direction of rotation is determined and the blade is screwed off *in the same direction as the motor rotates.*

Another method of attaching the blade to the shaft is by use of a setscrew. The Allen setscrew shown in Figure 7-3 is most commonly used. Special wrenches used with the Allen setscrew may be obtained in sets to cover a large range of sizes.

The Woodruff key, also shown in Figure 7-3, is likewise used, along with a nut on the end of the shaft to prevent endwise movement of the blade.

## 7.3. Electric Circuit

The electric circuit of the vacuum cleaner consists of a motor, a single-pole toggle switch, and the attachment cord. This cord is peculiar in two respects: it is of a special type developed particularly for vacuum cleaners, and is classified as type SV. It is similar in construction to the type SJ (Fig. 3-1), but of a smaller diameter. The cord is longer than that affixed to any other appliance. The usual cord length for an appliance is 6 feet, but since the vacuum cleaner is to be moved all over one room, and the housewife often finds it more convenient to vacuum an adjoining room or hallway without changing connection, the standard

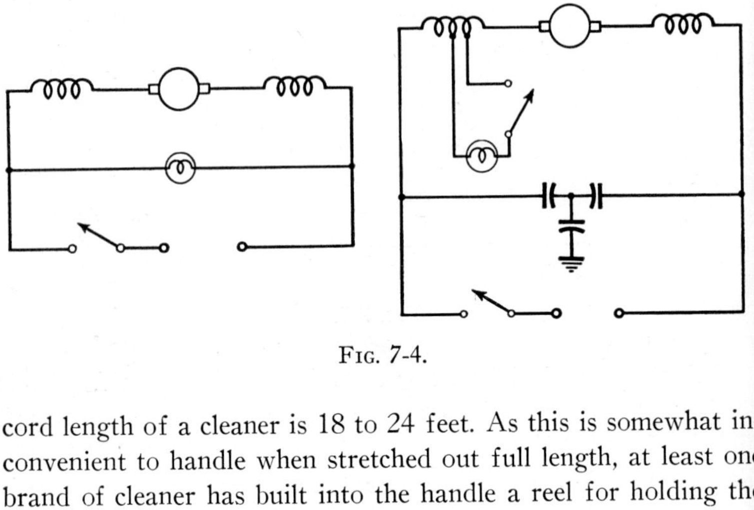

FIG. 7-4.

cord length of a cleaner is 18 to 24 feet. As this is somewhat inconvenient to handle when stretched out full length, at least one brand of cleaner has built into the handle a reel for holding the portion of cord not in use.

As a convenience for cleaning in dark corners, some manufacturers have equipped their products with a light, mounted a the front of the cleaner. As may be seen in Figure 7-4, this bulb is connected in parallel with the motor and is controlled by the switch on the handle.

The switch on a vacuum cleaner is a single-pole toggle type usually located on the handle at a spot convenient to the operator An alternate arrangement is to mount the switch alongside th motor; the handle bracket automatically turns the switch off whe handle is pushed forward (as is the case when machine is no in use) and on when handle is pulled back toward user.

The vacuum-cleaner motor is shown in Figure 7-5. This is the universal motor, operation of which is described in Chapter 6. As indicated in Figure 7-4, the field coils and armature of this motor are all connected in series. A motor designed in this manner has the characteristic of very high speed, especially when operated with a load as light as one fan blade. This characteristic

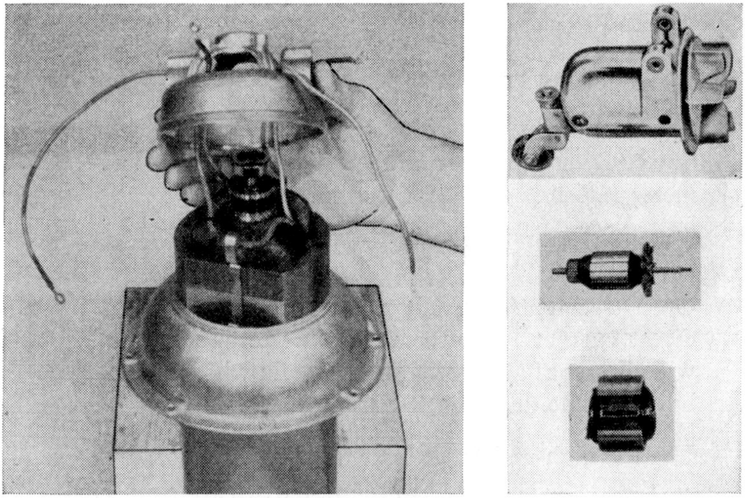

FIG. 7-5. Two Types of Vacuum-Cleaner Motors. (*Left:* Courtesy, Landers, Frary, & Clark)

makes it particularly well suited to vacuum-cleaner service, the high speed providing a substantial vacuum. The speed regulation of this type of motor is somewhat poor; however, in a vacuum cleaner the load remains fairly constant, so poor regulation is no drawback. The universal motor operates equally well on alternating current or direct current; this information is often stamped on the motor name plate. The only noticeable difference is a slightly higher speed on direct current.

Referring once again to Figure 7-4, it will be seen that a capacitor is connected across the brushes of the motor to reduce interference with radio and television reception. This is highly important, since a vacuum cleaner is one of the worst offenders in this respect, mainly because of the high speed of the motor. Sometimes a triple-section capacitor is used. Three wires extend from this type of capacitor; one has no insulation, and it is connected to the frame of the motor (grounded), while the other two lead wires are attached to the motor brushes. The circuit and connections are shown in Figure 7-4.

## 7.4. Testing the Capacitor

The capacitor may be tested in the following manner:

Short circuit: Use ohmmeter or series test lamp across capacitor terminals. If lamp lights to full brilliance, or ohmmeter registers zero ohms, capacitor is shorted, and should be replaced with one of identical size and value (capacity and voltage rating).

Open circuit: A capacitor is an open circuit insofar as a direct current is concerned, so the test for an open circuit will consist of attempting to ascertain whether the lead wires have become disconnected from the foil plates.

Use the high-resistance scale of the ohmmeter, and carefully observe the meter needle when the test wires are connected to the capacitor. If the capacitor is good, the battery in the ohmmeter will charge the capacitor, and in so doing will cause a momentary deflection of the needle. If it is open-circuited, no such deflection will be observed. After the capacitor has been charged through the ohmmeter, the connections between ohmmeter and capacitor may be reversed; the capacitor will discharge through the meter, adding its voltage to that of the meter battery, and causing a more definite movement of the needle. The higher the value of the capacitor, the more positive are the indications of this test; therefore, a very small-value capacitor may not respond to this test with a readily discernible deflection.

Another way to detect an open-circuited capacitor is by use of a 1/4-w neon test bulb in the circuit shown in Figure 7-6. The neon bulb is placed in series with the capacitor across a 120-v a-c source. Because of the minute current required to operate this lamp, the capacitor will (if good) allow sufficient current for operation to circulate in an a-c circuit. A glow indicates a good capacitor; no glow, an open capacitor. This test should be made in conjunction with the test for shorts outlined at the opening of this section, since a good capacitor and a shorted one may both give the same indication: a glow in the neon lamp.

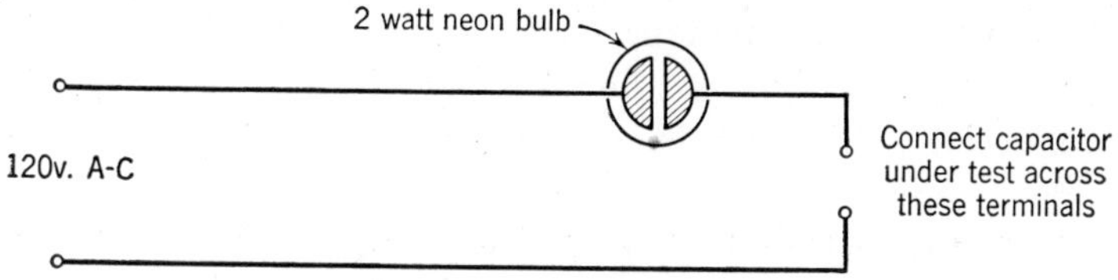


FIG. 7-6.

## 7.5. Testing the Motor Fields

The field of the universal motor has a *concentrated* winding. This type of coil is wound on a form and taped, then slipped over the field poles. A two-pole motor will, of course, have two such windings (Fig. 6-4). This type of winding is easily replaceable; the coil is merely tied or clamped into place, and loosening the clamp, or cutting the tie cord, allows the winding to be pulled out without the use of tools.

Often a new field coil can be prepared in the shop as follows. Obtain a block of wood, larger than the field coil. Drive four nails into the block, forming a rectangle exactly the same size as the internal dimensions of the coil. Mount a 3- or 4-inch bolt in the exact center of the rectangle, with its head on the same side as the nailheads, and pull down tight with a nut. Mount the end of the bolt in a hand drill which is held in a vise. Having determined the size of wire used in the coil to be replaced, together with its type of insulation (whether enameled or cotton-covered), and having counted the number of turns, wind an identical new coil on the form. Usually two persons are needed to operate this improvised coil-winder, one feeding the wire off its spool onto the coil form while the other counts the turns and operates the drill.

When the proper number of turns have been wound, the corners of the coil should be fastened by a loop of string so that the coil will not fall apart when the nails are loosened. A length of heavier wire with substantial insulation, such as that contained inside the outer sheath of type SJ or SV cord, should be soldered to the coil ends. These will act as the lead wires for the coil. Next, wrap the coil with linen tape, enclosing the soldered joints within the tape, and, finally, coat the assembly with insulating varnish.

Special equipment is available for coil-winding. A well-equipped shop will find it advantageous to have such equipment, which allows easier winding of a well-made coil and also eliminates the possibility of error, since an automatic counter is attached to the winder.

The coil thus made must be connected in the circuit so as to provide the proper magnetic polarity of the field poles. This means, in a two-pole motor, that when one is a north pole, the other must be a south pole; in a motor with many poles, any two *adjacent* poles must be of opposite polarity. One way to check the polarity is to connect the motor line-cord leads to a source of low d-c voltage. A couple of dry cells will do. With armature removed, connect the brush leads together so as to complete the circuit. Test the magnetic polarity produced by the d-c source with a small pocket compass. If opposite ends of the needle are attracted by adjacent pole pieces, the connections are correct. In a two-pole motor, the needle will swing very noticeably into line with the center of the poles when placed within the motor.

Another way to check a two-pole universal motor for proper field connections is to assemble the motor and connect it momentarily to its rated voltage source. If the motor turns, the field connections are correct. If it merely hums, the leads from one field coil should be reversed. If the motor runs backward, reverse the leads from the coils to the brushes. Reversing the brush connections causes current to flow through the armature in the opposite direction, effecting a reversal of rotation.

The condition of a field coil may be determined by testing with an ohmmeter. The resistance of one coil should measure between 5 and 100 ohms, depending upon the wire size and number of turns. Usually it is possible from visual examination of the coil to judge where in this range the measurement should be. If in doubt, a small portion of the tape covering the coil may be removed so as to make the wire size visible. If the coil contains a broken wire, the ohmmeter will point to an infinite or very high resistance; if shortened, the coil will measure zero ohms or very nearly so. A test between the coil ends and the motor frame will show a ground if the reading is a measurable resistance value or zero ohms. Any of these three—open, shorted, or grounded coil—indicate that the coil should be replaced.

## 7.6. Testing the Armature

The ohmmeter is also used to check the armature. A resistance measurement should be made from every commutator bar to that next to it, and all measurements should read about the same resistance value. Generally this value is quite low—between 1/2 ohm and 10 ohms—so a meter which covers this range with the major portion of its scale should be used to obtain the greatest accuracy. Any measure of a higher resistance between some bars and others is indicative of an open coil.

To test for shorted coils, an instrument known as the growler is used; it is pictured in Figure 7-7. It consists of many turns of wire around a laminated iron structure, designed so that the armature may be placed in the V-shaped top. The growler is connected to a 120-v a-c source, and the armature set in place. A thin piece of iron, such as a knife blade or hack-saw blade, is placed on top of the armature. If the iron part of the armature displays a magnetic attraction for the blade, a coil is shorted. This test should be made for all the armature coils, the armature being turned so as to bring all parts to the top.

The test for a grounded coil may be made with a series test lamp or an ohmmeter. Connect one test lead to the shaft or the iron laminations. Touch the other test lead to all the commutator bars in turn. Low resistance on the ohmmeter, or a glow of the lamp, is evidence of a grounded coil. A readable value of high resistance on the ohmmeter indicates weakened insulation and the probability of a total ground within a short time.

Often the running condition of a motor indicates the status of the motor windings. A motor that smokes or becomes excessively hot should be tested for grounds and shorted turns. Excessive sparking at the commutator is often caused by a shorted armature

FIG. 7-7.

coil. If these symptoms are observed, the motor should be disconnected to prevent further damage, and tested as described.

No attempt will be made here to set forth in detail the methods used for armature rewinding, or the various windings used in appliance motors. The appliance man without this kind of experience will find it wise to take advantage of the exchange plan made available by most manufacturers.

## 7.7. Brushes and Bearings

The universal motor requires carbon brushes for its operation. Since the motor operates at a high speed, some brush wear is to be expected. Very often when a motor will not run it is because the brush, or brush spring, is worn. The usual brush length is about 1/2 or 3/4 inch; if the brushes are much shorter than this length, it is an indication of brush wear, and they should be replaced. A spring holds the brush against the commutator, and for proper motor operation the spring tension should be maintained. If brush springs show evidence of loss of tension, or are misshapen, they too should be replaced. It is important that brushes and springs be replaced with exact duplicates. A wrong-size brush will wobble and wear unevenly if too small, and bind if too large. A brush of the wrong shape will bind or be too loose. Proper design calls for a brush tension of 1.5 to 2 pounds per square inch of brush surface, and the manufacturer will provide this in his motor. Replacement with exact duplicate springs will prevent trouble from improper tension.

The new brush should be shaped by sanding it to the contour of the commutator. This is often difficult to accomplish on a small motor; if it is possible, sandpaper (not emery cloth) should be placed around the commutator, rough side out, and the armature turned by hand, allowing the sandpaper to shape the brush end to the same curvature as the commutator.

The commutator is also subject to wear. This is especially true if ill-fitting brushes are used; a groove worn into the commutator may result. The worn commutator should be trued on a lathe. If a lathe is not available, and the wear is not excessive, the commutator may be sandpapered to remove blackened spots, thus effecting an improvement in the operation of the motor.

Each bar of the commutator is insulated from its neighboring bars by a mica sheet. The mica used is carefully selected so as to have the same rate of wear as the copper commutator bars. Even so, often the copper will wear more, resulting in so-called "high mica," and the brush will not be able to make proper contact with the commutator. If the commutator has been trued in a lathe, the level of copper and mica will be even. To prevent the occurrence of high mica, the mica should be undercut. A used hack-saw blade may be used for undercutting, as its thickness is about the same as that of the mica. The sharp edge formed by breaking the blade can be used to cut down the mica to a depth of about 1/32 inch below the copper. If a grinding wheel is available, the hack-saw blade may be ground to shape as shown in

Figure 7-8. The hook formed by grinding is a convenient shape to pull through the mica slot.

Two types of bearings are used on vacuum cleaner motors: the sleeve bearing and the ball bearing. There is very little wear, even at high speed, on ball bearings, and they will operate satisfactorily as long as sufficient lubricant is present. A ball bearing, however, which is run dry, or has grit mixed with the lubricant, will soon bind or destroy itself, and must be replaced.

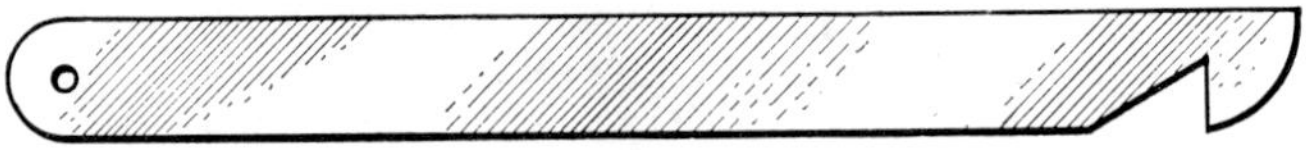

FIG. 7-8.

The ball bearing inner race is pressed onto the motor shaft, while the outer race is fitted less snugly into a recessed place in the motor end bell. A bearing puller is required to remove the ball bearing from the shaft. To replace the bearing, a block of wood with a hole in it the size of the motor shaft may be used to drive the new bearing into place. A good grade of fiber grease should

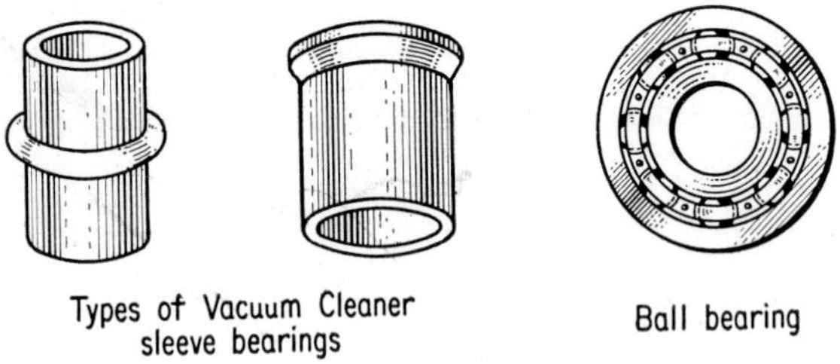


FIG. 7-9.

be used on the new ball bearing, and care should be exercised to make sure that the grease gets inside the ball bearing assembly, not just on the surface.

The sleeve bearing (Fig. 7-9) is more subject to wear than the ball bearing, and, even if properly lubricated, will eventually wear to the extent that it becomes too loose and must be replaced.

Some sleeve bearings are threaded on their outer surface and screwed into a threaded hole in the motor's end bell; a screw driver or wrench is all that is required to remove this type of bearing. Another type is pressed into place, and for its removal a tool such as shown in Figure 7-10 must be used. The angle bracket is placed over the end bell of the motor. The bolt used is

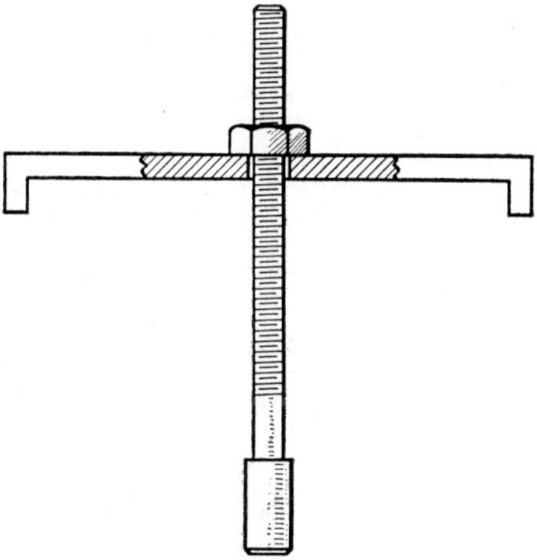

FIG. 7-10.

one of such size that its end flange just fits the outer diameter of the bearing. It is run through the bearing and angle bracket. The nut when pulled down tight will cause the bolt to pull the bearing out of its housing. A new bearing may be pulled into place in the same manner.

Invariably there is a slight misalignment between the two new bearings, and if the motor is assembled in this condition the armature will bind. To correct this situation, a line reamer with a long shaft is used, so that it can fit in both bearings at the same time. The procedure is as follows:

Remove one bearing. Replace with new one. Assemble motor without armature.

Using old bearing as guide, ream out new bearing.

Disassemble motor. Replace other bearing. Reassemble motor without armature.

Using bearing already reamed as a guide, ream out second bearing.

When the motor is reassembled, the bearings will be in perfect alignment and the armature will turn freely. Line reaming should be done to both the screw-in and the press-in types of sleeve bearings. Proper alignment of the bearings in all motors is so important that no well-equipped shop should be without a complete set of line reamers.

One type of bearing which requires no reaming, provided the size is a satisfactory fit for the armature shaft, is the self-aligning or floating bearing. As shown in Figure 7-9, this bearing is egg-shaped and is held in place by a plate fastened to the motor's end bell. The construction of this bearing and its housing is in the form of a partial ball and socket, which allows the axis of the bearing bore to be shifted (by a light pressure) through a rather large angle. Pulling the through bolts of the motor down tight will cause these bearings to align themselves naturally with the armature shaft.

This type of bearing will wear down just like any other sleeve bearing, and when worn must be replaced. In some cases, especially on inexpensive motors, the bearing retainer plate is riveted onto the end bell of the motor, and the rivets must be drilled out in order to remove the bearings. It is advisable to use bolts rather than rivets when reassembling the bearing housing, since with bolts there is less likelihood of distorting the end bell, and future dismantling will be simplified.

Some sleeve bearings are turned from a piece of bronze alloy. Others are formed under pressure from fine particles of bronze and a binder. The latter type is porous and will retain lubricating oil within its pores; this is the type of bearing used in the motor which the manufacturer advertises as requiring no oiling during its lifetime. Mounted beside the bearing is a felt wick saturated with oil. As the bearing and wick become warm owing to motor operation, the lubricant becomes more fluid and seeps from the bearing pores to lubricate the bearing surface and shaft. Cooling of the motor after shut-down allows the lubricant to become more viscous and soak back into the bearing pores.

The bearing fashioned from solid metal will require oiling from time to time. The bearing is made with an oil hole drilled in its side, and grooves in the bearing surface to distribute the lubricant. A felt wick is mounted so as to feed oil through the bearing onto the shaft; at its top end is a hole through which oil may be added. When the oil hole is provided on the vacuum cleaner, the owner should be advised to add a few drops of No. 10 motor oil every three months. It should be emphasized, however, that overlubrication is injurious to a motor, since excess oil saturates the windings, causing the insulation to deteriorate.

## 7.8. Tank-Type Vacuum Cleaners

The tank-type cleaner is shown in Figure 7-1. In use, this cleaner is placed on the floor and a long flexible hose attached. At the other end of the hose is fitted a length of rigid tube to which is connected a flared nozzle. The cleaner may be left in the middle of the room, since the attached conduit is long enough to allow the cleaning end to reach any part of the room.

Figure 7-11 shows an exploded view of a tank-type vacuum cleaner. The external parts appear at the lower left of the picture. Compare this with the photograph of the same appliance in Figure 7-1. The lower left part of the exploded view illustrates the sequence of parts within the tank. First is the dust bag, which can be removed by merely opening the tank end; loosening two clamps accomplishes this removal. Next is the dust filter, which traps small particles of dust which might seep through the bag, preventing them from entering the next part of the cleaner—the motor and fan assembly. The construction of the cleaner is such that air circulated by the fan must pass through the motor, and any dust here would do considerable damage to bearings, commutator, and windings. The manufacturer recommends that the dust filter be changed regularly. Finally, there is a vent at the motor's end for expelling air after it has done its job.

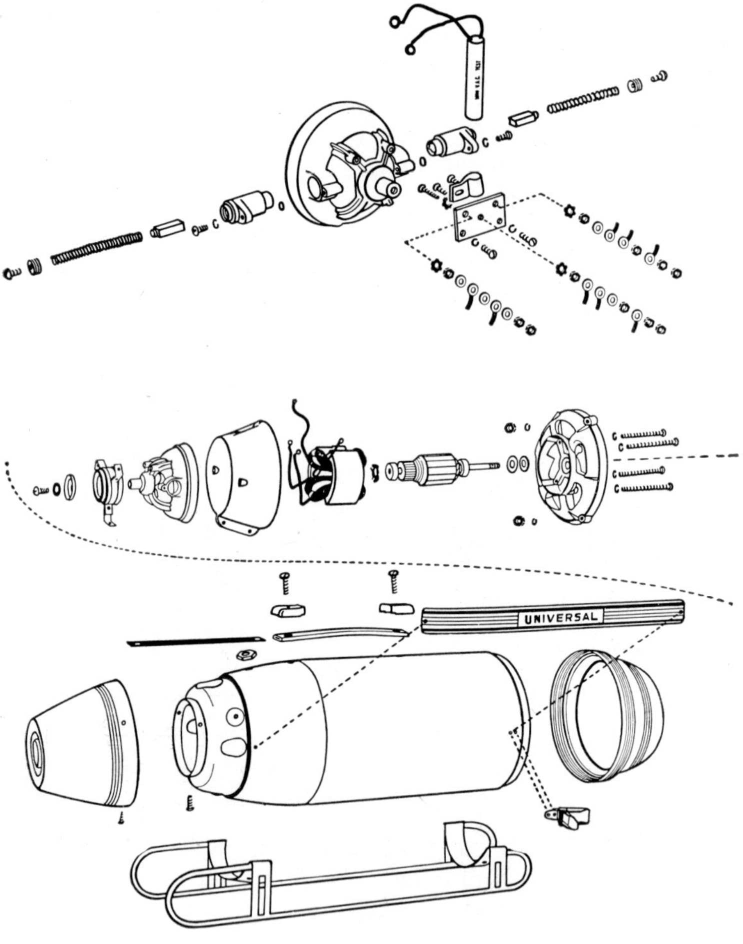


FIG. 7-11. Universal VC 6026 Vacuum Cleaner.

The central portion of Figure 7-11 displays the motor-blower assembly. Two moving and one stationary blades are used in a turbinelike array. The proper location of spacing devices (to be observed upon disassembly to assure proper reassembly) is important; otherwise, the blades will rub against one another, or adjacent metal, and at the high speed of the fan motor the noise of this rubbing can be quite startling.

The motor is shown at left center. It is seen to be a conventional, although rather well-built, universal motor equipped with ball bearings. Notice the peculiar shape of the motor end bell at

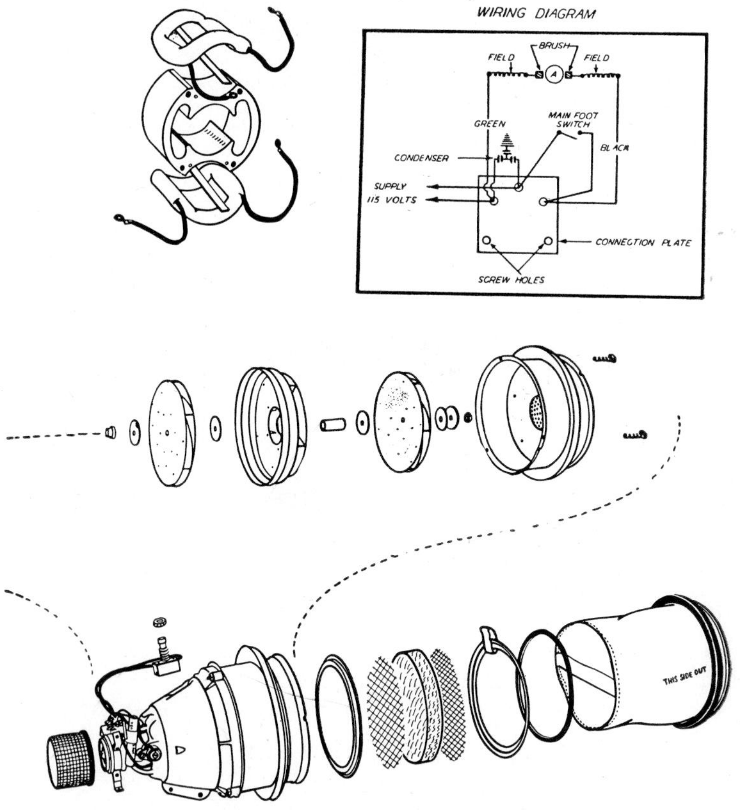


Fig. 7-11 (cont.). (Courtesy, Landers, Frary, & Clark)

the shaft end. When properly placed on the motor it looks as if it were on backward. The reason for this shape is twofold: it flares out to be fitted with a gasket which provides a rubber mount for the blade end of the motor, and the flared shape provides the correct path for air flow. Connections of wires to the terminal block are shown at the upper left of the figure in accordance with the wiring diagram at the upper right of the figure.

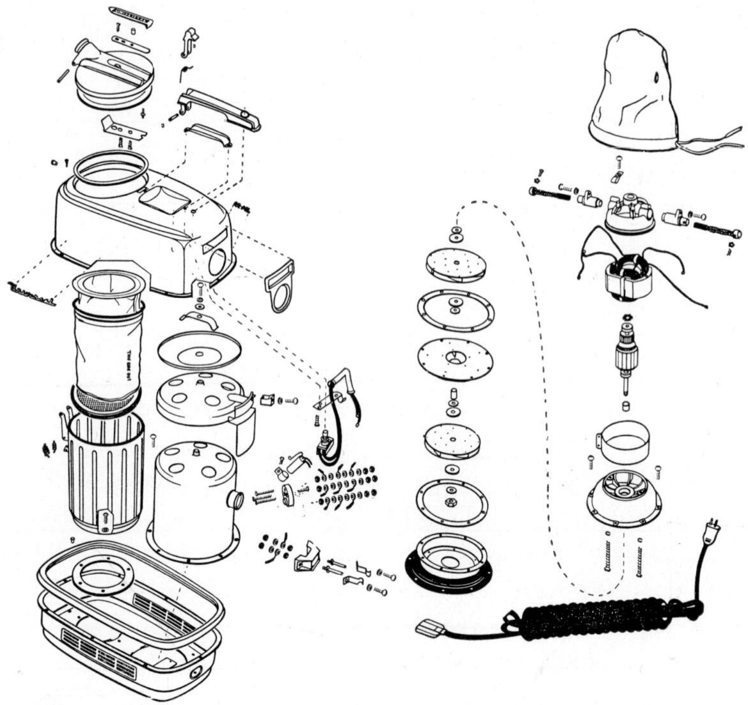

FIG. 7-12. Universal VC 6710, Jet 99 Vacuum Cleaner. (Courtesy, Landers, Frary & Clark)

Figure 7-12 is the exploded view of a newer style of tank-type vacuum cleaner which the manufacturer calls the Jet. The parts used are noticeably similar to those in Figure 7-11, but have a different arrangement. The exterior view of this appliance appears in Figure 7-1. Whereas the flow of air through the tank cleaner is in a straight line, the path is U-shaped in the Jet. The air enters the bottom and passes out through the louvres at the lower sides so as to give a more silent exhaust air flow. The motor used on this appliance is approximately 50 per cent more powerful than those on earlier models; otherwise, it is the familiar universal motor—the most suitable type for vacuum cleaners.

A number of fittings are supplied with the cleaner for the various tasks it may be called upon to perform. Among these are a small flared fitting for cleaning upholstery, a long slender piece for cleaning radiators, a brush-equipped fitting for polishing floors, and, for use when the tubing is fitted into the blowing end of the cleaner, a paint spray gun and a disinfectant dispenser. The versatility of this type of cleaner is increasing its popularity, and its distribution is rapidly catching up with the older, more familiar upright type.

The electric circuit of the tank-type cleaner is substantially the same as the upright vacuum cleaner, except that there is no headlight attached to the tank-type cleaner. The motor is of the same type as in the upright, a universal motor, and testing and servicing procedures are the same as those described for the motor of the upright vacuum cleaner. The off-on switch is electrically the same, but more substantially built. Mounted on top of the tank, it is intended to be operated by foot pressure.

To keep the tank-type cleaner from being too noisy, the motor is mounted in rubber at both ends. A small rubber ring is clamped aroung the motor at the brush end, and a larger rubber ring is fitted onto the fan end. This larger gasket is of such a size as to fit snugly against the inner perimeter of the tank, making an air-tight fit. The motor vibration is absorbed by the rubber mountings.

The motor and fan assembly is easily removed from the tank. The motor switch is loosened, the three bolts holding the brush end in place are removed, and the entire assembly is pushed out of the tank, fan end first. The fan assembly consists of a moving vaned disk and two stationary vaned disks. The bolts that hold the stationary disks in place are visible from the outside. A nut and a Woodruff key hold the moving blade in place. The retaining nut may be removed by holding the blade stationary and turning the nut in the same direction as the motor rotation.

Returning the motor and fan assembly to the tank is more difficult than removing it. The larger rubber gasket is so shaped as to spread out and bind when the assembly is pushed into the tank. It is often possible to install the rest of the assembly with the gasket removed, then put the gasket in place after the brush end of the motor has been made fast. Manufacturers of this type of vacuum cleaner have developed a special tool for replacing the motor and fan assembly, and it may be obtained from them at a reasonable price.

## 7.9. Indicating Devices

At least one brand of tank-type vacuum cleaner is equipped with an indicating lamp which glows when the dust bag is full. Beneath the bag is a hinged metal strip, and under the strip is a switch. The bag, when full, rests on the strip, and when it grows sufficiently heavy its weight will cause the switch to close, completing the circuit of the indicating lamp.

The indicating lamp bulb operates from a low-voltage source: 2.5 v or 5 v is the usual voltage applied to this small-size bulb, of the type used for pilot lights. To obtain such low voltage from a device operated on 120 v, one of the motor field coils has a tap located at such a point in the field winding that the voltage difference between the tap and the coil end is the required voltage for the lamp.

This principle is illustrated in Figure 7-13A. Here is shown a coil of wire connected across 120 v. Let us assume that the coil itself has 120 turns of wire. If, therefore, there are 120 v across 120 turns, there will be 1 v across any one turn. In like manner, there will be 5 v across five turns (any five adjacent turns). If a wire is tapped into the fifth turn from the bottom, and a 5-v lamp placed between the bottom wire and the tap, the bulb will have its proper voltage applied and will burn. Since it is not likely that any coil with as few as 120 turns will be put across 120 v, the same idea can be expanded to a larger coil of, say, 1,200 turns, wherein a tap at 50 turns will produce 5 v. In Figure 7-13B is shown the electric circuit of the motor with its tapped field and pilot lamp. The voltage between the field tap and one end of the field *only* provides the pilot-lamp voltage. If the pilot lamp should be placed across some other part of the circuit, the higher voltage would burn it out.

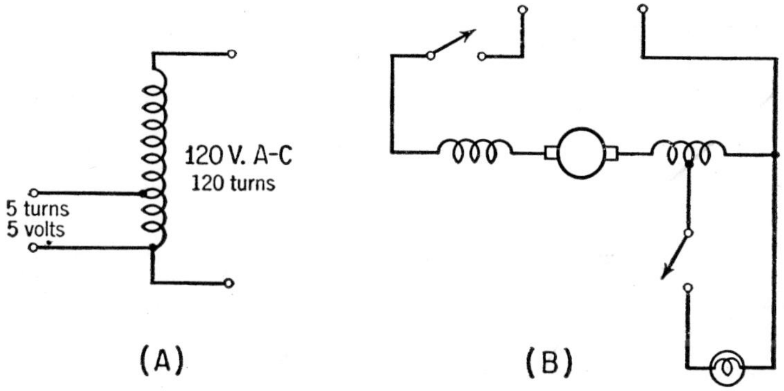


FIG. 7-13.

When a circuit such as this is disassembled, it is advisable to mark the wires so that no mistake will be made when reassembling. If such a motor should be received for repair already dismantled, the tapped coil may be checked with an ohmmeter to determine which wire is the tap. There are three wires extending from the tapped coil. Measure the resistance between all these wires; the two which register the highest value in ohms are the end wires, and the third is the tap. It still will not be known, however, which wire is used with the tap to obtain the pilot-lamp voltage. This can be determined when the motor is running by taking a voltmeter reading between the tap and each end wire.

The most commonly used types of small pilot lamps are Numbers 40, 46, and 47, rated for 6 to 8 v, and Number 41, rated at 2.5 v. A complete listing of pilot lamps is given in the following table.

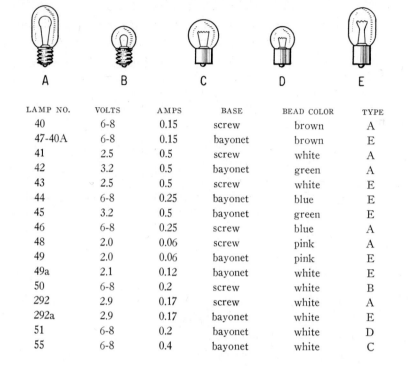

| LAMP NO. | VOLTS | AMPS | BASE | BEAD COLOR | TYPE |
|---|---|---|---|---|---|
| 40 | 6-8 | 0.15 | screw | brown | A |
| 47-40A | 6-8 | 0.15 | bayonet | brown | E |
| 41 | 2.5 | 0.5 | screw | white | A |
| 42 | 3.2 | 0.5 | bayonet | green | A |
| 43 | 2.5 | 0.5 | screw | white | E |
| 44 | 6-8 | 0.25 | bayonet | blue | E |
| 45 | 3.2 | 0.5 | bayonet | green | E |
| 46 | 6-8 | 0.25 | screw | blue | A |
| 48 | 2.0 | 0.06 | screw | pink | A |
| 49 | 2.0 | 0.06 | bayonet | pink | E |
| 49a | 2.1 | 0.12 | bayonet | white | E |
| 50 | 6-8 | 0.2 | screw | white | B |
| 292 | 2.9 | 0.17 | screw | white | A |
| 292a | 2.9 | 0.17 | bayonet | white | E |
| 51 | 6-8 | 0.2 | bayonet | white | D |
| 55 | 6-8 | 0.4 | bayonet | white | C |

## *Repairing Vacuum Cleaners*

### 7.10. Vacuum Cleaner Will Not Operate

Failure of the vacuum cleaner to operate is caused by the following:

Power failure
Defective cord and/or plug
Defective switch
Open circuit in motor
Jammed motor

Proceed as follows. Plug the vacuum cleaner into the appliance tester (Chap. 2, Fig. 2-2) and observe:

1. If the vacuum cleaner runs, the cause of failure to operate is a defective receptacle or blown fuse.

2. If the lamps on the appliance tester indicate a normal circuit and the motor will not turn, the motor is jammed.

This may be due to "frozen" bearings, the blade rubbing, or foreign object wedged in blade.

3. If the tester indicates an open circuit, the vacuum cleaner must be tested further to isolate the trouble.

Next test the cord and plug. This is done by removing the cord, placing a jumper across the ends, and plugging it into the appliance tester. A short-circuit indication shows that nothing is wrong with the cord; an open-circuit indication means there is a break in the cord, which must be replaced.

To remove the cord for testing, it is necessary to partially dismantle the appliance. If it is an upright model, the cord must be pulled out of the handle, the switch first having been removed. If it is a tank model, the rear cover must be removed and the cord disconnected from the terminal block. If the cord has been severed deliberately (that is, for the insertion of a switch), twist the severed ends together before making the continuity test. The purpose of the test is to locate a hidden, not an intentional, break in the cord. If the cord is defective and must be replaced, small-diameter S.V. wire should be used, since type S.J. cord is too bulky, particularly in the length required for a vacuum cleaner.

The switch is tested with an ohmmeter or series test lamp, with the switch lever in the ON position. When turned to the ON position, the switch should test as a short circuit.

If none of the foregoing is the trouble, the motor should be tested next. (Note that servicing has now progressed to a point where troubles listed under item 2 can be soon observed, if they are present.) Place an ohmmeter across the motor wires and turn the shaft by hand.

If the ohmmeter needle fluctuates wildly, the brushes are making poor contact.

If the ohmmeter needle fluctuates slightly, the brushes are making satisfactory contact.

If the needle remains at ∞, the motor is open-circuited and must be dismantled for further testing.

On either the upright or tank model it is necessary to remove the blade to dismantle the motor. The blade on either type is held in position by a hexagon nut on the end of a threaded motor shaft. The nut is screwed onto the shaft in such a manner as to cause the nut to tighten rather than screw off as the shaft turns. To remove this nut, the motor shaft or the blade is held firmly in a fixed position while the nut is turned with a hexagon wrench *in the direction in which the motor shaft normally rotates.* It cannot be assumed that an ordinary right-hand thread will be used; quite often it is a left-hand thread. In all likelihood the blade can easily be taken off the shaft after the lock nut is removed. If, however, it is stubborn, a gear puller will assist removal. As an extreme measure, a "frozen" blade can be shattered to give access to the motor, and a new blade supplied when reassembling.

Having removed the blade, the repair man will find four bolts holding the motor end bell in place. Removal of these allows the motor to be opened and tested as a cause of failure to operate. The procedure is as follows:

1. With an ohmmeter, test the several field coils for continuity. The individual coils should all have the same resistance value. Infinity on the meter scale indicates an open coil. Replace it with a new one. (Section 7.5 gives instructions on how to wind a new coil.)

2. Make a bar-to-bar test of the armature (Sec. 7.6). A single high-resistance reading indicates an open-circuited armature. With the armature in a certain position—brush contacting the commutator bar connected to the open coil—the motor may fail to run; in other positions, the motor may start, but will run slowly, with much sparking at the brushes.

3. Examine the brushes and brush springs for defect. Brushes worn short and discolored, or misshapen or weak springs, should be replaced with new ones.

A "jammed" motor is due to "frozen" bearings or a foreign object which has got into the motor—wedged between armature and field—thus preventing rotation. The latter trouble is easily remedied, once located; the former is apparent in the refusal of the shaft to turn when twisted by hand. Sleeve bearings, when deprived of lubrication, will bind onto the shaft. Cleaning and oiling will often cure this trouble; in more severe cases, bearing replacement is necessary (Sec. 7.7). Ball bearings when "frozen" are, by their nature, rendered useless, and must be replaced.

## 7.11. Motor Troubles in Vacuum Cleaner

External indications of a faulty motor are the following:

Motor will not operate.
Motor runs too slowly.
Motor smokes (or gets too hot).
Motor is noisy.

The circumstances under which the motor will not operate are described in the preceding section.

The most frequent reason why the motor runs too slowly, or overheats, is a defective armature: one that is shorted, grounded, or open-circuited. The chart on the following page will aid in diagnosing armature defects.

Another reason why a motor runs too slowly may be defective motor brushes or a badly worn commutator. Either cause is clear upon observation. Bad brushes should be replaced, and a worn commutator trued on a lathe.

The noisy motor is one with worn bearings or a bent fan blade. Looseness due to worn bearings is noticeable when manipulating the shaft. The obvious repair is replacement of the bearings (Sec. 7.7).

A cast-iron (or cast-aluminum) blade is not readily bent; by the same token, it is difficult to straighten if it should somehow have become misshapen. Furthermore, the blade may cause motor noise if it is unbalanced as a result of having been chipped or cracked. It is thus apparent that unbalance noise due to a

## Armature Defects

| CONDITION OF ARMATURE | CAUSE | EXTERNAL EVIDENCE | TEST |
|---|---|---|---|
| Grounded | Defective or worn insulation causing wiring to contact frame | Armature "thumps" while rotating. Armature turns too slowly. Armature may smoke. | Ohmmeter or series test lamp check from commutator bar to armature shaft. Continuity indicates ground. |
| Open circuit | Broken armature wire or armature wire loosened from commutator bar | Armature "thumps" while rotating. Armature turns too slowly. Armature may smoke. Brush arcing. | Bar-to-bar test of commutator using ohmmeter (Sec. 7.6). |
| Short circuit | Armature wires contacting one another due to a. defective insulation b. damaged mica c. conducting substance lodged between commutator bars | Armature heats rapidly and smokes. Long blue arc visible along commutator. If it is possible to dismantle motor rapidly enough, the shorted coil may be located by its excessive heat. | Use Growler (Sec. 7.6). |

defective cast-metal blade (conventional in the upright machine) is best cured by replacement of the blade. On the other hand, the formed sheet-metal blade used on the tank-type cleaner can be readily bent. If a deformity is causing motor noise in a tank-type model, the blade can easily be reshaped, and the noise will be eliminated once the balance of the blade is restored.

Less frequently a noisy motor can be traced to a bent motor

shaft. If other indications are lacking, and a bent shaft is suspected, it may be tested as follows. Remove the armature from the motor. Place it on a perfectly flat surface and allow it to roll through a few revolutions. Observe the shaft from an endwise viewpoint. If the shaft is bent, it will be observed to move up and down while rolling. If the shaft remains in a perfectly horizontal plane, it is not bent. The armature with a bent shaft should be discarded and replaced with a new one.

## 7.12. Vacuum Cleaner Does Not Draw Up Dirt

Causes of failure of a vacuum cleaner to pick up dirt when to all external appearances the machine is operating normally are these:

Clogged dust bag
Broken brush belt
Worn-out brush
Loose fan blade

The dust bag on a vacuum cleaner is made of a somewhat porous fabric. The weave is such that when dust-laden air is forced into the bag by the action of the fan, the air can seep through the pores but the dust cannot. The reader has no doubt observed that when a dust bag is emptied, some of the dust clings to the fabric. Eventually the pores of the dust bag become thoroughly clogged with dust particles, and this condition blocks passage of air. When this occurs, the fan fills the bag with air, which then becomes trapped within the bag, preventing further entry of air and destroying vacuum action; the appliance will no longer pick up dirt. Periodic laundering is helpful, but some of the dust material is insoluble in soapy water and will not wash out. The importance of the porosity of the dust bag is such that the appliance repair man is advised to examine every cleaner received for repair, no matter what the complaint, to see whether performance could not be improved by replacement of the dust bag. The behavior of the dust bag is tested indirectly. After all repairs have been made, observe the actual performance of the cleaner in picking up dust and lint, and compare with the normal performance of this type of cleaner. It may even be advisable to have in the shop a small so-called throw rug for making this test. Talcum powder is good sample "dust," since it is so easy to see whether the machine is picking up the white powder. If the performance of the cleaner is noticeably below standard, a new dust bag should be put on the machine.

A part of the cleaning performance of the vacuum cleaner consists in loosening imbedded dirt by means of the brush. The brush is rotated at a rather high speed through a rubber belt driven by the motor shaft. The belt may become stretched and loose, and consequently fail to drive the brush. Or, it may break or slip off its pulley. Any of these conditions will impair the performance of the cleaner. There is no servicing problem involved here; it is quite easy to observe whether the belt is driving the brush properly, and belts are readily obtained and easily installed.

The bristles on the brush are normally about 1/4 inch long. If they are badly worn—a condition instantly obvious to anyone who has seen a brush in new condition—the brush should be replaced.

As has been previously mentioned, the fan blade is held onto the shaft by a screw thread (nut, or threaded blade and shaft) arranged so that normal rotation of the motor tends to tighten rather than loosen the blade attachment to the motor shaft. This principle is excellent, but its application may occasionally fail from such causes as soft material, burred threads, and so forth, and the blade as a result becomes loosened on the shaft. Of course, the vacuum property of the appliance fails as a result; but the blade also vibrates violently, giving rise to what might be construed as a motor noise (described in Sec. 7.11). Any defective parts must be replaced; otherwise, merely tightening the blade onto the shaft will eliminate the trouble.

## 7.13. Vacuum Cleaner Blows Fuses

When a vacuum cleaner is received with this complaint, it should be checked with the appliance tester.

If the tester gives indication of a normal vacuum-cleaner circuit, the probable cause of blown fuses is an overloaded circuit. If, however, the tester indicates a short circuit, the source of the blown fuses lies within the appliance—in the cord, the motor, or the capacitor if one is present.

The cord is tested by disconnecting it from the motor (both wires) and plugging the plug cap into the appliance tester. The ends just loosened are *not* jumpered together to make this test.

If the tester indicates an open circuit, the cord is in good condition. If the tester indicates a short circuit, the cord is defective and should be discarded.

If the capacitor is suspected as a cause of blown fuses, it can be tested with an ohmmeter.

If the capacitor is normal, the meter needle will fluctuate briefly and return to the left end of the scale. If the capacitor is faulty, the ohmmeter will register zero or a relatively low value of ohms.

For convenience in plugging into the appliance tester, the motor lead wires should be fastened to a short length of appliance cord. It will then be easy to determine whether the short causing blown fuses lies in the motor. If so, the motor should be tested as indicated in Section 7.11.

# FANS

## 7.14. General Discussion

The basic electric fan consists merely of a motor with a blade attached. However, a number of auxiliary devices are to be found on fans which add to the convenience of their use, such as multispeed controls, oscillating mechanism, on-off switches, and the like.

*Fan Motors*

Three kinds of motors are used on fans. A fan for service on either a-c or d-c will be equipped with a universal motor of the same type used on vacuum cleaners. The servicing and testing procedure for the universal motor is described in Sections 7.5–7.7.

Some older fans intended for use on a-c only have a split-phase motor. The newer type fans contain a shaded-pole motor. A description of these two motors is to be found in Sections 6.3 and 6.4.

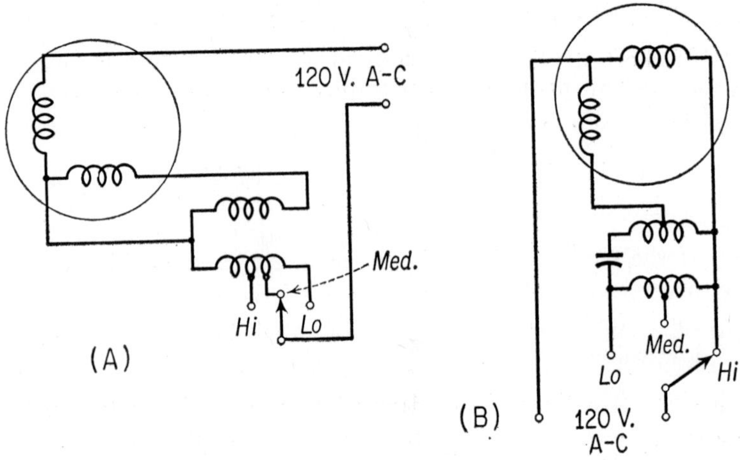


FIG. 7-14. (A) Circuit of Split-Phase Fan Motor. (B) Capacitor Fan Motor.

## 7.15. Speed Control

The split-phase motor used with fans is a type developed especially for fan use. This motor has two windings, a main and an auxiliary. There is no cut-out switch, however, in the auxiliary winding; it is always in the circuit.

The circuit of this motor is shown in Figure 7-14A. A special coil is used with the motor, which serves two purposes: it allows the speed to be varied, and reduces the voltage applied to the auxiliary winding to a lower value than that of the main winding, thus eliminating need for a starting switch. A coil used in this manner is called an autotransformer. Because of the auto-transformer action, the motor operates at a reduced voltage on the high position, and the taps for medium and low speeds reduce the motor voltage even further. With lowered voltage there will be less torque and a consequent reduction of speed.

The autotransformer is mounted in the base of the fan, and there is a three-wire cord for the electrical connections extending from the motor down to the base of the fan. If the fan has an oscillating mechanism, the connecting cord will be constantly flexed, and there is a possibility that the cord may become worn or broken. When repairs are made on any fan having an oscillating mechanism, this cord should invariably be checked for worn places and tested for continuity.

In order to reduce the size and weight of the motor, and to obtain improved performance with a reduction in watts consumed, the split-phase fan motor may have a capacitor in the circuit. The use of a capacitor increases the efficiency of the magnetic action of the auxiliary winding and supplies more torque so that a smaller motor may be used. As shown in Figure 7-14B, in the high position of the speed control, full-line voltage is applied across the main winding. The auxiliary winding has a lowered voltage because some of the autotransformer windings are in series with it. Moving the switch to the medium and low positions reduces the voltage to both windings proportionately. The effect of the capacitor is increased by the autotransformer action of the coil. Instructions for testing a capacitor are given in Section 7.4.

The shaded-pole motor finds its most common use in the smaller, inexpensive desk fans. This motor is small in size and quite rugged in construction. The simplicity of its construction makes it easy to repair in the shop. The only part of the electric circuit that could become defective is the field coil; however, being wound in a bundle and then placed around the field poles, this coil is easy to repair or replace. The shaded-pole motor is silent in operation, a characteristic which makes it ideal for fan service.

It is usually possible to determine the type of motor used in a fan without actually opening the motor. If brushes are used,

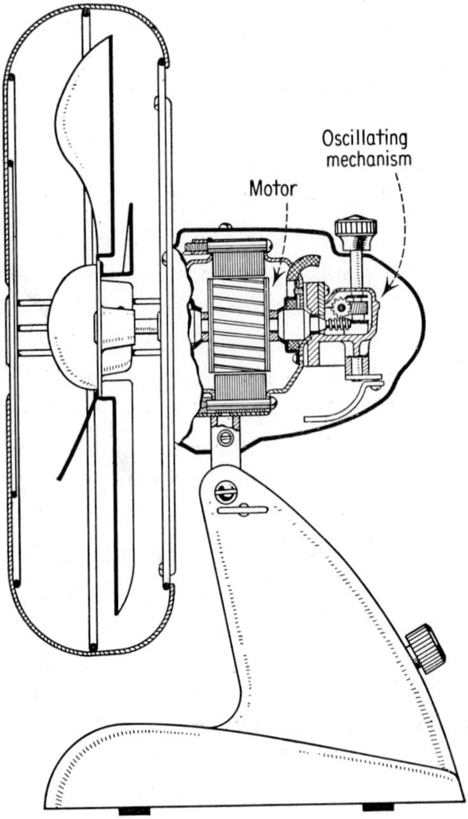


Fig. 7-15. (Courtesy, Knapp-Monarch Co.)

it is a universal motor. If no brushes are present, and if the fan is a small one (8 inches or under), the probability is that it contains a shaded-pole motor. In larger sizes the split-phase motor is employed.

The speed-control system of the split-phase motor, as already explained, consists of a tapped coil in series with the motor. A similar coil is sometimes used with the shaded-pole motor to vary its speed (Fig. 7-16). Generally speaking, it is impractical to try to vary the speed of an induction motor: this type of motor attempts to operate at a speed that is a function of the alternator supplying it with current. If a lowered voltage is applied to this motor, it will still try to uphold its speed regulation, but at a reduced torque. If the load on the motor is sufficient it will place a drag on the motor, resulting in a reduction of speed, but with a severe increase in the current flow through the motor. These facts, however, are ignored in the induction motors used with fans. The current demand of this small motor is very moderate, and the increase resulting from speed reduction is not very great. The motor load is not constant as is the case with most larger motors, since, with a decrease in fan-motor speed, less air is moved and the motor load is thereby lightened. Thus it is possible with a fan motor to use speed-control systems which would be considered impractical with a larger induction motor or one with a constant load.

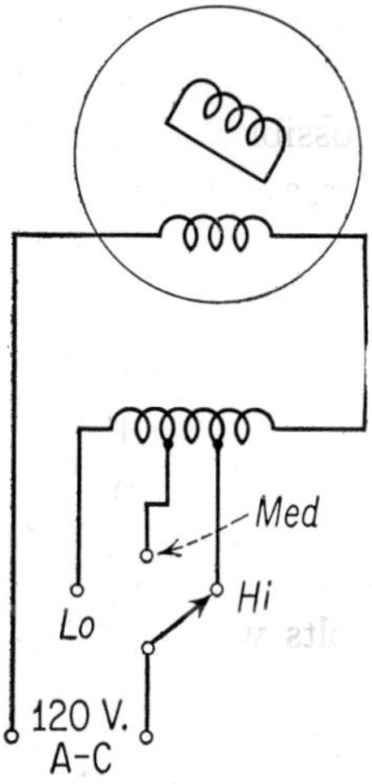

FIG. 7-16. "Speed Coil" Used with Shaded-Pole Fan Motor to Vary Its Speed

Two devices are used to vary the speed of a universal motor when used on a fan. One is the tapped coil (autotransformer), and the other is a tapped resistor, or rheostat. Both operate on the principle of a voltage drop preceding the motor and a consequent reduction of motor voltage. The universal motor readily responds to a lowered voltage with a proportionately lowered speed.

## 7.16. Disassembling the Fan

A fan motor contains ventilating holes at each end so that the blade can accomplish the dual purpose of providing comfort to the user while at the same time cooling the motor. During a single hot season sufficient air will be drawn through the motor to deposit a substantial quantity of dust in the motor. Whenever possible, it is wise to dismantle a fan after one season of use for a general cleaning and reoiling; and, of course, this is also a good time to examine all parts for possible wear or damage, and make the necessary repairs or replacements, in order to avoid midsummer breakdown when the services of the fan are sorely needed.

In disassembling a fan, the first part to be removed is the guard. It is usually held in place by two or four of the same bolts which hold the end bells onto the motor. The open spaces in most fan guards are large enough so that the guard can easily be slipped off the blade. The blade is next removed by loosening its setscrew and pulling it off the motor shaft. One manufacturer uses a threaded-bore fan blade which is screwed onto the rotor. To remove the blade it is necessary to engage the rotor by means of a tool (such as a punch) inserted through the ventilating holes in the back of the motor, holding it stationary while turning the blade in the same direction as it normally revolves. Another unusual constructional feature of this particular make of fan is the bored rotor. The shaft is securely mounted to the motor frame, and there is a hole through the rotor which allows it to be slipped onto the shaft. The operation is, of course, unchanged from an electrical standpoint.

The next step in disassembly is removal of the frontal end bell of the motor. Sometimes two, sometimes four bolts are used to hold the motor together. When the nuts at the front are removed, the end bell will come off. This exposes the rotor, which can be pulled out next. Observe the location of the spacing washers on the rotor shaft so that they may be replaced exactly as they were. At this point the bearings should be examined. A fan bearing should be an easy sliding fit, but there should be no wobble. Replacement of bearings in a fan motor is identical with the process outlined for vacuum-cleaner motors (Sec. 7.7).

The fault in the fan may be a damaged or defective field winding, making it necessary to remove that part of the motor. Examine the motor to see if the name-plate bolts are fastened to the motor-field core. If so, remove them before attempting to remove the field. Only in a few cases is it possible to remove the field structure from the motor housing with a wheel puller; more often it is necessary to drive it out. This is done from the back end of the motor through the bolt or ventilating holes. Using a slender punch, and being careful not to damage the field-coil wires, place the punch through the bolt holes and onto the laminated field core. Strike sharply with a hammer. Remove the punch, and repeat the process on the other side of the motor. Continue alternating the site of punching until the field structure is removed. When driving it back into place, take care to have the bolt holes in the field structure properly aligned with the holes in the motor housing.

## 7.17. The Oscillating Mechanism

On the back of the motor is mounted the oscillating mechanism. It is driven by the motor. A favorite method of drive is to cut threads on the shaft of the rotor, the threads acting as a worm to drive a reduction gear whose shaft has at its bottom end an eccentric arm. The eccentric is attached to a rod which is in turn connected to the base of the fan (Fig. 7-15). The supporting rod for the motor is swivel-mounted so that the eccentric arm will cause the fan motor to oscillate. If the oscillating mechanism is designed to be turned off, the reduction gear will not be fastened to its shaft, and when turning will not cause the shaft to turn. However, right above the reduction gear is a nut, fitted onto a threaded portion of the shaft, and when this nut is tightened, it will act as a clamp to hold the reduction gear tightly against a flange which is part of the shaft. Thus, tightening the nut will cause the reduction gear to drive its shaft; loosening the nut will free the reduction gear from its shaft and stop the oscillating mechanism from operating. The nut has a shaft attached which extends up through the top cover of the oscillating mechanism, with a knob attachment making it possible for the user to turn the oscillating mechanism on or off at will.

A similar arrangement is shown in Figure 7-17. Notice that the reduction-gear shaft has a disk at its bottom rather than the eccentric arm, and two threaded holes in the bottom of the disk which allow the oscillating mechanism to be adjusted for a greater or lesser angle of swing. The reduction-gear shaft has a knob, located at the top of and external to the mechanism housing, which is lifted up to turn the oscillating mechanism off and pushed down to turn it on. Two things happen when the knob is pushed down. A gear cut into the bottom of the shaft engages the rocker-arm disk, and a ball and spring mounted in the side of the shaft enter the reduction gear, applying a pressure against it so that the rotation of the gear will be transmitted to the shaft.

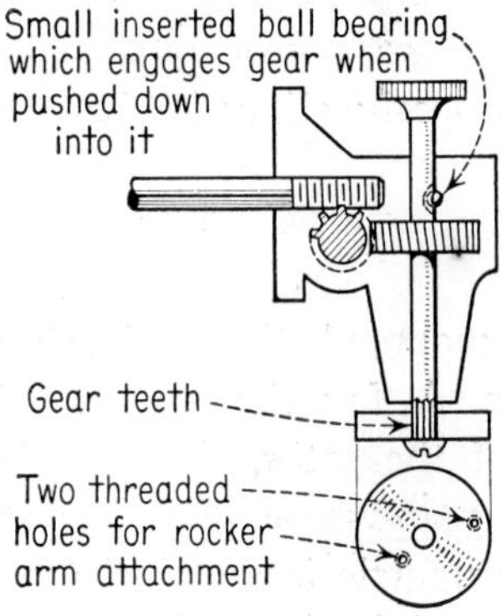


Fig. 7-17.

It has been mentioned that one manufacturer makes a fan whose motor shaft is stationary and fastened to the motor housing. The oscillating mechanism used in this fan is shown in Figure 7-18. Through the shaft is run a thin rod. One end of this rod has two flats milled on it, and fits into a corresponding slot in the fan blade. At the other end of the rod, on the back end of the motor, is a worm. Turning the fan blade causes the worm to turn. By means of a series of reduction gears this motion is transmitted to a disk under the oscillating-mechanism housing. Bolted to this disk is the rocker arm. The bolt through the rocker arm screws into a block mounted in the disk; turning the knurled outer edge of the disk causes the block to move to the outer edge of the disk for a wide-angle oscillation, or to move to the center of the disk, preventing oscillation.

The three types of oscillating mechanism just described are those most commonly encountered, and although some manufacturers employ a slightly different design, the principle is the same. A brief examination will reveal the purpose of the component parts of the oscillator.

When making repairs to the oscillating mechanism, all parts should be removed and completely cleansed of grease. On examination, any parts that give evidence of wear—gears with worn or broken teeth, loose bearings, or scored shafts—should be replaced with new parts. It is advisable to put a few drops

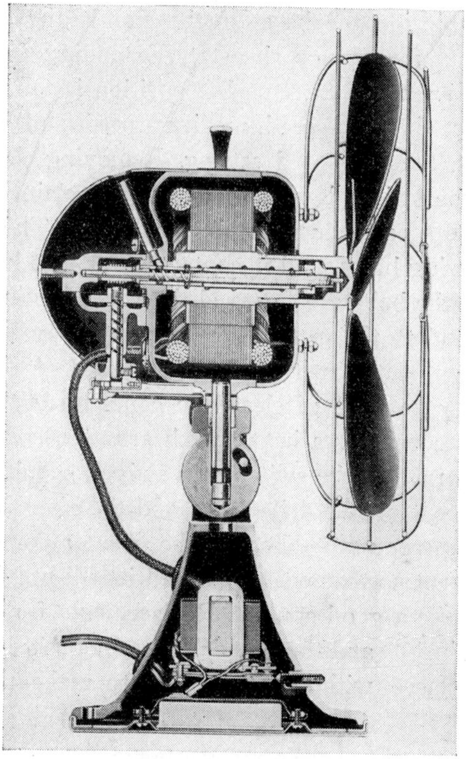

FIG. 7-18. (Courtesy, Emerson Electric Company)

of No. 30 motor oil on all shafts, gears, and bearing surfaces when reassembling, and then fill the gear housing with a good grade of fiber grease. The motor bearings should be lubricated with a few drops of No. 30 motor oil.

At the bottom of the motor is a rod fitted into the top of the base in a swivel arrangement, allowing the motor to be turned by the oscillating mechanism (Fig. 7-18). Sometimes a ball bearing is used here so that the motor will turn freely and silently. This bearing surface should be cleaned and oiled when repairing the fan. As these are slow-moving parts, there is seldom any wear calling for replacement; however, the lubricant does become dirty and gummed, and jamming may occur, causing damage to the oscillating mechanism as it tries to turn.

Mounted inside the base of the fan is the speed-control choke, autotransformer, or rheostat. Extending from the base is the control lever. Its extreme left position is OFF. Following to the right are the high-speed, medium-speed, and finally, to the extreme right, the low-speed setting. Removing the base cover reveals that the switch is mounted on a porcelain or fiber base along with the speed-reducing coil or rheostat. The switch arm is made of spring brass, and it contacts four bolt heads. To the other ends of the bolts are fastened the wires leading to the coil or rheostat, and to the motor. The contacts may become pitted and make poor contact with the moving arm. A fine grade of sandpaper may be used to clean the contact surfaces. Another cause of poor contact is a bent switch arm. To correct this, the bolt or rivet on which the switch arm swivels should be removed (if it is a rivet it can be drilled out and the rivet replaced with a bolt), taking care not to damage the fiber or porcelain mount, and the arm bent so that when replaced it will provide sufficient pressure to make a good contact. Replacements for any of these parts are obtainable, and those which are obviously beyond repair should be replaced without attempting to make the old parts serviceable.

## 7.18. Reassembly and Lubrication

When the fan is reassembled after repairs are made, the surfaces where the base and motor are joined together should be cleaned and lightly oiled so that the fan will tilt without forcing. When the rotor is replaced in the motor it should be checked for end-play. If necessary, use additional fiber spacing washers. They should be distributed between the two ends in such a manner as to allow the rotor and field to line up as closely as possible—that is, the front edge of the rotor should be flush with the front edge of the field core. It is not wise to remove all the end play lest the motor bind. About 1/32-inch end play is ideal, although as much as 1/8-inch in a fan motor is tolerable. In any event, some end play is preferable to binding.

On many models there is some provision for lubrication at either end of the motor. This may be merely a drilled hole, or an oil cup may be fitted into the end bells of the motor. Some manufacturers have installed an oil cup at the front and rear of the motor, located below the bearing and containing a felt wick held up against the motor shaft by a spring. Capillary action draws the oil up through the felt wick and keeps the shaft lubricated. The oil cup, if kept filled with oil, will provide lubrication for many seasons; if this is neglected, however, the oil will be used up and the wick will dry and harden. This condition is injurious to the motor, for the hardened wick will soon cut a groove in the motor shaft. The wick should be cleaned in gasoline or carbon tetrachloride to remove the gummed lubricant and new oil (not grease) put in the cup whenever the fan is repaired, so as to forestall the occurrence of hardening of the wick and damage to the shaft.

## 7.19. Aligning the Fan-Blade Assembly

Before the fan blade is replaced it should be examined for balance. Most fans received in the shop for repair will have one or more leaves of the blade bent, and the resultant misalignment will cause much vibration and noisy operation. Aside from visual observation of wobble and vibration of the entire fan, the alignment of a blade may be tested in two ways. One method is to lay the blade, shaft end up, on a flat surface to determine if all leaves touch the surface while the shaft bore is absolutely perpendicular to the flat surface. If only a slight misalignment exists, it may be corrected by using this method and bending any out-of-line leaves until a uniform blade is obtained.

If only one leaf of the blade is bent out of place, it may be determined by the following method. Mount the blade in place on the motor shaft. Place the blade of a screw driver on top of the motor so that it is parallel with the motor shaft, and with the tip of the screw driver just touching the leading edge of one blade leaf. Turn the blade by hand, holding the screw driver in one spot. If the blade is in proper alignment, all leaves will just brush the end of the screw driver; any bent leaves will either miss the tool tip altogether or bump into the screw-driver shaft. If only a slight misalignment exists, bending the offending member into line will correct the trouble, and provide noise- and vibration-free operation.

If the blade is severely bent, more drastic steps must be taken. It is, under these conditions, quite difficult to obtain the exact pitch originally put into the blade by the manufacturer. However, every effort should be made to come as close as possible to the original pitch, since the motor characteristics and blade pitch are carefully matched. With a length of rod of the same diameter as the motor shaft affixed to the blade, place each leaf in a vise and with a protractor measure the angle the rod makes with the bench. Use the average of these angles as the probable original pitch angle. Now, if each leaf is placed in the vise in turn, and the rod bent backward or forward until with each leaf the rod forms the angle, as calculated, with the bench on which the vise is mounted, the blade will be balanced. When the leaves are placed between the jaws of the vise, every leaf should be positioned exactly alike, preferably with the center line of the leaf located halfway down the depth of the vise jaws, and with the center bracket of the blade also between the jaws of the vise. The bending should be done to this bracket rather than to the thinner metal of the leaves.

Although this method does assure a balanced blade, it is possible that the pitch may be somewhat different from that for which the fan was designed. If the pitch is too great, there will be a definite drag on the motor, and the fan will be unable to get up to full speed. If the pitch is less than the original, the blade will be unable to move as much air as before.

If the fan motor is of the split-phase or shaded-pole types, its speed (high setting of the switch) may be checked by comparison with another fan with the same type of motor. With both fans running, look at the blade just repaired through the moving blade of the other fan. If the speed of the fan under test is correct, its blade will appear to stand still, or rotate very slowly. The results of this test will be more pronounced if a single fluorescent lamp is used for the only illumination. The particular property of the fluorescent lamp which makes it suitable for this test is explained in Section 11.8.

The blade with too great a pitch may be readjusted by using this test to observe the results. If the pitch is too slight, and not enough air is being circulated by the fan, the pitch may be increased until the foregoing test shows the blade to appear to stand still.

## 7.20. Circulating Fans

A discussion of fan servicing would hardly be complete without mention of the larger circulating pedestal fan, which is becoming increasingly popular. This fan, with blades 18 and 24 inches wide, uses the larger split-phase or capacitor motor in 1/4 and 1/3 hp sizes. Some are equipped with an oscillating mechanism and multispeed field windings. With the exception of the motor, the servicing procedure on all other parts—oscillating mechanism, blade alignment, and so forth—is the same as for the smaller fans.

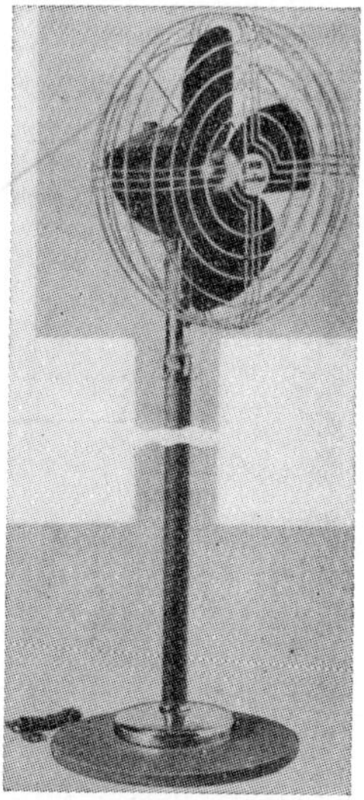

FIG. 7-19. (Courtesy, Knapp-Monarch Co.)

In Chapter 6 is a discussion of the split-phase motor. This motor has two distinct separate windings, electrically displaced from each other and wound in slots in the motor frame (distributed windings). This is a constant-speed motor, its speed being dependent upon the applied frequency and the number of poles in the motor. A four-pole motor runs at 1,725 rpm. The speed of a six-pole motor is 1,140 rpm. While it is not possible to vary the speed of a motor with a fixed number of poles, it is possible to rewind any one motor for a different number of poles. Therefore it is also possible to put two windings in a motor, each winding for a different number of poles, and, by means of a

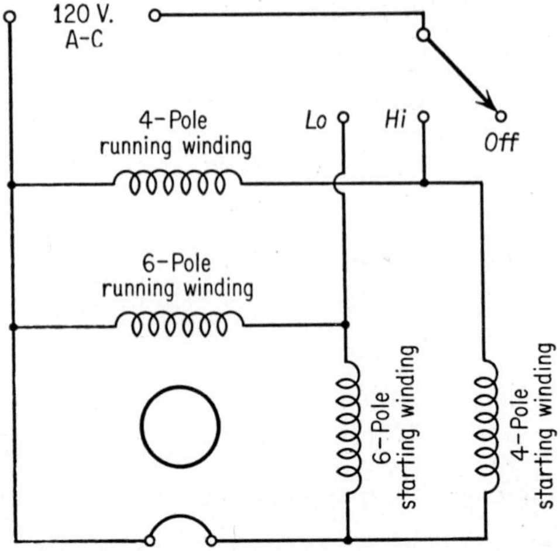


FIG. 7-20.

switch, effect the necessary circuit changes to change the speed. This is what is done in the split-phase motor used for a two-speed circulating fan. The circuit of Figure 7-20 shows the two separate windings, consisting of a main and an auxiliary winding of four poles, and the same for six poles. The same starting switch is used for both auxiliary windings. A double-pole double-throw switch of the rotary or pull-chain style is used to switch the line wires into the circuit of one or the other set of windings.

The windings of this motor are tested in the usual manner with series test lamp or ohmmeter for open circuit, short, or ground. The servicing procedure for split-phase motor is described in Chapter 9 in connection with the use of this motor for washing-machine service.

## Repairing Electric Fans

### 7.21. Fan Will Not Operate

Failure to operate is due to five factors:

Power failure
Defective cord and/or plug
Defective switch
Open circuit in motor
Open circuit in speed coil (autotransformer)

Plug the fan into the appliance tester (Fig. 2-2), and observe the following:

1. If the fan blade turns, and the tester gives a "normal" indication (both lamps glow with reduced brilliance), the cause of failure to operate is a defective receptacle or blown fuse.

2. If the lamps on the appliance tester indicate a normal circuit and the fan motor will not turn, this indicates a burned-out speed coil, motor shaft jammed due to frozen bearings, or coil of one phase open-circuited (split-phase motor).

3. If the tester indicates an open circuit, the fan should be tested further to isolate the trouble.

(The general nature of the trouble is now known. The tests and repairs which follow are all-inclusive, and any one not pertinent to the trouble in any individual fan may be deleted in the servicing procedure for that appliance.)

Test next the cord and plug. This is done by removing the cord, placing a jumper across its ends, and plugging it into the appliance tester. A short-circuit indication shows that the cord is in good condition. An open-circuit indication means there is a break in the cord and it must be replaced.

The switch on a single speed fan motor is a simple on-off switch, and may either be given a continuity test or jumpered around to determine if it is the cause of failure. On a multispeed fan, the switch has a series of contacts; however, a switch defect will show up if each contact is jumpered onto the main switch arm. If the fan runs under these conditions, the switch is the faulty part.

An autotransformer—known to the trade as a speed coil—is used for speed control on the majority of modern multispeed desk fans. The scheme of the connections between motor and speed coil is shown in Figure 7-16. By the nature of its use, a fault in the speed coil will be reflected in the performance of the fan motor; in general, the fan will not run with a defective speed coil.

The test for a defective speed coil consists of measuring continuity with an ohmmeter. A relatively low resistance (less than 1,000 ohms) should exist between any pair of lead wires, the amount of ohms being variable due to the possible random choices of pairs of wires. If, however, there is measured between any two wires a very high resistance or an open circuit, the speed coil is defective.

The iron forming the speed-coil core is operated at a critical magnetic flux density, so the possibility of obtaining satisfactory performance by rewinding a speed coil is questionable; it is better practice to obtain a replacement coil. When servicing the speed coil, note carefully the connections of the coil to the remainder of the circuit. Identification is aided by the color-coded wire leads used on the coil.

The motor as a possible cause of failure to operate may be checked by testing for continuity. Further motor tests are described in Sections 7.10 and 7.11.

A somewhat trivial cause of failure to operate is a fan blade so badly bent that it locks against the guard. This cause is quite obvious, and of course no tests are necessary.

## 7.22. Fan Is Noisy

There are three causes of fan noise:

Unbalanced fan blade
Worn or damaged oscillator mechanism
Worn bearings

The fan blade must be properly balanced and aligned to prevent noisy operation. The tests and procedures for fan-blade balance and alignment are given in Section 7.19.

The oscillator mechanism of a fan is driven by the motor through a high-ratio gear assembly. Not infrequently fiber gears, or those made of white metal, are used, either of which materials are more readily damaged than iron or steel. In addition to causing erratic oscillator operation, worn or damaged gears are noisy —two symptoms which will help the repair man in his diagnosis. The oscillator mechanism is serviced by removing it from the rear of the fan motor, disassembling it, and cleaning all parts. Examination will reveal the faulty gears, which can then be replaced with new ones.

Worn bearings are, perhaps, the most common cause of noise in motor operation; the fan motor is no exception. Usually it is possible to detect worn bearings by observing the extent to which the shaft has vertical freedom of motion when the motor is held stationary and the fan blade lifted by hand. Servicing is a bit more difficult than testing, since the motor must be disassembled in order that the bearings may be replaced. (Section 7.7 gives details regarding replacement of bearings.)

Elimination of noise caused by worn bearings is not possible on all fans. On very inexpensive fans, the bearings are fastened onto the end bells in such a manner as to discourage removal and replacement, being either welded or riveted into place. Furthermore, replacement bearings for these fans are not obtainable. The repair man would do well to consider this type of fan as being economically beyond repair. The time wasted on trying to patch such an appliance would be more wisely spent on repairs to a well-known brand.

## 7.23. Motor Runs Too Slowly

In connection with the troubles caused by bearings, wear may become so great as to cause the rotor to rub the stator and reduce motor speed. The worn bearings may be detected by observing the looseness of the fit of the shaft in the bearings, as mentioned above, with the additional indication of actual rubbing by observation of worn places on the iron of rotor and stator. Replacement of the bearings (Sec. 7.7) is, of course, the remedy.

The motor may run too slowly if the fins on the fan blade have somehow been bent to too great a pitch. The volume of air the blade would move represents an overload to the motor. This condition (too great a pitch) can be detected with the aid of another fan—one known to be in good working order—having the same style of a-c motor, with the same number of poles, as the one being serviced. Observe the rotation of the blade of the defective fan through the revolving blade of the good one. If the faulty fan's blade seems to be slowly turning when so observed, its motor is revolving too slowly; if the effect is that of the blade standing still, then both blades are rotating at the same speed. This illusion is similar in cause to the stroboscopic effect described in the chapter on fluorescent lamps, and can be taken advantage of only when the fan has an a-c motor. (Recall that the speed of an a-c motor depends upon the frequency of the a-c supply, rather than voltage or current.) In use, the foregoing test is applied before and after reducing the pitch of the blade of the faulty fan, and if the described difference is observed, it is conclusive that the pitch was incorrect.

## 7.24. Motor Hums but Will Not Turn

This trouble may be a duplicate of those just described if caused by a defective oscillator mechanism or badly worn bearings, either of which may cause the motor to bind. As the servicing procedure for these faults has been described, it will not be repeated here.

The real intent of this section—"motor hums but will not turn"—is to introduce the listing of faults which may occur in a fan motor having split-phase windings, one of which is inoperative. The motor will then be energized but unable to start rotation. However, if the blade is given a spin by hand, the motor will run in the direction it was started.

To begin with, there may actually be a severed wire in the

winding, causing one phase to become open-circuited. Using the diagram of Figure 7-14A as a guide, check both windings with an ohmmeter. If either ohmmeter reading is very high or at infinity, that winding is open-circuited. Only rarely can the break be found by inspection and repaired; otherwise, the motor field must be rewound. Many manufacturers make available a replacement field assembly as a servicing convenience to the repair man who is without training in motor rewinding or does not have access to a rewinding establishment.

Again referring to Figure 7-14A, note that an open circuit in the speed coil also interrupts the circuit to the phase-winding energized by the speed coil. This possibility should be suspected if the preceding test—that for the field winding—fails to disclose the cause of trouble. It is usually possible to trace through the circuit and locate the wires leading to the section of the autotransformer across which the phase winding is connected. Having located these leads, disconnect them from the remainder of the circuit and test across them for continuity. A reading of high ohms, or infinity, on the ohmmeter indicates a faulty speed coil. As previously mentioned, the speed coil should be replaced, since repair involves technical difficulties beyond the scope of the appliance repair shop.

Some older fans—many of them still in service—contain a centrifugal switch connected in the circuit in such a manner as to de-energize the starting winding when the motor approaches full speed. Wear or damage to this switch will cause the motor to fail to start. The switch consists of a massive brass split ring mounted on one of the motor end bells. Three brass levers ride on this ring, jumpering together the halves of the ring and completing the starting winding circuit. Rotation of the motor causes these levers to fly away from the ring by centrifugal action, opening the starting winding circuit. A visual examination of the switch parts will usually reveal the wear or damage causing it to be inoperative. A part of the examination should be a test of the condition of the springs fastened to the centrifugal levers. A weak or broken spring should be replaced.

If the fan has a capacitor motor (Fig. 7-14B) the capacitor should be tested as a possible source of trouble. The test for the capacitor is given in Section 7.4.

## 7.25. Trouble-Shooting Chart: Vacuum Cleaners

| SYMPTOM | CAUSE | TEST | REMEDY |
|---|---|---|---|
| Will not run | Open circuit in a. cord | Remove cord, fasten wires together, and test other ends with series test lamp or ohmmeter. | If discontinuous, replace |
| | b. switch | Remove switch and test for continuity in ON position with ohmmeter or series test lamp. | If defective, replace. |
| | c. motor | Check motor brushes and springs (visual examination). | If defective, replace. |
| | | Check field coils for continuity with ohmmeter. | Replace or rewind field coils. |
| | | Check armature for open circuit (Sec. 7.6). | Replace with exchange armature. |
| Is noisy. | Worn bearings | Test motor shaft for "wobble." | Replace bearings. |
| | Bent fan blade | Test in same manner as bent blade on electric fan (Sec. 7-19). | Straighten blade (Sec. 7-19) or, if too badly bent, replace with new blade. |
| Motor runs too slowly. | Dry bearings | Turn shaft of motor by hand to determine whether it is binding. | Oil in accordance with manufacturer's instructions. |

| SYMPTOM | CAUSE | TEST | REMEDY |
|---|---|---|---|
| | Electrical defect in armature | See Chart (Sec. 7.11). | Replace or rewind armature. |
| | Bent shaft Low voltage | Remove armature from motor. Roll along flat surface, noticing if ends of shaft appear to move up and down. | Replace armature. |
| Cleaner does not draw up dirt | Worn-out brush | Noticeable upon visual examination. | Replace brush. |
| | Broken brush belt | Same as above. | Replace belt. |
| | Fan blade loose or detached from shaft | Same as above. | Replace or repair. |
| | Dust bag clogged | (After prolonged use, pores in bag become so clogged with dust that air cannot escape.) | Replace bag. |
| Blows fuses. | Shorted cord, capacitor or motor | Check with ohm-meter. Very low or zero ohms indicate short. | Dismantle appliance, testing for short at each step. When short disappears, defective part is indicated. Replace offending component. |
| Appliance shocks user. | Internal wiring grounded to frame of appliance | Test with test lamp or ohmmeter from line cord to frame. Continuity indicates ground. | Same as above. |

## 7.26. Trouble-Shooting Chart: Electric Fans

| SYMPTOM | CAUSE | TEST | REMEDY |
|---|---|---|---|
| Will not run. | Open circuit in a. cord | Remove cord, fasten wires together, and test other ends with series test lamp or ohmmeter. | If discontinuous replace. |
| | b. switch 1. line switch 2. centrifugal starting switch | Remove switch and test for continuity in ON position with ohmmeter or series test lamp. | Replace switch. |
| | c. motor | Check motor brushes and springs (visual examination). | New brushes and/or brush springs. |
| | d. speed coil | Test various taps on speed coil with ohmmeter. | Replace coil. |
| Is noisy. | Worn bearings | Test motor shaft for "wobble." | Replace bearings. |
| | Bent fan blade | (Sec. 7-19) | Align or replace blade. |
| | Worn oscillator mechanism | Dismantle oscillator mechanism on rear of fan; clean and examine for worn or damaged parts. | Replace parts or entire assembly as necessary. |
| Runs too slowly. | Worn bearings causing rotor to rub on stator | Dismantle appliance. Open motor and examine for evidence of rubbing. | Replace bearings (Sec. 7.7). |
| | Bent blade | Test as explained in Sec. 7-19. | Align or replace blade. |

| SYMPTOM | CAUSE | TEST | REMEDY |
|---|---|---|---|
| Hums, but will not turn. | Open speed coil | Test the several taps on speed coil for continuity with ohmmeter. | Replace coil. |
| | Open starting winding (split-phase type) | Test individual windings for continuity with ohmmeter. | Replace or repair field assembly. |
| | Worn bearings causing rotor to "lock" against stator | Test as above for worn bearings. | Replace bearings. |
| | Jammed oscillator mechanism | Dismantle oscillator mechanism on rear of fan; clean and examine for worn, broken parts. Examine shafts for dryness, rust, and so on, causing binding. | Repair or replace offending component. |
| Blows fuses. | Shorted cord or motor | Test at plug cap with ohmmeter. Very low or zero ohms indicates short. | Replace or repair offending component. |
| Appliance shocks user. | Internal wiring grounded to frame | Use series test lamp or ohmmeter from line cord to frame. Continuity indicates ground. Dismantle appliance, testing for short or ground at each step. When fault disappears, defect is indicated. | Same as above. |

# HAIR DRIERS

## 7.27. General Discussion

The hair drier is a fan-type appliance containing also a heating element. Figure 7-21 shows the appliance, with heating-element location revealed, also wiring diagram. A shaded-pole motor is used to drive a small fan blade. The path of air is through

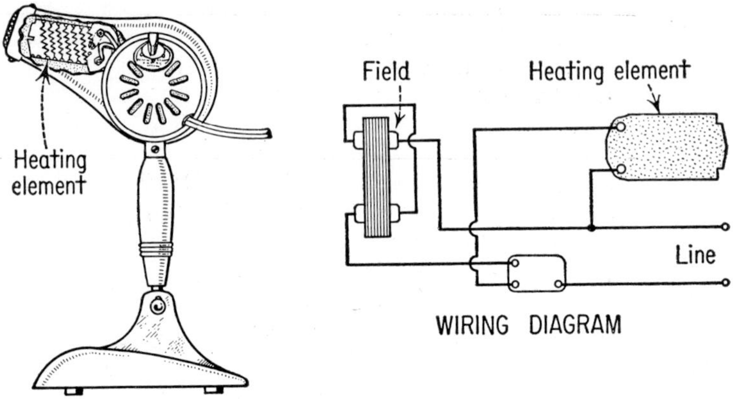


Fig. 7-21.

the motor, across the heating element, and out the vent at the left of figure. When the wiring diagram is examined, it will be seen that heating element and fan-motor wires are brought to separate terminals on the switch. The switch itself is of a type that, in one position, connects both motor and heating element into the circuit, thus supplying hot air; another position of the switch disconnects the heating element so that cool air can be obtained. The third switch position turns both off. (The switch positions are not necessarily in this sequence.)

The circuit of this appliance is not very complicated, and servicing from a technical viewpoint is relatively simple. The usual test for open circuits, shorts, and grounds apply, and motor- and heating-element tests and repairs are given in the preceding pages. The only difficulty is that the hair drier is a rather small appliance; especially is the heating element a small item; and standard nichrome elements are not suitable for replacement. While this need not necessarily complicate repairs, a delay is almost inevitable, as it is frequently necessary to obtain replacement parts from the manufacturer.

## Now that you have read this chapter, can you answer these questions?

**1.** In general, which requires more current for its operation, a motor-operated appliance, or one with a heating element?

**2.** The vacuum cleaner is so designed that the motor is sealed off from the dirt in the air stream. In what way, if any, will dirt damage a motor?

**3.** What is the proper adjustment for a vacuum-cleaner brush?

**4.** Will the quality of the bag affect the performance of a vacuum cleaner? Explain.

**5.** How can you determine, without experimenting, in which direction to turn a fan- or vacuum-cleaner blade so as to unscrew it from the threaded motor shaft?

**6.** To eliminate radio interference, a vacuum-cleaner motor has a "filter" capacitor across its brush terminals. How would you check this capacitor for shorts? For an open circuit?

**7.** What is meant by a distributed winding? A concentrated winding?

**8.** A vacuum cleaner motor is plugged into 120-v direct current. The newly replaced field coils are connected so as to make the magnetic polarity of both field pieces a north pole. How will the motor behave?

**9.** How would you reverse the direction of rotation of an universal motor? A shaded-pole motor? A split-phase motor?

**10.** When a motor is used in an application where it is necessary to change abruptly the direction of rotation, it is said to be "plugged." Is it possible to plug a split-phase motor? Explain.

**11.** What is a growler? How is it used?

**12.** The air drawn into a tank-type vacuum cleaner goes through the motor. How is the motor kept free of dirt?

**13.** An appliance is fitted with a screw-base pilot lamp with a blue bead visible inside the bulb. What are the specifications of this bulb?

**14.** What is an autotransformer?

**15.** Describe the procedure for aligning a fan blade.

**16.** How can you determine if the blade of a fan having a shaded-pole motor has too great a pitch?

**17.** Is it possible to control the speed of a 1/4 hp split-phase motor? Explain.

**18.** What is a self-oiling bearing?

**19.** What is a self-aligning bearing?

**20.** What two methods are used to vary the speed of a fan?

**21.** Why is the universal motor ideally suited to vacuum-cleaner service?

**22.** Does the universal motor have the same speed on alternating current and direct current?

**23.** Does the universal motor have the same direction of rotation on alternating current as on direct current?

*chapter* **8**

# Food Mixers

A food mixer (Figs. 8-1A and B) is, basically, a motor with whippers or beaters attached for the purpose of mixing or rapidly stirring food where this work would be laborious by hand. Many other features of convenience have been incorporated into its design, such as speed-control devices, reduction gears, on-off switch, swivel and removable motors, and, on some few models, a pilot light.

## 8.1. Attachments

The modern mixer is provided with attachments which allow it to wander far afield from its original purpose. The manufacturer can now supply attachments which will perform such tasks as chopping and grinding meat and other foods, mixing drinks, grinding coffee, turning an ice-cream freezer, churning butter, peeling potatoes, shelling peas, opening cans, and even sharpening knives and polishing silverware.

The motor may be detached from its base with the mere flick of a lever, and carried to the stove or table to perform its duties of beating, mixing, and whipping. Truly, the manufacturer has done all in his power to make this appliance irresistible to the housewife who has once witnessed its amazing versatility.

Supplied with the mixer as standard equipment are an

attachment for juicing, a juice strainer, two mixing bowls, and a ball bearing mounted pedestal on which the mixing bowl rests. Some mixers are provided with two mounting holes. If the pedestal is placed in one mounting hole, the beaters are in the center

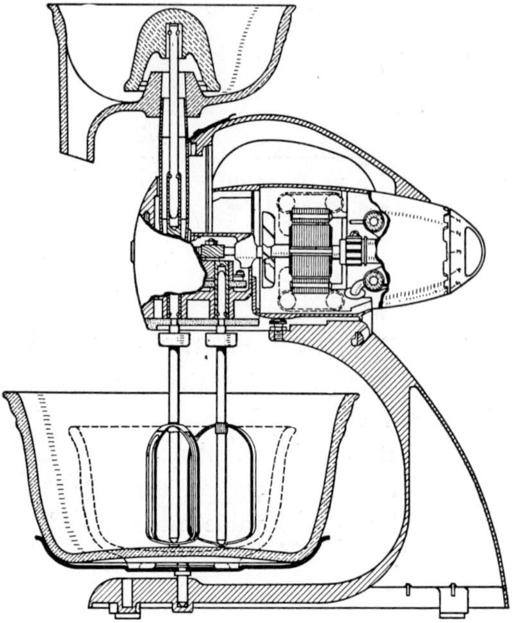

Fig. 8-1A. (Courtesy, Knapp-Monarch Co.)

of the mixing bowl, which remains stationary while the beaters operate. If the other mounting hole is used, the beaters are close to the side of the mixing bowl and cause the bowl and pedestal to rotate so that all parts of the mixture are automatically reached by the beaters.

## 8.2. The Mixer Motor

Insofar as styling is concerned, there are two types of mixers, one with a horizontal motor and the other with a vertical motor. The type of motor is the same in either case. With very few exceptions, the universal motor is used for mixer service, since this style, more than any other in the small-motor field, lends itself to speed-control methods.

Upon removal of the front cover of the mixer, it will be seen that the armature shaft has a worm gear attached (or turned on

FIG. 8-1B. (Courtesy, Knapp-Monarch Co.)

the shaft itself), which drives a pair of reduction gears. These gears reduce the speed of the motor from around 9,000 rpm to 1,000 rpm, the highest beater speed. The shafts of the reduction gears are hollowed and fitted with flats or drive rods, serving as spindles for the beater shafts. Figure 8-2 illustrates the commonly used types of beater drives. Notice that the spindles are set at an angle so that the beaters will not bump against each other when rotating. A 45° angle is used between beaters with four blades, 60° for beaters with three blades. This fact should be remembered when the reduction gears or spindles have been removed and are being reassembled. Most mixers are provided with some marking to assure proper alignment of beaters, such as a flat or depressed place in the reduction gear shaft for placement of the reduction-gear setscrew.

The reduction gears are generally made of a hard fiber, which provides more silent operation than would a metal gear. The lubricant for the gear box should be ordered from the manufacturer, since a special type must be used which will not seep down the spindle and beater shaft into the foodstuff.

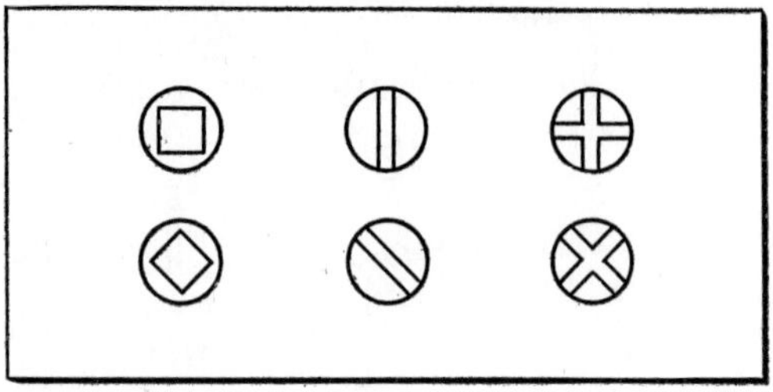

FIG. 8-2.

The beaters snap into place in the spindles with only a slight pressure. When it place, the beaters should come close to the bottom of the bowl, but not touch it. If the beaters touch the bottom of the bowl, there will be a drag on the motor which will cause it to overheat, thus shortening its life. It is possible, in some mixers, to adjust the spindle position by placing spacing washers below the reduction gears. Other mixers are provided with an adjusting screw which allows the beater depth to be varied.

The sleeve bearing below the spindle, in which the shaft of the beater rides, may become worn, allowing the beater to vibrate. The manufacturer makes an oversize bearing which may be used to replace the old one; being oversize, it will compensate for wear in the beater shaft.

## 8.3. Speed Control

On the back end, or side, of the motor housing is a switch for varying the motor speed. It may be calibrated from high to low speed, or it may be marked for the speed that is proper for the various types of food preparations which are to be mixed. Some mixers have but three speeds; others provide a smooth, gradual increase from low (275 rpm) to high (1,000 rpm). Four speed-control systems are used on the various brands of mixers: a rheostat, a tapped motor-field winding, adjustable motor brushes, and the Lee governor. These systems will be considered in the order named.

## 8.4. The Rheostat

This system of speed control has been discussed with respect to its use with fan motors (Sec. 7.15). A rheostat is a variable resistor with an external control knob. It is placed in series with the motor, and provides a voltage drop preceding the motor,

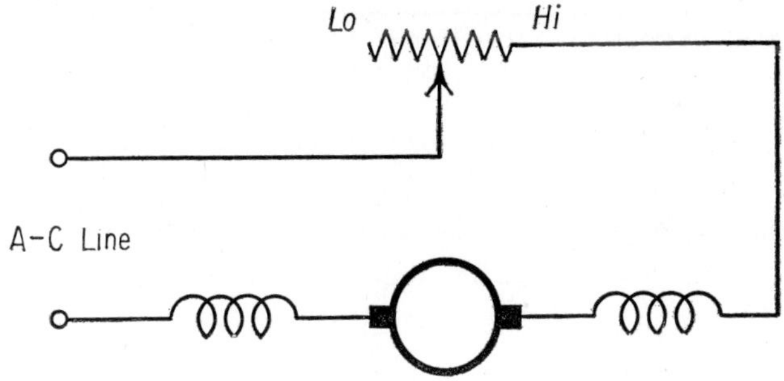


FIG. 8-3.

thereby reducing the value of the voltage available for the motor itself. The circuit of a mixer motor and control is shown in Figure 8-3. The setting of the rheostat arm to the extreme right is highest speed, and to the extreme left is lowest speed.

## 8.5. The Tapped Field

The tapped motor-field winding of Figure 8-4 provides but three speeds—low, medium, and high. One of the field coils of the motor has three taps on it, and a switch which completes the circuit from one line wire through some one of the three tap wires. Thus, the entirety of the tapped field may be in the circuit, or just a part of it, or none of it—depending on the setting of the speed-control switch. The switch position which allows current to go through the entire field coil is the slow-speed setting. The next, or medium, speed setting of the switch selects the tap at the center of the field. There is now less motor wire in the

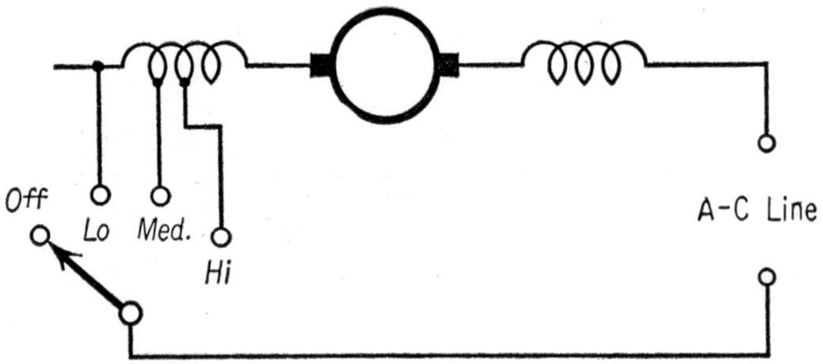


FIG. 8-4.

circuit, and consequently more current will flow through the motor. This produces a stronger magnetic field from the field poles and a consequent increase in speed. This condition is carried to a further extreme in the high-speed switch position, where the current flow is still greater and produces an even stronger magnetic field.

If an ordinary motor had some of its field-coil turns removed in an attempt to produce a higher speed, the motor would likely overheat and burn out from excessive current. The tapped field motor is, therefore, designed around its high-speed position, and extra turns added to its field coils to produce the lower speeds obtained. The wire used for these extra turns is, in most cases, of a smaller gauge than that which is in the circuit all the time.

This motor speed-control system has a distinct advantage over the rheostat method in that it is more economical. With a tapped field, the watts of power required for the motor to operate are proportional to the speed and consequent power exerted by the motor. When a rheostat, on the other hand, is used for speed control, some wattage is dissipated as heat in the resistance wire forming the rheostat; and only at high speed, where no external resistance is in the motor circuit, is the motor operating at top efficiency. A serious limitation of the tapped-field method is that very few values of speed may be obtained, and the speed changes are abrupt.

## 8.6. Shifting Motor Brushes

Figure 6-1 illustrates a single-coil armature and its commutator bars and brushes. The relationship between the location of the brushes and commutator bars is normally set, and the position called neutral. The action in the motor is such that the current-carrying coil removes itself from the magnetic field of the pole nearest it. In moving away from this pole it will eventually move into the influence of a pole of opposite polarity, which will cause the current-carrying coil to reverse its direction of motion. At a point midway between the two poles, there is an equal force on the wire in opposite directions. This is the neutral position, and the brushes are located so as to cause a current reversal through the coil at this position by means of its commutator, thus continuing its rotation in the original direction. If the brushes are moved past this neutral position there will be some back pressure or force on the armature coils, resulting in a reduced armature speed.

This principle is used in varying the speed of a mixer motor. There is an externally controlled lever attached to the brush holders. The brush holders are mounted so as to be movable, and the attached lever moves the brushes off neutral to reduce the motor speed. This system allows many speeds and a smooth, gradual speed change.

## 8.7. The Lee Governor

Invented by Dr. Royal Lee, the Lee governor (Fig. 8-5) is a fairly new speed-control device. It operates on the principle of making and breaking the circuit to the motor by vibrating contacts, the motor speed being determined by the vibration rate. In terms of one make-and-break cycle, while the contacts are closed the motor is carrying current and accelerating; during

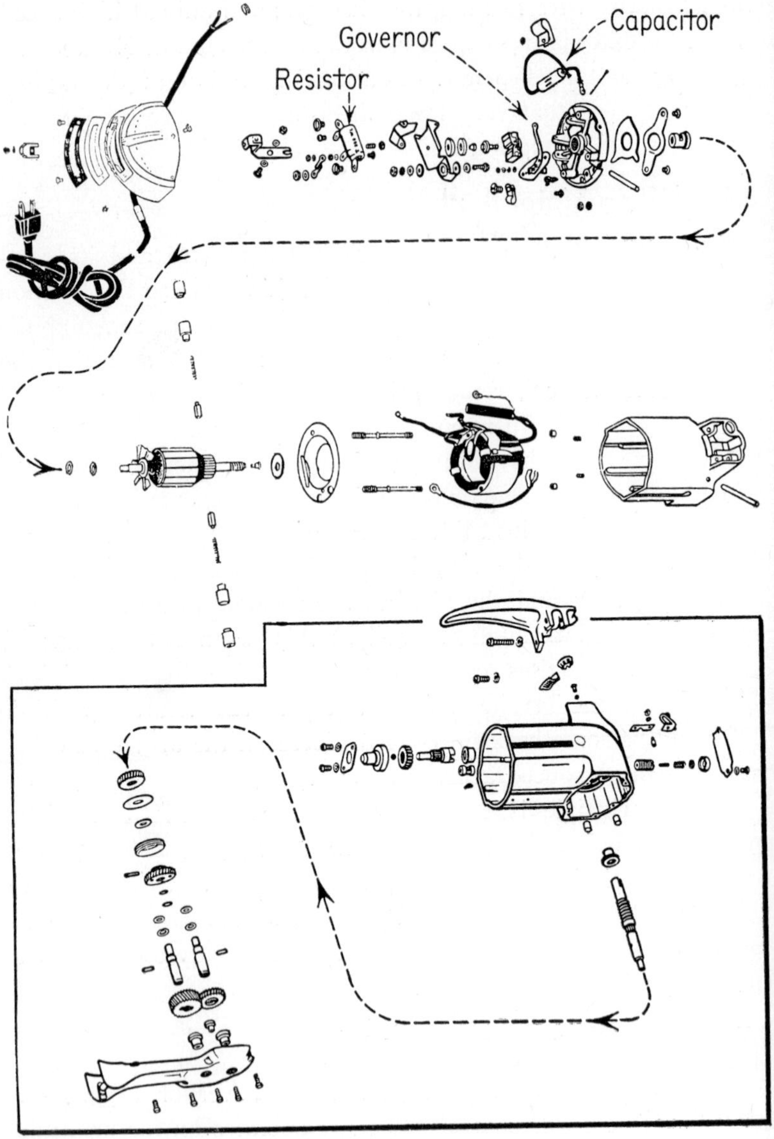


Fig. 8-5. (Courtesy, Landers, Frary, & Clark)

the time the contacts are open, the motor receives no current and is decelerating. There is a certain *average* speed for this one cycle. If make-and-break occur fast enough, acceleration and

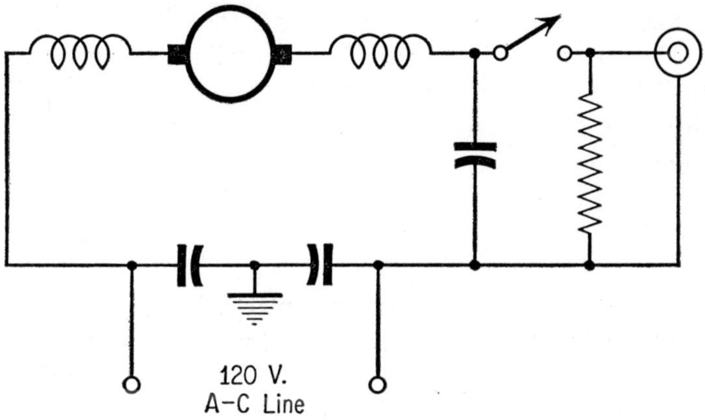


FIG. 8-6.

deceleration will not be noticeable—only the resultant average speed.

The governor assembly is fastened to the motor shaft and rotates with the armature. There are two tungsten contacts on the governor, one stationary and the other movable. The movable contact is counterbalanced by a piece of iron integral with its construction. A spring holds the contacts closed until the motor reaches a predetermined speed, and then centrifugal force on the counterbalance opens the contacts against the spring tension. This breaks the motor circuit, and it slows down. Centrifugal force is reduced, the contacts close, and the motor, again receiving current, speeds up. The speed at which the contacts open and close is approximately 100 or 200 times per second.

The governor contacts open and close the circuit of the 120-v line to the motor (Fig. 8-6). Therefore the governor is equivalent electrically to any on-off line switch. However, the governor is rotating with the armature, and some provision must be made to introduce current to its contacts. For this purpose, the governor assembly has two slip rings, one electrically connected to each contact, and a pair of brushes, one contacting each slip ring. The mixer motor with governor control has a total of four brushes, two for the governor and two for the armature commutator.

The governor is adjustable externally. On mixers, the method is to allow the control knob to move a cone in and out against one of the contacts, varying the spring tension between them and, consequently, the vibration rate. Hence, the customary speed range of from 300 to 1,000 rpm may be obtained with governor control.

As may be seen in Figure 8-6, a resistor and a capacitor are in parallel with the governor contacts. The opening of the contacts does not totally interrupt the motor circuit; the value of the resistor is such as to allow a small current to flow through the motor. Reduction of motor current rather than total interruption allows the motor to operate more smoothly, and there will not be any chattering of the motor from contact vibration. The capacitor is used to increase contact life by reducing the severity of the arc accompanying the breaking of the circuit.

The governor is an economical speed-control device, thanks to its characteristic of opening the motor circuit to reduce speed, thus reducing power consumed. Since the closed contacts, at any speed, allow full current through the motor, the power of the mixer is not reduced; even at lowest speeds, full power is obtained.

The capacitor shunting the governor contacts, and its purpose, have been discussed above. Another capacitor unit is often included in the mixer circuit. As shown in Figure 8-6, this acts as a filter across the line to eliminate radio interference originating at the motor brushes. The value of these capacitors is such as to make sparking noises unnoticeable in a radio located 6 feet or more from the motor. (When replacing capacitors, always use an identical value.)

A pilot light is found on some mixer models. A small lamp is used, operating on from 6 to 8 v. The motor field is tapped to provide this voltage. Figure 7-4 shows a similar circuit used for a pilot light on a vacuum cleaner.

A thrust screw is located at the rear of the motor to adjust the armature alignment and to take up the back pressure exerted by the gears driving the beaters. It should be adjusted so as to allow about 1/32-inch end play in the motor shaft.

## 8.8. Testing the Motor

The motor is tested in the manner described in Sec. 7.11 for universal motors and as outlined below.

*Motor Field*

Test with ohmmeter or test lamp for continuity.

No meter movement or no glow on test lamp indicates open circuit.

Full glow on test lamp indicates continuity.

A reading of from 5 to 100 ohms indicates a normal circuit.

A reading of zero ohms indicates a shorted coil.

Test from coil leads to frame. A glow on the test lamp or a deflection of the meter needle indicates a grounded coil.

This type of coil may be easily made and installed in the shop. Count the number of turns, and check wire size, to assure an exact duplicate. If motor does not turn, reverse leads from new coil.

If motor runs hot, this may indicate a shorted or grounded field coil.

*Armature*

If armature coils are open, motor may refuse to turn, or may have a thumping or surging sound while operating.

A long blue spark at the brushes indicates a shorted coil.

Test from bar to bar on the commutator with ohmmeter. The same resistance measurement should exist between any two consecutive bars. Too high a resistance measurement indicates an open coil. Zero ohms indicates a shorted coil.

Test from commutator bars to shaft. If either test lamp or ohmmeter shows continuity, coils are grounded. If armature is open, shorted, or grounded, it should be replaced or rewound.

## *Servicing Food Mixers*

### 8.9. Mixer Will Not Run

The motor on a food mixer may fail to run for one or more of the following reasons:

Defective cord
Defective off-on switch
Defective speed controller
Defective motor or brushes

As an initial test, connect the mixer to the appliance tester (Fig. 2-2). If the indications are those of a normal circuit, the trouble lies in the power line: receptacle or fuse. If the tester indicates an open circuit, the fault lies in the mixer, and it must be disassembled for further testing.

Test next the cord and plug. This entails partially dismantling the appliance, the method and extent depending upon the brand and model. Having removed the cord, jumper together the appliance ends and plug the cord into the appliance tester. A short-circuit indication means the cord is in good condition. An open-circuit indication means the cord is defective and should be replaced.

The off-on switch is generally not a separate unit, but integral with the controller, and operated by the controller knob or lever. Thus, it is necessary to dismantle the controller assembly to the point where the portion of the controller acting as off-on switch is accessible for examination and testing. Operate the switch while observing its action. Defective metal pieces or points will usually be revealed by this examination. If any doubt exists, the switch parts can be jumpered around and the appliance connected to the power line. Normal operation indicates the switch to be the faulty component.

The speed controller is actually a sort of switch in series with the off-on switch. The tapped field controller has switch parts easily recognizable as such; the governor is a vibrating switch, and the rheostat is a sliding switch. If the controller is handled as if it were a switch, servicing of the controller follows the same line of reasoning as switch servicing, and re-establishing the broken circuit continuity will restore operation.

The rheostat type of speed controller may suffer from two defect types: broken resistance wire, or poor sliding contact. If the resistance wire is broken at the high end, the mixer motor may fail to operate at all. If the break is elsewhere, the mixer may operate through a short range of controller-knob rotation, then suddenly stop. Operation may be intermittent, or totally lacking, if the slider is making poor contact. Jumpering around the rheostat will restore mixer operation (but only on high speed) if the rheostat is faulty. In any event, a faulty rheostat must be replaced; such units are not built so as to allow of repairs.

The tapped-field controller usually fails in such a manner that one or more, but not all, speeds will operate. This may be due to a broken wire at the switch buttons, or pitted contacts, either of which is visible upon inspection. If the switch seems in good condition, and the mixer still operates on a few of the speeds only, the motor is to be suspected as the faulty part.

Speed control by shifting brushes is a purely mechanical operation. Any defect in the shifting mechanism is apparent upon examination. One very common cause of failure is a break in the wires leading to the brushes. Inasmuch as the wires are flexed each time the brushes are shifted, this is only to be expected.

Servicing by observation is less useful on the governor than on other types of control devices. Furthermore, additional electrical parts are associated with it: capacitor, resistor, and brushes. The sum total of the interacting effects of all these parts must be considered when analyzing governor failure. Defects in the capacitor or the resistor are not direct causes of the motor's failure to operate; however, through damage done to the governor they can become the *indirect* cause. Bad brushes will disrupt circuit continuity and result in failure of the motor to rotate.

The capacitor paralleling the governor (Fig. 8-6) is tested with an ohmmeter, or as described in Section 7.4. As tested with the ohmmeter, the capacitor should cause the meter needle to move a short distance up scale, and then return to infinity. Any other behavior of the meter—including no perceptible motion of the needle whatsoever—indicates a defective capacitor.

The resistor consists of a length of resistance wire wound on a porcelain tube. As tested with the ohmmeter, it should measure as having between 100 and 1,000 ohms. Watch especially for a reading of infinity, which indicates a resistor whose defect is a break in the resistance wire.

The governor itself may suffer from damaged parts, broken springs, or faulty contact between brushes and points. The contact points on a governor are made of tungsten, a very tough metal which will withstand the impact of the vibrating action of the governor without damage—silver or copper would be flattened out within a few minutes of operation. Do not try to file tungsten contacts; instead, replace the governor assembly. A broken spring or other damaged or broken parts will be revealed by examination, and any such condition requires that the entire governor be replaced, since replacement parts for it are not available. Continuity of the governor may be tested between the slip rings with a series test lamp or ohmmeter. Again, a defective governor or defective brushes must be replaced.

Finally, the motor itself, or its brushes, may be the cause of failure to operate. The procedure outlined in Section 7.11 for motor servicing, and the chart contained in that section, may be used as a guide in servicing a mixer motor.

## 8.10. Mixer Hums but Will Not Turn

The cause of this type of defective operation is any condition which might cause the motor shaft to be locked into position and prevent the armature from turning. Possible sources of binding are the following:

- Damaged gears
- Damaged controller
- Dry bearings
- Worn bearings
- Open-circuit coil in armature
- Food which has leaked into motor and dried, causing motor to lock

There is no test which will reveal which of the foregoing is the cause of trouble. It is therefore necessary to disassemble the mixer and examine the interior until the trouble is isolated, checking in turn each of the possibilities listed.

To repair broken gears, it is necessary that the parts in the gear case be removed and cleaned for examination. It is, of course, necessary to find the broken piece(s) which caused the failure, making sure that no particles remain in the gear case to cause future trouble. When replacing gears, the angular displacement required of the drive spindles should be kept in mind, or beater-blade interference trouble will be experienced. The type of lubricant used in the gear case has a consistency which prevents leakage of the lubricant onto the foodstuff under preparation. This lubricant may be obtained from appliance parts outlets, and should invariably be used in the mixer gear case.

If the controller is a governor, there is always the possibility that some part of it may become broken off and wedge the governor into a locked position. No tests are required, as this condition is noticeable upon inspection.

Either dry or worn bearings can prevent the motor from rotating. Either condition is apparent when an attempt is made to turn the motor shaft by hand. Perhaps the dry bearings can be cleaned and relubricated to restore service. The worn bearings must be replaced; the procedure is explained in Section 7.7.

To determine if the trouble is due to an open-circuited armature coil, rotate the motor shaft by hand with the motor plugged in. If the motor attempts to run, or does run slowly and haltingly, the armature is the probable faulty component. Test it further as described in Section 7.6.

Some mixers have a spindle atop the motor housing for insertion of a juice-extractor attachment. When the extractor attachment is removed, the spindle opening offers an excellent receptacle for spilled flour, baking powder, and so forth, and the drying and caking of these ingredients can cause the mixer mechanism to become so jammed as to interfere with operation. No test is required to isolate this cause, which reveals itself upon inspection. Ordinarily, cleaning out the mechanism will restore normal operation.

## 8.11. Speed Will Not Vary

This trouble may occur on the mixer having a tapped field as speed-control device, resulting from an open-field circuit; or it may occur on the mixer with a governor as a result of welded governor contacts or a shorted governor capacitor.

Consider the first case, that of the defective tapped field. The circuit is shown in Figure 8-4. A break in the field-winding section located between medium and high speeds will allow operation at high speed only. This condition can be verified by plugging the mixer into the appliance tester (Fig. 2-2) and observing the lamps on the tester with the mixer control knob in the low and medium positions. If the field is open-circuited, the tester will give the indication of an open circuit. When the mixer is dismantled, the continuity between field taps can be tested with an ohmmeter or series test lamp. An examination of the field coils may reveal the location of the break; otherwise, the field coil must be either rewound or replaced.

Single-speed operation (high only) of the mixer with a governor is due to failure of the make-and-break property of the governor. This can result from stuck contacts. The appliance-tester indication in this case is somewhat indefinite; it is better to examine the governor for visual evidence of damaged contacts. If defective, the governor must be replaced.

If the capacitor paralleling the governor should develop an internal short—and a capacitor can do just that—it acts as a jumper around the governor, and effectively eliminates it from the circuit. The capacitor is tested as explained in Section 7.4, or with an ohmmeter. A shorted capacitor will register zero ohms on the ohmmeter.

## 8.12. Motor Runs Too Slowly

This condition is usually accompanied by a thumping sound and the odor of burnt insulation. It is the result of a defective armature; the armature may be grounded, shorted, or open-circuited. As verification, the armature is given the tests listed in Section 7.6; however, it will be necessary to replace the armature or to have it rewound. The original direction of rotation of the armature should be determined and recorded. If the replacement armature does not rotate in the correct direction, the wires to the commutator brushes can be interchanged, thus reversing to the original direction of rotation. Note that the governor-controlled mixer has two sets of brushes—the governor-slip-ring brushes and the armature-commutator brushes. Only the latter can be interchanged to obtain a reversal of direction of rotation. Interchanging governor brushes has no effect on the motor operation. Such a change is equivalent merely to reversing the wires fastened to an off-on switch.

## 8.13. Mixer Blows Fuses

Plug the mixer into the appliance tester (Fig. 2-2). If a normal indication is obtained, the cause of blown fuses is an overloaded circuit. If the tester indicates a short circuit, the cause of blown fuses is within the mixer and may be one of these:

Defective cord
Defective internal wiring
Short within the motor

To test the cord, remove it from the mixer and plug it into the appliance tester *without a jumper across the appliance end.* If the tester indicates an open circuit, the cord is in good condition. If the tester indicates a short circuit, the cord is defective and should be replaced.

Defective internal wiring can be located by examination, or by an ohmmeter test between the wiring and the frame of the mixer. Manipulation of the wiring, along with observation of the meter-needle deflection, is helpful in spotting the site of the wiring defect.

To isolate a short circuit within the motor, it should be carefully disassembled with the ohmmeter attached to the motor leads. When the location of the defect is agitated, the meter needle will move off zero to a normal resistance reading. Field and armature can, if necessary, be further tested as described in Sections 7.5 and 7.6.

## 8.14. Trouble-Shooting Chart: Electric Mixers

| SYMPTOM | CAUSE | TEST | REMEDY |
|---|---|---|---|
| Motor will not run. | Open circuit in a. cord | Remove cord, fasten wires together, and test other ends with ohmmeter or series test lamp. | Replace cord. |
| | b. switch | Test switch with ohmmeter. | Replace switch. |
| | c. speed controller | Dismantle appliance to point where controller is exposed. Examine and test parts of controller for 1. burned-out rheostat, 2. bad contacts on governor, 3. wire broken at speed switch, 4. bad brushes. | Replace defective component. |

| SYMPTOM | CAUSE | TEST | REMEDY |
|---|---|---|---|
| | d. motor | Check motor brushes and springs. | Replace brushes and/ or springs. |
| | | Check field coils for continuity. | Replace or rewind field coils. |
| | | Check armature for open circuit (Sec. 7.6). | Replace with exchange armature. |
| Motor hums but will not rotate | Jammed mechanism | Open gear box examine for broken gear, dry spindle, dry motor shaft, foodstuff spilled into gear box. | Replace or repair as necessary |
| | Armature open-circuited | Armature test given in Section 7.6. | Replace armature. |
| Motor speed will not vary. | Defective governor mechanism: a. shorted capacitor | Capacitor test given in Section 7.4. | Replace with capacitor of identical value. |
| | b. "welded" contacts | Visual examination. | Replace governor. |
| | Open field coil (on appliance with tapped field-coil speed control) | Measure resistance of the portion of field coil between speed switch and line. | Replace or rewind field-coil sections. |
| Blows fuses. | Shorted cord or motor | Check at plug cap with ohmmeter. Very low or zero ohms indicates short. | Dismantle appliance, testing for short or ground at each step. When fault disappears, defect is indicated. |
| Appliance shocks user. | Internal wiring touching frame of appliance | Use series test lamp or ohmmeter from line cord to frame. Continuity indicates ground. | Same as above. |

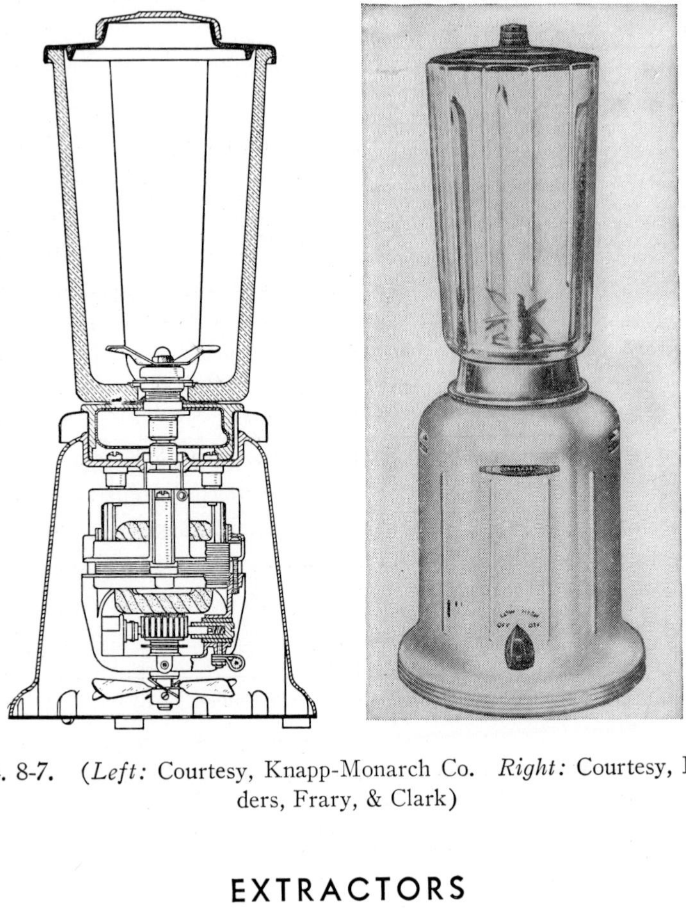

FIG. 8-7. (*Left:* Courtesy, Knapp-Monarch Co. *Right:* Courtesy, Landers, Frary, & Clark)

# EXTRACTORS

## 8.15. General Discussion

The juice extractor is a mixer-type appliance; typical are the Liquidizer and Mixablend shown in Figure 8-7. This appliance has a vertically positioned universal motor which is accessible for servicing by removing the screws holding the bottom plate in place. Depending upon the brand of appliance, the motor is either a single-speed or a three-speed motor. The single-speed motor is controlled by a simple off-on switch. The speed control for the three-speed motor is obtained by tapping the field; a four-position switch (off-high-medium-low) is provided on the appliance.

The contents of the extractor are removed by lifting the upper bowl off the remainder of the appliance (that part which contains the motor) so that the juice can be poured out without lifting the entire appliance. Such an arrangement requires that the coupling between motor and cutter be of a type which will readily come apart and can be reassembled just as easily. Splined shafts, gear-tooth engagement clutches, and tongue and groove couplings are the type of connectors used.

The bearing for the cutter shaft has a gasket at either end to prevent the contents of the bowl from leaking through to the motor compartment. The gasket is forced against the shaft by a retaining nut. This assembly should be checked for wear and/or leakage when servicing the appliance. It might be well to examine the coupling for indications of wear or breakage which would prevent positive engagement.

The problems of servicing and testing a universal motor have already been detailed (Chap. 7). As this appliance motor operates in a vertical position, extra attention should be given to the possibility of the motor armature rubbing because of improper positioning or bearing and spacer washer wear.

## Now that you have read this chapter, can you answer these questions?

**1.** What is a rheostat?

**2.** Explain the control of a universal-motor speed with a rheostat—a governor—a tapped field—by shifting motor brushes.

**3.** What provision is made to prevent beater blades from hitting one another?

**4.** What type of lubricant is used in the gear housing of a mixer?

**5.** What type of mixer speed control will give best performance at low speed? Why?

**6.** What method of speed control will give poorest low-speed performance? Why?

**7.** A mixer with governor speed control is defective in that it will operate at high speed only. Upon examination it is found that all mechanical parts are satisfactory. What is the probable cause of trouble?

**8.** If the rotation is in the wrong direction, what effect will it have on the speed and/or behavior of a governor-controlled motor?

**9.** Concerning a universal motor, what is meant by "neutral"? By "off neutral"?

**10.** Some mixer motors have a small fan-blade mounted on the armature shaft. What is its purpose?

**11.** What determines the value of resistance used across the contacts of the governor?

**12.** What determines the make-and-break speed of the governor contacts?

*chapter* **9**

# Electric Laundry Equipment

## WASHING MACHINES

### 9.1. General Remarks

The greater part of repair work in the appliance shop will be on washing machines. This appliance is, perhaps, more of a necessity than any other; it is owned by more families, and any failure to function is a severe blow to the housewife, especially in a household with small children. As a consequence, the service man will usually be called upon to repair it the same day it stops running.

The first washing machines built were of the cylinder type. The huge cylinder into which the clothes were put rotated in a tub half filled with soapy water. By periodically reversing the direction of cylinder rotation, this machine did agitate the clothes to some extent. But the process was slow and the washing machine bulky. It has been totally replaced by the agitator-type machine, which, thanks to its smaller size and modern improvements, is more easily operated and may be rolled out of the way when not in use.

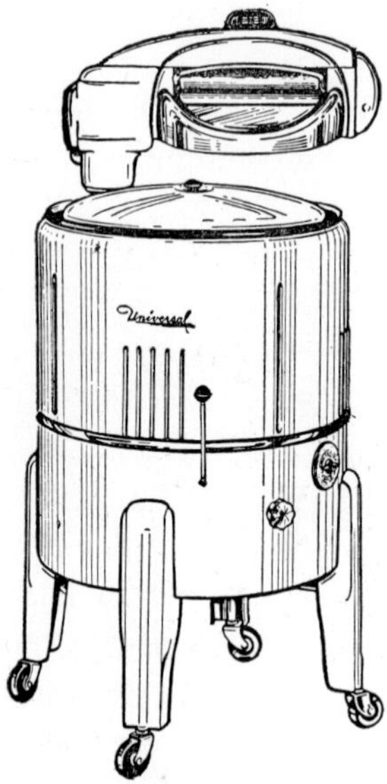

FIG. 9-1. · (Courtesy, Landers, Frary, & Clark)

The modern washing machine, Figure 9-1, consists of a 1/4-hp split-phase motor, a gear case for agitator drive, the agitator, the tub and its lid, the wringer drive-gear assembly, and the wringer.

## 9.2. The Washing-Machine Motor

The motor used for washing-machine service is a 1/4-hp split-phase short-hour motor. The split-phase motor is described in Section 6.4. By short-hour is meant that the motor is intended to be used intermittently, not constantly, as in the case of a refrigerator motor. The split-phase motor is intended for use on a-c only. If plugged into a d-c source it will quickly burn out. The motor has two sets of windings, and both are wound in slots in the stator (stationary member of motor). The winding in the bottom of the slots is the running winding, and consists of many turns of heavy wire. Wound on top of this is the starting winding with its fewer turns of finer wire. The windings are arranged so that there is a 90° electrical difference between the centers of starting and running windings. In other words, a starting-winding pole is centered midway between two adjacent running-winding poles. The running winding with its many turns has electrical characteristics which differ from the resistive nature of the fine wire used for the starting winding, providing the motor with the equivalent of a rotating magnetic field. Thus the motor starts in a predetermined direction of rotation. When it reaches approximately 80 per cent of full speed, the starting winding is removed from the electrical circuit by means of a centrifugal switch. Having reached this speed, the motor will continue to rotate without benefit of the starting winding. A four-pole motor, as used on a washing machine, operates at 1,725 rpm. This speed will vary slightly depending upon the load. The motor draws in excess of 15 amp while starting; 4 amp (approximately) while running.

The difference between the starting and running currents is accounted for by the current drawn by the starting winding.

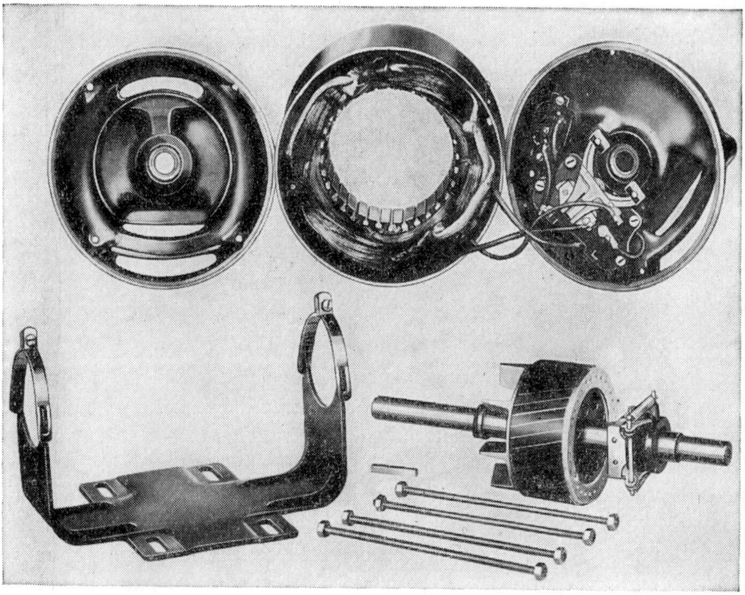

Fig. 9-2. (Courtesy, Emerson Electric Company)

With such a heavy current through a small number of turns, this winding will rapidly overheat, and can burn out within a very few minutes. So that this will not happen, it is switched out of the circuit as soon as the motor comes up to almost full speed. The switch is built into the motor. It is operated by a system of weighted levers mounted on the rotor, and a certain rotor speed causes the levers to fly out and open the switch. A typical starting-switch assembly is shown in Figure 9-3.

A squirrel-cage rotor is used in this motor. Its winding consists of heavy uninsulated copper bars riveted or welded into slots in the laminated rotor structure. Current is induced into these wires by the rotation of the rotor. This induced current makes of the rotor an electromagnet. The running windings produce a magnetic field from the stator, and the interaction of these two magnetic fields causes continued motor rotation.

FIG. 9-3. Centrifugal starting switch. The function of the centrifugal starting switch is to open the circuit of the auxiliary stator winding after the motor has reached a predetermined speed. This consists of two parts, the switch and the actuator. The switch is mounted on the inside of one of the end shields. This part carries a pair of contact points in series with the auxiliary winding. These points remain in contact until the predetermined speed is reached at which time the actuator on the rotor rapidly moves axially, causing separation of the contact points, thus opening the circuit of the auxiliary winding. The contacts operate with a wiping action which keeps them clean. (Courtesy, Emerson Electric Company)

This motor cannot be reversed while running at full speed. It is necessary to bring the motor to a stop and then reverse the connections of the starting winding or the running winding (not both), and restart in the opposite direction.

On most washing machines it is essential that the motor have the proper direction of rotation. The motor is coupled onto a worm which, because of its high speed and the load on the gears, is provided with a thrust bearing. If the motor turns in the wrong direction, the pressure of the worm will not be against the thrust bearing. Instead, it will be exerted against a surface not designed for the purpose of a bearing, and excessive wear will result. Some machines are designed so that the wringer will not turn, others so that the agitator will not engage, if the motor is turning in the wrong direction.

Generally, it is possible to tell by the operation of the wringer whether the motor is turning in the right or wrong direction. As a matter of convenience to the operator, most manufacturers design the washing-machine wringer so that the user may, regardless of where the wringer is located around the tub, pull the roll-reverse lever toward herself, and have the rolls turn in the proper direction to take clothes from the side on which the operator is standing through to the other side of the wringer. If the reverse lever is pulled toward the operator and clothes will not feed into the wringer because of improper direction of roll rotation, then the motor is rotating in the wrong direction. The new washing machine as it comes from the factory will, of course, have a motor with the correct direction of rotation. If a motor turns the wrong way, it shows that a motor repair or replacement has been made. Before the motor is removed, the repair man should determine whether the motor rotates in a clockwise or counterclockwise direction.

## 9.3. Motor Servicing

The split-phase motor normally does not require brushes for its operation. However, one manufacturer has made a motor with a wound rotor and squirrel-cage stator. The rotor has a starting and a running winding just like the stator on a more conventional machine, and the stator has current induced into its copper bars the same as in a regular squirrel-cage rotor. Brushes are used in this motor to conduct the line current through slip rings to the rotor windings. The brush holder is bolted onto the back-end bell, and the brushes are flat at the end, since they fit against flat, not curved, slip rings. This brush should be about 1 inch long. If it is shorter, or if the brush spring has lost its tension, the brush and spring should be replaced.

The slip rings may be examined through the opening in the

end bell for the brushes. If the slip rings are pitted or grooved, the rotor should be removed, and the slip rings smoothed in a lathe.

Examine the starting switch for pitted contacts, worn parts, and springs with weakened tension. It is important that this switch operate properly lest the starting winding be damaged.

Test separately the starting and running windings with an ohmmeter. The running winding should measure from 2 to 5 ohms, the starting winding 5 to 10 ohms. A measurement that is too high indicates an open circuit. Zero ohms indicates a short. Either of these indications calls for the motor to be rewound.

A motor that has been in a damp place, or subject to condensation from hot water, may have had its insulation penetrated with moisture, and running such a motor will totally destroy the insulation. It is sometimes possible to bake the moisture out of the motor and reinforce the insulation with a suitable varnish. A baking time of four or five hours in an oven whose temperature is just above the boiling point of water (212° F.) will generally drive out all the moisture. All accessible coil wires should be painted with an insulating varnish, and sufficient time for the varnish to dry should pass before the motor is assembled. Test with series test lamp for grounds (from coil leads to frame) before operating the motor.

If an oven is not available, a motor may be dried in the following manner: Connect the two windings in parallel. Connect a 100-w bulb in series with the windings. Place the bulb inside the field structure, and plug into a 120-v a-c receptacle. The bulb current through the field wires will cause a temperature rise, and the bulb will radiate heat. If the entire unit is covered with a piece of canvas, the heat will be kept inside the motor. Twelve to twenty-four hours is sufficient time to dry out the motor by this method. If after drying and revarnishing the motor continues to test grounded or shorted, or runs hot, it must be rewound.

A grounded motor is always a hazard to the user. This is particularly true of a washing machine, which is often used in a basement; dampness from concrete floors, and moisture from hot wash-water in the air and on the person of the user, when combined with a grounded motor will result in a severe shock every time the machine is touched. Newer-type motors are rubber-mounted, insulating them from the washing machine; but the rubber does deteriorate in time, and moisture on the rubber will carry a current. If the washing machine shocks, the motor should be rewound or replaced. Most manufacturers of motors make provisions for a motor exchange at a price that compares favorably with the cost of rewinding.

Examine the bronze sleeve bearing in each motor end bell. As originally manufactured, this bearing has a clearance of 1/1,000–3/1,000 inch. If the bearing is worn to an extent that a noticeable wobble exists when the rotor shaft is moved sidewise in the bearing, it is too loose, and both bearings should be replaced. A bearing that is too loose will cause the motor to chatter, or run hot, or, perhaps, fail to start. The bearing is replaced by use of a bearing tool and line reamer similar to that described in Section 7-7, and the procedure is the same as with the vacuum-cleaner motor bearing.

When the motor is installed it must be properly aligned with the gear case it is to drive. If a direct coupling is used, the motor shaft must be exactly in line with the worm gear shaft to which it is coupled. If a belt drive is used, the motor pulley must be in line with the gear-case pulley, and the belt must not be too tight. Failure to observe these precautions will result in excessive wear on the motor bearings and belt or coupling, plus noisy operation and an overheated motor. Washing-machine motors are allowed a 40° C. temperature *rise* above room temperature. If the room temperature is 25° C. (77° F.), a 40° C. temperature rise will bring the motor temperature to 65° C. (149° F.). The motor will normally feel quite warm, but if the odor of scorching insulation is present the motor is definitely overheating. Its exact temperature can, of course, be checked with a thermometer.

Although belt drive is satisfactory in every respect, most

manufacturers prefer a direct coupling from motor to gear case. The coupling is made of a semiflexible material (rubber-impregnated fabric), since it is almost impossible, with the limited supply of tools that can be taken into the field, to obtain an absolutely perfect alignment between motor shaft and worm shaft. A straight edge will help to bring about a degree of alignment sufficient to hold flexing of the coupling, and resultant wear, to a minimum, and make possible silent operation.

## 9.4. The Gear Case

Located underneath the tub of the washing machine is the gear case. A typical example is shown in Figure 9-4. Observe that the worm mentioned in the preceding section is common to all gear cases, as is the large main reduction gear which it drives. The reduction gear engages another gear whose purpose is to operate a shaft which rises upward and into the wringer, causing it to turn. In some models, the wringer drive-shaft gear is eliminated, the wringer drive shaft being attached directly to the main reduction gear.

An offset block or disk is cast integral with the main reduction gear. The *Pitman arm* fits onto the offset, so that a reciprocating motion is applied to the Pitman arm. A partial or *segment gear* is connected onto the other end of the Pitman, and its reciprocating motion results in oscillation of the segment gear. The segment gear drives the *pinion* gear, whose shaft extends up into the tub. This is the *agitator drive shaft,* and it has at its upper end a block, or spline, or similar device to drive the agitator (gyrator, dasher, turbulator).

A number of methods are employed to disengage the agitator through manipulation of an external lever, in order that the operator may stop it from turning. The segment gear may be on an eccentric shaft; turning the shaft will move the segment gear out of range of the agitator-drive pinion. The eccentric block on the main reduction gear is often a separate piece, attached to the main reduction gear only when the operator flips a lever allowing a pin to drop through the eccentric block and the main reduction gear, joining them together. Some washing machines have a knob on top of the agitator. To put the agitator in motion this knob is depressed, and a bar attached to the agitator slips into a slot in the top of the agitator-drive shaft.

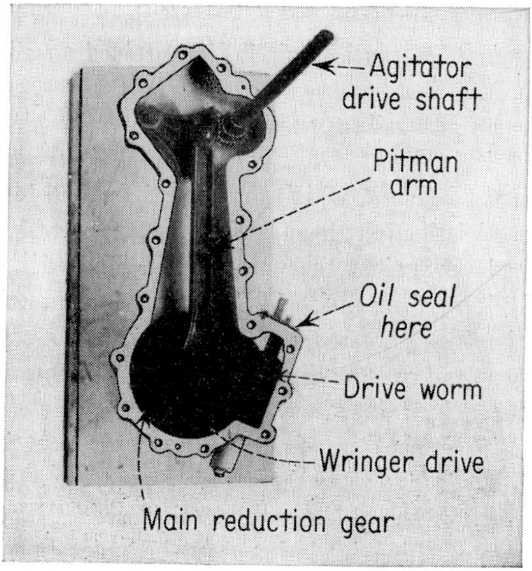


Fig. 9-4.

When this arrangement is used, all the gears in the gear case are in motion at all times when the motor is turned on.

The gear case contains a quart of oil, the equivalent of a No. 30 SAE motor oil. The oil level does not reach to the top of the gears. When in motion, the gears will cause enough splashing of the oil to keep all parts lubricated.

The gear case is a solid casting, open at the top. The top covering generally consists of a sheet-metal piece bolted to the gear-case housing, and a gasket used in between the two to provide an oil seal. The only other opening in the gear-case casting on most machines is the place where the worm shaft extends out to the motor coupling. A seal is used here to prevent oil leakage. The oil seal is composed of a length of packing and a pressure ring with a concave surface pressing against the packing, holding it against the shaft. A flange bolted onto the outside of the gear case holds the packing and gland in place. The flange should be pulled down tight enough to prevent oil leaks, but not so tight that the packing will bind against the shaft and prevent it from turning. Some manufacturers use a fabricated seal which requires no flange. A special spindle is required to slip this seal onto the shaft.

The worm generally turns in such a direction that the pressure against it is directed away from the driven end. Here is located a thrust bearing, which may be of the ball bearing type, or just a steel ball and an adjusting screw by which the steel ball is pushed up against the worm shaft. The adjusting screw is externally located, and should be turned far enough to eliminate any noise from looseness of the worm, but not so tight as to bind the worm and cause a drag on the motor. The screw adjustment is secured by a lock nut.

The worm is the only fast-moving component in the gear box. The other gears move at a lower speed, and if properly lubricated will not be subject to appreciable wear. The gear case of a washing machine is designed to be quiet but not silent; consequently, the parts are not as snug-fitting and the tolerances not as precise as, for example, in an automobile engine. Inadequate lubrication and years of service will, however, produce sufficient wear to cause the machine to become quite noisy. When replacing worn gears with new ones, to obtain like-new quietness it is advisable to compare the old part with a new one as to fit and appearance at surfaces where wear may occur.

There is a seal, or packing, around the agitator shaft where it enters the tub. Often the water level exceeds the height of the tube which supports the agitator-drive shaft, and were it not for the seal the water would go down the tube and into the gear case. Some brands are provided with a watershed or slinger to prevent water entry into the gear case.

Wear at the seal (or its equivalent) ultimately does allow water to enter the gear case. If clear water gets into the gear case, it, being heavier than the oil, will sink to the bottom, causing the oil to float; and, as the level rises, the oil will leak out through the nearest opening, which is usually a breather hole in top of the gear case or gear-case cover. When hot, soapy water gets into the gear case, the soap causes the water and oil to emulsify, forming a substance resembling chocolate pudding in appearance and consistency. In either case, the lubricating quality of the oil is destroyed, and damaging wear begins immediately. If not checked at this point, the gears will wear until some one of them, probably the worm, will no longer engage the other gears which it drives, and a complete replacement of all parts in the gear case will be required.

Unfortunately, it is impossible to clean out a gear case containing water without disassembling the machine and cleaning all parts individually. Kerosene and other flushing compounds do not thoroughly clean these parts, and the addition of new oil is useless, since it either floats above the water or combines in the emulsion. The water seal on the agitator shaft should be replaced when repairing the machine; and the user should be warned as to proper observance of the water-level marker on the tub or agitator in order to avert a reoccurrence of the water leakage.

## 9.5. Overloading Motor and Gear Case

It is sometimes found that a washing machine is used in a basement that does not contain a furnace or other heating source. In such a place the winter temperatures are often low enough to harden the oil in the gear case. If the motor is started under these conditions, it may not be able to turn, or else will turn very slowly. Within a few seconds the motor will begin to smoke as the insulation on the field coils scorch, and soon the motor will have "burned up." This may be prevented if hot washwater is put into the washing machine tub thirty minutes to an hour before starting the motor. The heat of the water will loosen the oil in this length of time.

Another precaution which will lengthen the life of the motor has to do with starting under a load. What, in the owner's opinion, constitutes a proper load of clothes for a washing machine may differ considerably from the load for which the machine was originally designed. While an overload strains the motor while running, to start it under too severe a load is even more detrimental to the motor; therefore, the agitator shift lever should always be off when the motor is started. When the motor is at full speed the agitator may be set into motion, for the

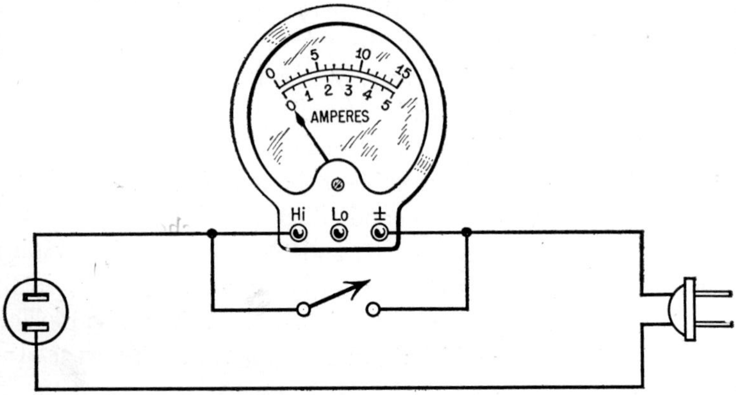


FIG. 9-5.

torque, or pulling power, of the motor is greater at full speed than starting from standstill.

Because of the repair man's superior technical knowledge, it becomes his responsibility to inform the owner as to the proper loading of the washing machine for best washing results, and to assure long life to the appliance. The salesman may have been overenthusiastic in his description of the fine qualities of the machine, and the owner consequently expects it to handle more clothes at one loading than was intended by the manufacturer.

On the name plate of the motor is stamped the full load current. A washing-machine motor draws 4 or 5 amp under a normal load. Measuring the current while the machine is washing clothes will make it possible to determine instantly whether the load is too great for the motor. Figure 9-5 illustrates the circuit of an ammeter used for the purpose of measuring motor current. Unplug the washing-machine cord from its receptacle, and in its place put the plug of the tester. *Close the meter switch.* Plug the washing-machine cord into the receptacle of the tester. When the motor is running at full speed, open the meter-shunting switch. The ammeter will then indicate the current used by the motor.

Note that the ammeter is in *series* with the motor, and the motor current goes through the meter. It is important that this connection be properly made, for if the meter is placed across the line (in parallel with the motor) it will be instantly destroyed. An a-c meter with a full-scale reading of at least 15 amp should be used. Because the starting current of the motor may exceed 15 amp (normally), the meter is short-circuited by the switch until the motor current has reduced its lower running value.

An overloaded motor will draw more than its rated current. A severely overloaded motor will, in addition to reading high, cause the ammeter needle to flicker each time the agitator reverses its direction. Remove clothes from the machine piece by piece until the ammeter reads the current value listed on the motor name plate. The amount of clothes remaining in the tub is the maximum quantity that should ever be put into the machine.

## 9.6. The Agitator

Within the tub of the washing machine is the agitator. A number of styles of agitators are in use; one manufacturer uses an arrangement consisting of three inverted cups which rise and fall vertically in the tub and at the same time rotate slowly so that all the tub area will be affected. The familiar three-vaned design of agitator, however, is the style most frequently encountered.

The purpose of the agitator is not to tumble the clothes, but rather to force the soapy water through the pores in the fabric, thus flushing out the dirt. The trend of modern engineering is toward an agitator designed so that it will not touch the clothes at any time. The action of this agitator may be observed by using clear water and small pieces of laundry such as handkerchiefs or hand towels. With the agitator in motion, place two or three pieces in the tub. It can be seen through the clear water that the clothes are moving in a circular path: down to the bottom of the tub near the agitator, along the bottom, and up to the top of the water on the outer side of the tub. The clothes do not touch the agitator at all. A number of pieces may be added and the same action will continue, the articles still moving in a circular path. However, if the quantity is increased still further, the general movement of the pieces will stop; the action of the agitator will produce only a slight movement of the article nearest it. This represents an overload from the standpoint of efficient cleansing action. As long as the pieces are circulating they are being rapidly and efficiently cleansed. The white pieces, such as shirts and bedclothes, need be allowed to remain in the machine only three to five minutes to become clean. Work clothes, of course, require a considerably longer washing period. Overloading, in addition to lengthening the washing time, allows the agitator to rub against the clothing, which will, in time, wear a hole through the fabric. A demonstration of this sort will soon sell the owner on the benefits of properly loading her washing machine.

When the washing is finished, the agitator should be removed from its post, and not replaced until next washday. Some agitators are removed by merely lifting out of place; others have a screw cap or through pin which must be loosed in order to lift out the agitator. The agitator is made of aluminum (some few are plastic). The agitator drive-post is made of a lightweight alloy known as white metal. Both materials are subject to a scale produced by hot, soapy water. If the agitator is *not* removed each time, and after a number of washings an attempt is made to remove it, it will have become tightly stuck because of the scale formation. Furthermore, the part of the tub covered by the agitator cannot be cleaned and, consequently, dirt and small objects such as string and buttons will accumulate under the agitator if it is left in place; these may become loosened by the next washing, sometimes causing spots and streaks of dirt to appear on the clothes.

Occasionally the service man must repair a machine on which the agitator has not been taken out for a number of years. Such methods as heating the top of the agitator with a blowtorch, and hitting the agitator near the top a few sharp blows with a hammer, may be tried, and sometimes are effective in loosening the scale and corrosion which holds the agitator. If these actions fail, however, it will then be necessary to break the agitator by hammering, and replace it with a new one.

Some agitators are adjustable. By means of a nut located in the top of the agitator, its height in the tub may be varied. It is desirable to have the agitator as low as possible in the tub without allowing it to scrape against the enameled surface. It is usually recommended by the manufacturer that a post card be used as a gauge, and the agitator be adjusted so that the post card can be slid, without forcing, under the agitator at all points.

## 9.7. The Tub

Washing-machine tubs are made of aluminum, copper, or porcelain-enameled steel. Of these, the enameled tub is most commonly encountered, probably because it has the neatest appearance and is most easily cleaned. The porcelain surface is, however, likely to be chipped if roughly handled. Porcelain-patching compounds are available, but, regardless of how carefully color is matched, the patch will discolor with age, while the porcelain surface will not. The porcelain tub should not be pried out of place with a metal bar or tool. It is unwise to use the tub as a container for parts or tools when making repairs on a washing machine, since this practice inevitably results in a chipped tub. In short, it is impossible to be too careful with a porcelain surface.

At the bottom of the agitator-post housing is the tub nut. This nut must be loosed in order to remove the tub for servicing the machine. Beneath the tub nut is a rubber or cork gasket. This gasket must be put back on reassembly to prevent the tub from leaking water. When in doubt, put in a new gasket to assure a water-tight fit at the tub nut.

In the bottom of the tub is a drain vent. Attached to the vent is a drain plug or a drain hose. For the purpose of emptying the tub into a sink rather than a floor drain, a pump is included in the drain equipment of some machines. The pump shaft has attached a rubber-covered wheel which is forced by spring pressure against a similar wheel integral with the motor coupling. Friction drives the pump impeller at a speed approximating that of the motor. The drain vent or pump hose must be unfastened before removing the tub.

Pumps will require periodic servicing because of the accumulation of lint, buttons, and strings in the pumping chamber. The pump is easily disassembled; one side may be removed by loosening a few bolts. The impeller blade is generally screwed onto its shaft, and may be removed by turning it in its normal direction of rotation while the shaft is locked. When reassembling the pump, a new gasket, applied with gasket shellac, should be used to make the assembly water-tight. The bearing through which the impeller shaft extends should be frequently lubricated with a water-repellent grease.

## 9.8. The Wringer

Extending vertically from the gear case to the top of the tub is a tube called the *wringer post.* This tube encloses a shaft driven by the main reduction gear, and provides power for operating the wringer. The wringer gear housing (wringer head) is on top of the wringer post, and contains the necessary gears for operating and reversing the wringer. A flange on the wringer post, near the top, determines the extent to which the wringer settles down onto its post. The wringer must be designed so it will be possible to move it to a number of positions, and must lock in place in each position. Figure 9-6 shows the customary wringer positions. An *index lever* engages in a slot in the wringer-post flange. To move the wringer from one position to the next, the index lever is depressed and the wringer started toward the next position. The index lever may then be released, and as soon as the wringer reaches its next position the index lever will snap into place, locking the wringer at that position.

The wringer-drive shaft fits into a coupling which is a part of a shaft inside the wringer gear case (Fig. 9-7). This shaft drives a pinion gear equipped with two sets of teeth, or a clutch which engages two pinion gears. By means of the *wringer reverse lever,* the pinion or clutch is moved upward and downward. In the neutral position, the clutch is not engaging any parts in the wringer gear case. When moved upward, the clutch slips into the teeth of the pinion, causing it to turn, and eventually causing the wringer roll to turn with it. Moving the clutch downward causes it to engage a pinion again. However, *the crown gear is now driven in the opposite direction,* and the wringer roll rotation has been reversed.

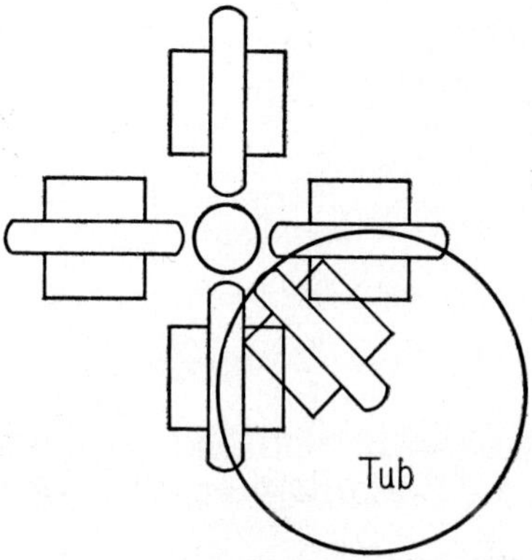

FIG. 9-6.

The clutch must slide to and fro on its shaft, and at the same time turn with the shaft in the wringer gear case. This is accomplished by use of a splined shaft, a squared shaft, or a pin through the shaft. Figure 9-7 illustrates how this will allow movement of the clutch on the shaft as the shaft turns the clutch.

The wringer head contains approximately half a cup of a heavy fiber grease. Most manufacturers put out a special grease for wringers which will cling to the gears and not leak out onto the roll, where it would soil the clothes.

Attached to the crown gear is a coupling into which the lower wringer roll fits. With the exception of a few models, only the lower wringer roll is driven, its friction against the upper roll causing the latter to turn. As had been previously mentioned, the wringer head is so designed that the operator always pulls the reverse lever *toward* herself when wringing clothes from the position in which she is standing toward the other side of the wringer. Pushing the reverse lever away will reverse the rolls, causing the clothing to come toward the operator. Therefore, if

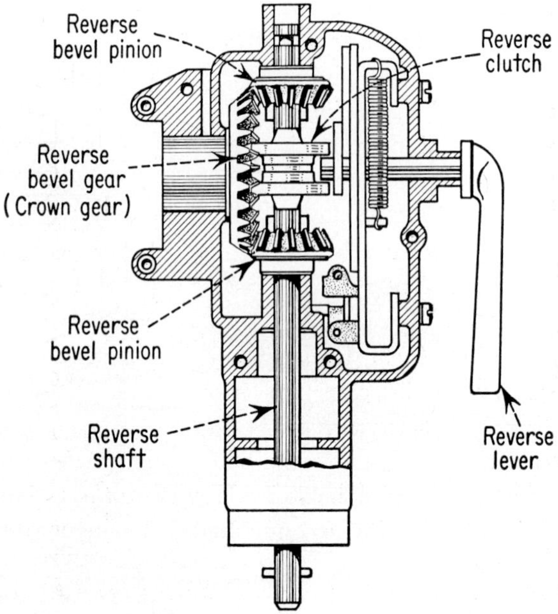


FIG. 9-7. (Courtesy, Easy Washing Machine Corporation)

she goes around to the other side of the wringer, she will still find it necessary to pull the reverse lever toward herself to make the rolls turn the right way.

## 9.9. Rolls and Bearings

Wringer rolls are made of a medium-soft rubber with a steel shaft through the center. One end of the shaft is milled so that it will fit the coupling which drives it. The surface of the roll has been roughened, giving it the appearance of crepe paper. This roughness is called the crepe of the roll. It is necessary that the roll be rough in order that it may possess enough friction to pull clothes through and to turn its companion roll. The crepe surface is often destroyed when the layers of soap accumulate and dry on the roll. This practice causes a slick glaze to form, which then slides against clothes without pulling them through. This condition may be avoided by washing off the rolls after each laundry. If the glaze is severe, the roll may be resurfaced in a lathe by use of a broad-edged chisel. The scraping action of this tool will remove the glaze and put a crepe surface on the rubber.

A tool for this purpose can easily be assembled in the shop. A 1/4 hp motor is coupled to the roll as it is held in a pair of mounted bearing holders of the proper size. An ordinary wood chisel is a good tool to use to scrape off the glaze and recrepe the surface. To hold the tool, a tool rest made from a block of wood should be mounted in front of the roll. The tool rest should be of such height as to be lower than the center of the roll by the thickness of the chisel used. This will put the chisel edge right at the center line of the roll.

If the roll is badly worn, if the rubber has become loosened from the shaft due to rust, or if the drive end of the shaft has become worn, the roll should be replaced. It will probably prove advisable to replace the roll coupling also.

Most roll bearings are made of wood. To minimize wear, a hardwood is used. It is processed by being impregnated with paraffin, and this paraffin is the lubricant for the shaft as it rides against the bearing. Wood is not damaged by the soapy water that invariably splashes onto the bearing to the extent that an ordinary bronze bearing with oil for a lubricant would be, since soapy water cannot wash away the paraffin.

Typical manufacturing procedure is to use a half bearing for the lower roll and a full bearing for the upper roll. The bearings are set in the side braces of the wringer, which have been formed into a channel shape.

Although the wood bearing is the longer-lasting type, it has a tendency to become glazed, and the shaft of the roll as it moves against the glazed surface of the bearing produces a very annoying squeal. The squeal is easily eliminated by scraping or sanding the glazed surface.

The wringer may also have a squeal which is not produced by a bearing. If the rubber part of the roll is improperly spaced, it may rub against the side of the wringer, and the friction of rubber against metal where water is present will produce an unpleasant high-pitched sound. This condition may be corrected by use of a fiber spacing washer made for that purpose. These

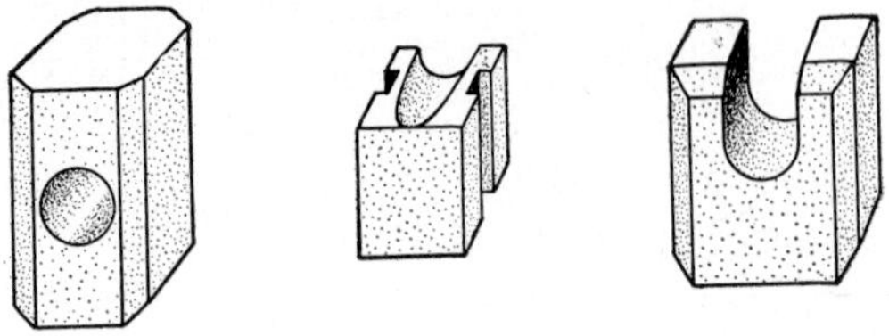

FIG. 9-8.

washers may be obtained from the dealer who sells wringer rolls. The washer is slipped onto the roll shaft, and when the roll is replaced the spacer is between the roll and the metal surface against which it was rubbing.

Spanning from one top roll bearing to the other, a heavy spring metal bar is held in place by the top of the wringer and provides a spring tension to press the rolls together. The wringer top itself does not bear against the spring; a bolt through the top, instead, allows the roll pressure to be adjusted by a knob externally located on the top of the wringer (Fig. 9-9). It has been found that the optimum adjustment of roll pressure is that which will remove just enough water from the clothes so that they will not drip when put on the line to dry. The action of the sun in evaporating the remaining water will, to some extent, bleach the laundry. This bleaching effect will be lost if the wringer is too tight and has squeezed out too much water, even though the drying time is thereby shortened. For this reason, a number of washing-machine models have no wringer-roll pressure control, the wringer having been factory-adjusted to the proper tension.

By examining the wringer construction, the repair man can easily locate this internal adjusting screw, and set it to the liking of the operator.

## 9.10. Safety Release

A constant hazard to the operator of a wringer is the danger that a hand may be pulled into the wringer rolls. The manufacturer uses a rubber soft enough so that the roll will not apply a bone-crushing force, but the bruise resulting from an accident of this sort may be quite painful. An important part of the wringer is the safety release—in the form of a bar on each side of the wringer, and easily accessible—which, with little pressure, will instantly release the roll tension. If the operator is alert, use of the safety release will eliminate all danger involved in operating a wringer. The repair man should always check and test the release mechanism, making sure that it is operating properly and that all parts are free-moving and well-lubricated. The mechanism of the release varies considerably with the different brands of wringers. However, it is fundamentally a latch which holds the top bar down against the tension spring pressure; the release bar loosens the latch, allowing the rolls to spring apart.

The top bar on some wringers is hinged at one end and latched in place on the other end. When the safety-release bar is depressed, the latch is loosed, and the top bar flies up. This type of construction is pictured in Figure 9-9. The top bar may be lifted high enough to make possible removal of the upper roll and its bearings. With the top roll out of the way, the lower roll in turn can be removed, facilitating the replacement of old rolls with new.

Another form of wringer construction is such that the safety release unfastens both ends of the top bar. For roll replacement, the entire top-bar and upper-roll assembly is lifted out of place. The lower roll lifts out, but the upper-roll bearing holder must be dismantled to remove the top roll.

The wringer release should always be depressed—removing the roll tension—after the wash is finished, and left disengaged until the next washday. If the rolls are allowed to remain under pressure, they may stick together. The film of soap remaining on the rolls should be washed off, since this encourages roll sticking. (The writer has observed in a number of homes the use of a clothespin as a spacer between the two rolls; this allows all parts

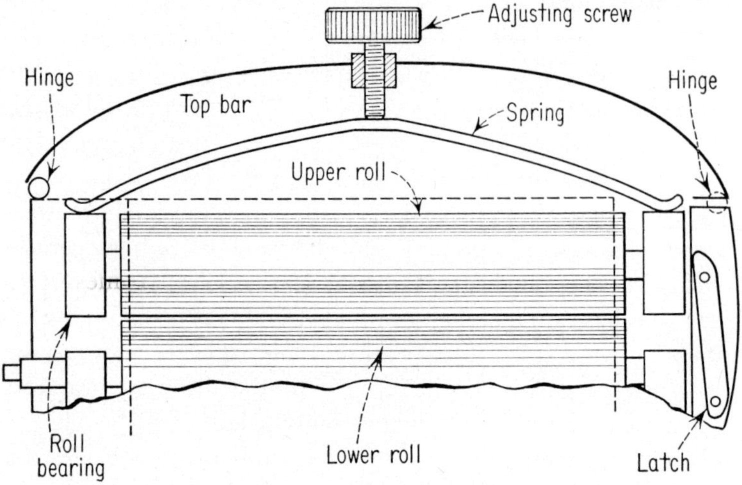


FIG. 9-9.

of both rolls to dry, and at the same time eliminates the possibility that rolls may stick together. This practice apparently does not in any way damage the roll.)

To prevent water wrung from the clothes from splashing onto the floor, or into the rinse water, a flipper board is included as a part of the wringer assembly. This flat (or slightly V-shaped) metal piece is mounted below the lower roll and is hinged right below the roll bearings. Most wringer models feature an automatic flipper board. However, the manually operated type is still to be found on some older models. The automatic flipper board operates by a friction-drive lever attached to the lower roll, which reverses its rotation and pressure against the flipper board as the roll direction is reversed, thus tilting the flipper board so as to drain the water back from the direction of wringing. A lever extending from the wringer frame is used to tilt the manual flipper board.

The mechanism of the flipper board is simple, and there are no parts subject to extreme wear. When the flipper-board mechanism fails to operate, the trouble is almost always rust, caused by the hot water to which the parts are subjected. There is no satisfactory lubricant; soapy water washes all types of lubricant away.

## 9.11. The Spinner

The fact that there is some hazard attendant on the use of a wringer has inspired manufacturers to devise various other methods of removing water from clothes which assure total safety to the operator. The most popular device of this type is the centrifugal spinner, which, operating at a high speed, flings all the water out of the clothes, leaving them (if desired) drier than is possible with an ordinary wringer.

The spinner (Fig. 9-10) consists of a basket driven from the main gear case. The basket moves at high speed, and the basket-drive shaft is driven directly from the main reduction gear, or from a gear train operated from the worm gear and providing a speed in excess of the motor speed.

A short shaft is used to drive the basket; it extends up into the spinner compartment only an inch or two. When the spinner is in use, the water expelled from the clothes is often above the top of the spinner drive shaft. Consequently, measures are taken to prevent leakage of water around the shaft and into the gear case. Both a water slinger and a water seal are used for this purpose.

Because of the high speed of the spinner it is not feasible to engage it directly with the driving gears, since this procedure would place an excessive load on both gears and motor. To start the spinner at a slower speed, and allow it to come up to full speed as the motor power normally overcomes the spinner basket and its clothes-load inertia, a clutch drive is employed. The clutch

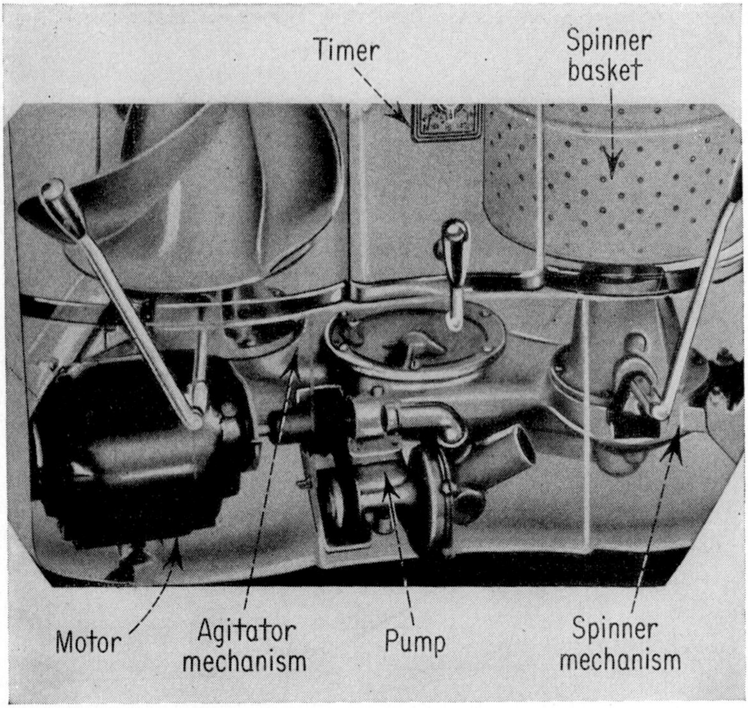


FIG. 9-10. (Courtesy, Easy Washing Machine Corporation)

assembly (Fig. 9-11) consists of two disks, (A) and (B), one of which (A) is turning all the time. The other disk (B) is held a short distance away by the spinner ON-OFF lever. Moving this lever to the ON position allows a spring to press the two disks together. The upper member (B) is fastened onto the basket drive shaft, and will, at first, slip against the driven disk (A). The friction resulting from this motion will set the basket-drive disk (B) into motion, slowly at first, but with ever-increasing speed as the slippage is reduced, until, finally, the basket is rotating at the speed of the driving disk (A).

The basket-drive shaft is machined to a square or splined shape, and the bottom bore of the basket is milled to the same shape, thus providing a positive drive for the basket. The basket is removable, and should be removed after each washing, so as to allow cleaning of the spinner tub, and also to prevent the basket from sticking onto its shaft.

A short shaft driving a tall basket would allow an excess of wobble at the top of the basket were it not that the lid of the spinner tub has a disk which just fits the inner edge of the basket and holds it steady. This disk rotates with the basket, and to allow smooth action is provided with a ball bearing where it is mounted in the lid (Fig. 9-12). Proper lubrication of this bearing may be a servicing problem, inasmuch as a frozen or worn bearing causes a drag on the basket, and unsatisfactory spinner operation. So that the disk will have the right amount of pressure on the basket when the lid is closed, the disk shaft is adjustable. This adjustment (left-hand screw) is made accessible by removing a small plug located on top of the spinner lid. The adjustment should be made with the lid closed and the spinner turning. Too much disk pressure will cause the spinner to drag, or become inoperative; too little will allow the basket to vibrate. These effects are quite pronounced, especially with a loaded basket, and it is not difficult to tell, by the sound of the operating machine, just what the optimum adjustment is for silent operation. A lock nut when pulled down tight secures the adjustment.

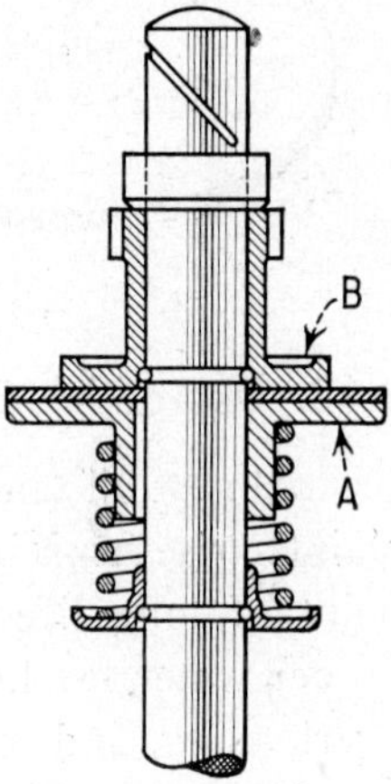


FIG. 9-11.

The water expelled from the clothes by the spinner action is removed from the spinner tub by a pump, which is driven either by a pulley on the motor coupling or by an extension of the gear-drive worm shaft.

Most spinner troubles result in vibration of the machine. If the washer is not level, it will vibrate. To prevent this, one of the three washing-machine legs is made adjustable. Improper loading of the spinner basket will cause vibration. The owner should be instructed as to proper loading method so that she may enjoy normal spinner operation.

When the spinner basket is being loaded, it is imperative

that the pieces be uniformly distributed in the basket. This is done by packing them evenly into the basket in layers, rather than tossing them in haphazardly.

FIG. 9-12.

## 9.12. Use of Machine

Almost all unnecessary or premature washing-machine complaints arise from improper operation. Important from the standpoint of long life and satisfactory service are such factors as proper water level, quantity of soap, washing time, avoidance of overloading, and so forth.

The water level is indicated on most machines by a mark on the agitator, or a ring embossed on the tub. This level is for water plus clothes, and should never be exceeded, since to do so is to shorten the life of the machine. The quantity of clothes placed in the water should not exceed that which will permit ready circulation of the clothes by the stirring action of the agitator.

There is a popular notion that soap must be added to the water until there is a froth of suds which is not dissipated by the washing process. Actually, this is both an extravagance and a deterrent to satisfactory washing. Common sense indicates that the washing action takes place in the water, not on its surface. Water set in motion by the agitator seeps through the pores in the fabric, flushing out the dirt, and only the quantity of soap required to accomplish this washing action is necessary or desirable. Two cupfuls of soap powder to a load is generally adequate. However, it is advisable to follow the instructions on the soap package, since the manufacturer has tested his product to determine the proper quantity for economical service.

There are now on the market a number of detergents, some of which perform their washing and cleansing actions without producing any suds. These detergent cleaners are quite effective, and are designed to be used in smaller quantities than the ordinary soap powders.

FIG. 9-13. (Courtesy, Easy Washing Machine Corporation)

## 9.13. The Automatic Washing Machine

The newest development in laundry equipment is the fully automatic washing machine (Fig. 9-13). To use this machine, it is necessary only to insert the clothes in the machine, pour in some washing powder, set a control knob—and that's all. The automatic features of the machine include the processes of soaking, washing, draining, rinsing, and spin-drying. When—after the machine has gone through its automatic cycle—it finally shuts itself off, and the clothes may be removed, they are dry enough to be ironed at once: damp-dry, it is called.

This cycle requires considerably more time than the washing period of a wringer-type washing machine, and the time required to complete four or five tubfuls of wash would be prohibitive. However, this objection is overcome when it is realized that the "no attention required" feature makes it convenient to use the machine daily, washing the clothes as they become soiled, and completely eliminating the drudgery of the old-fashioned washday.

## 9.14. The Motor

The automatic washing machine is powered by a 1/6- or 1/4-hp split-phase motor, the same type used on the nonautomatic machine. Methods of testing and servicing this type of motor are discussed in Sec. 9.3.

The motor is fitted with a belt which drives a two-speed transmission. The lower speed is the washing speed, while the higher is for spinning the clothes dry. From the transmission a belt goes to the clothes basket, which is thereby rotated. This basket, which is supported by a shaft at its lower end, is located inside the tub. The tub itself is weighted and suspended by springs, to reduce the vibration of the speeding basket. Attached to the tub are hoses for filling it with hot and cold water. A thermostatically operated valve determines the correct ratio of hot to cold water. A part of the tub-filling equipment is a device to limit the water to the proper level. One such device is a small tank called the water weigher, connected to the tub by a hose. As the water weigher fills up to the same degree as the tub, its increased weight lowers it from the spring on which it is suspended, until it eventually hits and closes a switch, and the water is thereby shut off.

## 9.15. The Solenoid

The device which shuts off the water, and performs the other automatic functions of the machine, is called a solenoid. The solenoid is more fully described in Chapter 10; briefly, it is an electromagnet without an iron core—that is, it consists of merely a number of turns of wire in a coil wound on a suitable fiber form, with a hollow space (air core) in the center. Its behavior is such that any magnetic substance will be drawn into the hollow center of the coil whenever current, either a-c or d-c, is applied to the coil. The coil behaves as if it were itself a magnet, and is often therefore called a "sucking coil." A solenoid is used in the automatic washing machine to shift the two-speed transmission from low-basket speed to high-basket speed, to turn the water valves on and off, and to operate the pump which empties the tub.

## 9.16. The Timer

A timer, somewhat similar to that used on the roaster oven and electric stove, is an essential part of the mechanism of the automatic washing machine. However, instead of being a clock-operated single-pole switch, the washing-machine timer is a multiposition switch: a combination of many switches. The need for switching in a number of circuits will become apparent as the timer operation is detailed. The timer must necessarily be a complex device, factory-set and adjusted; hence, it is advisable to replace it rather than attempt to repair a defective one. A number of wires are connected to the timer terminal screws, and, although a color code is used, it is advisable as an extra precaution to label each wire as it is disconnected, to make sure that the proper reconnection will be made when replacing the timer.

## 9.17. Operating Cycle

The timer is set (by means of the calibrated control knob on front or on top of the machine) to heavy, medium, or light, depending upon the type of clothes and how soiled they may be;

and the machine goes into its automatic operation cycle. The timer circuit has put into operation the motor and the solenoids which open the two water valves, one for hot and one for cold. An additional thermostatic valve adjusts the hot-water flow so that the combination of hot and cold water is from 125° F. to 150° F. The thermostat is purely mechanical in its operation, and in no way connected in the electric circuit. The water level rises until the shut-off device opens the circuit of the water-valve solenoids and the water shuts off.

The timer ticks on until the washing period is ended (about 15 minutes). A set of timer contacts then close, completing the circuit of the solenoid, which moves a hinged pump, forcing its drive pulley against the motor pulley. Thus the pump drains the tub. The timer works move to a position where the pump solenoid is open-circuited, and the water solenoids are reactivated. This rinses the clothes briefly. The timer acts again to operate the pump and reempty the tub.

During all the foregoing, the basket has been operating at low speed. Now, the timer operates a solenoid which shifts the speed to high and damp-dries the clothes.

The timer next takes the machine through a repetition of the washing cycle except for the lack of soap. This is called a deep rinse. The deep rinse is followed by a longer high-speed drying period than before, and finally the timer has moved to a point where all circuits are turned off. The clothes may now be removed, almost dry enough to iron.

The clock-controlled switching by the timer is, obviously, the heart of the operation of the automatic washing machine. It is possible to check the action of the timer itself; however, it is generally more satisfactory to check it indirectly. The pump solenoid, the basket-speed solenoid, and the valve solenoids are all operated at 120 v. By placing a lamp bulb in a pigtail socket across the terminals of the wires leading to one of the solenoids, it can be determined whether the switching action of the timer is actually applying voltage to the solenoid during the portion of the washing cycle it is supposed to operate.

## Servicing Washing Machines

### 9.18. General Procedure

The proper method of servicing the automatic washing machine is, first, to determine the nature of the trouble by observation or from the operator; and, second, to test, while in operation, the part, or parts, which might cause the trouble. Of course, along with failure of electrical components are the customary mechanical troubles characteristic of any washing machine. The nature of these troubles, and their remedies, are discussed earlier in this chapter.

If a voltage test (using a test lamp) indicates that a solenoid is inoperative, it may be further checked in two ways. Disconnect it from the circuit—if necessary, remove it from the machine entirely—and check its resistance with an ohmmeter. The exact value of ohms is relatively unimportant unless it is possible to compare this value with that of a known good solenoid. However, the very fact that there is a measurable amount of resistance indicates that the solenoid is neither open-circuited nor totally short-circuited. A second test is to apply 120 v directly to the solenoid by means of a temporarily connected attachment cord, and observe if it will draw in its plunger. It should operate indefinitely without overheating. If the solenoid will operate thus, but not when connected in its regular circuit, then either the connecting wires are open-circuited, a poor connection had been made to the solenoid or timer switch, or the timer itself is defective.

Any circuit that might be illustrated here would, obviously, apply to one model of one manufacturer only, and hence would have a limited usefulness. It is not difficult to draw up such a diagram from examination of the wiring of the machine; furthermore, the very act of drawing such a diagram imparts familiarity with the functions of the various components. If the service man feels that he is too inept at circuit tracing to draw such a diagram, the manufacturer will, upon request, supply the circuit diagram of his machine. The use of the specific diagram of the machine requiring servicing is emphasized because the automatic washing machine is more an electrical problem than a mechanical one.

A requirement of the original installation of the automatic washing machine is that it be firmly fastened to the floor. The speed of the basket when spin-drying is almost 500 rpm., and if the clothes are not evenly distributed about the basket, any unbalance will cause excessive vibration. A light load will naturally distribute itself more evenly than a heavy load. A possible cause of noisy operation is an overloaded basket. The owner should be correctly informed as to the proper quantity of clothes the machine will accommodate and still operate satisfactorily. This information is usually contained in the literature supplied with the machine, along with instructions as to the water pressure required to fill the tub in its allotted fill-time.

Neither the solenoids nor the motor will operate satisfactorily with improper voltage applied. If the machine is operated on a circuit with other heavy-duty appliances (iron, ironer, refrigerator), or if excessively long extension cords are used, this will contribute to a lowering of the circuit voltage, together with the probability of the washer motor's overheating, or the solenoids having a reduced and inadequate magnetic pull. The ideal arrangement would be a separate circuit for the washing machine alone. However, it will operate satisfactorily in the receptacle of a circuit which is carrying an otherwise light load.

## 9.19. Motor Will Not Operate

This may be due to a fault in the motor or in the cord leading to the motor. Often it is more convenient to remove both motor and cord as a unit from the washing machine, since the skirt of the machine may interfere with access to the terminal block of the motor to which the cord is attached. The design of all but a few older-style motors is such as to allow easy removal of the motor. Two clamps, each fastened with a single bolt, hold the motor to its bracket. A setscrew fastens the coupling to the motor shaft. Loosening the setscrew and the two bracket bolts is all that is necessary to allow removal of the motor.

A single test will determine whether cord or motor is at fault. The cord enters the motor under a cover plate; remove this plate and unfasten the screws which hold the cord in place. Temporarily fasten another cord onto the motor and plug into the power line. If the motor runs, the cord was the defective component. If the motor does not run, it is faulty, and should be opened for further testing. For making these and similar tests it is convenient to have available a test cord—an ordinary attachment cord with spring clips at the appliance end so that it can be rapidly fastened to the terminal connections of an appliance.

If the motor is open-circuited it will fail to operate, but the open-circuit condition must be such as to disable both starting and running windings. If only one winding is made inoperative by the fault, the motor will hum but fail to turn. This condition is considered in the next section (9.20). The leads from the terminal block to the motor windings may cause a motor to be totally open-circuited. This is usually noticeable upon inspection. If the motor is "burned up" it will, of course, fail to operate. This is also plainly evident upon inspection: the windings are discolored, the insulation crumbles, and the odor of burnt insulation is in evidence. The "burned-up" motor must be replaced or rewound.

## 9.20. Motor Hums but Fails to Turn

The motor may be unable to turn because of a fault in the mechanism to which it is attached; or, the defect may be within the motor itself. To isolate the cause to either motor or mechanism, loosen the setscrew in the motor coupling. If the motor will now run when the cord is plugged into the power line, the fault is known to be within the washing-machine gear mechanism. If the motor, however, still refuses to turn, the motor itself is due for further testing. The method of testing the split-phase motor is given in Section 9.3. The following summary of tests and repairs is intended to serve as a guide for servicing the specific fault described above. The motor which hums but fails to turn may have the following defects:

Frozen bearings
Open-circuited starting winding
Open-circuited running winding
Defective centrifugal switch

If the motor shaft cannot be rotated by hand, the first item is the fault. Frozen bearings can often be loosened by cleaning and lubricating the shaft and bearings. If, however; the bearings are worn to an appreciable extent, replacement is necessary. The procedure for bearing replacement is given in Section 7.7.

The starting or running winding can be tested with an ohmmeter. Both have a rather low resistance, ordinarily less than 10 ohms. If either winding tests as having a high resistance or infinity, it is open-circuited and must be rewound.

The centrifugal switch in the starting winding circuit is normally in the closed position, opening only when the motor approaches full speed. A continuity test across the switch itself should indicate a closed-circuit condition (zero ohms). If otherwise, the switch is defective and should be replaced.

Having serviced the motor and returned it to its mounting beneath the washing machine, the service man may occasionally observe that the motor is more noisy in operation than before. The noise is due to misalignment between motor shaft and worm shaft, and can often be reduced by turning the motor a few degrees in either direction. Experimenting with different positions of the motor will soon reveal the position of minimum noise.

If the cause of failure of the motor to turn is found to be a jammed mechanism, proceed as follows. Remove the wringer from the machine. Attempt to turn the motor coupling by hand. If it turns freely, the defect lies in the wringer gear box. If the shaft refuses to turn, the fault is in the agitator-drive mechanism—the gear box under the tub.

If the wringer is found to be the cause of trouble, it is serviced in the following manner:

> Open the wringer gear case and examine the gears for indications of breakage. It may be necessary to remove the gears and shafts from the gear case and wash all these parts in order to make a careful examination. Replace all damaged or worn parts.
>
> Observe the condition of the wringer drive shaft and its bearing. Water splashed onto these parts may have caused rusting and freezing of the shaft in the bearing, in which event bearing replacement may be in order.
>
> Examine the wringer shift lever, its shaft and bearing, its drive block. A broken part or frozen bearing may act as a lock on the entire wringer mechanism. Replace all defective parts. Use the proper type of lubricant and necessary gaskets when replacing gears in the wringer gear box.

To service the main gear box it is necessary, initially, to remove the tub from the machine. Notice if the drain is fastened to both the skirt and the tub. If so, loosen whichever fastening is more readily disconnected. Notice, further, if the wringer post is fastened to the tub. If so, remove the bolts as may be necessary to loosen this connection. In the center of the tub, screwed onto the agitator post (or occasionally integral with the agitator post) is the tub nut. Removal of this nut allows the tub to be taken off the machine and permits access to the hardware holding the gear box in place. The tub nut is somewhat large and occasionally awkward to remove. A repair man specializing in one particular brand of washing machine will find it convenient to obtain a special tool (obtainable from the manufacturer) for the tub nut, use of which greatly facilitates removal.

Having removed the tub, place it in a location where there is little likelihood of the enamel's being chipped. Loosen the bolts holding the gear case onto the frame of the machine (and, of course, the motor coupling), taking care not to allow the gear case, which is quite heavy, to drop suddenly, since such a jolt may cause unnecessary damage. Place the gear case on the work-bench and, having removed the necessary hardware, open it up. The contents of the gear case are described in Section 9.4. Observe particularly the following:

The worm gear bearing and oil seal should be examined for wear and/or breakage.

The agitator-drive engage mechanism should be examined for wear or breakage.

The lubricant should be changed, and if what was in the gear case was contaminated, the agitator-drive shaft seal, bearing, and water flinger should be renewed.

Any worn or damaged parts should be replaced, with special emphasis on the particular one which caused failure of operation. A new gasket between the halves of the gear case is essential. Test the mechanism by hand before attaching the motor.

## 9.21. Motor Turns, but Mechanism Will Not

Either the motor coupling or drive belt, whichever is used on the machine, may be at fault. This can be determined by observation. In either event, the coupling or belt must be removed.

In replacing the coupling, the motor must be removed from its mount. The style and length of the replacement coupling must be the same as the original. Be sure to tighten the set-screws onto the flat places on motor and drive shafts. Position the motor so that alignment between drive and motor shafts will be as nearly perfect as possible; this will result in a minimum of noise and wear.

In replacing a drive belt, the motor-mounting bolts can be loosened just a few turns. The motor can be shifted toward the gear case, allowing enough slack in the belt to permit its removal. The number on the belt serves as a guide to its replacement. The motor is moved away from the gear case just enough to cause the new belt to fit snugly, but not be tight; at a point midway between the pulleys the belt should "give," under moderate hand pressure, a distance equal to its own thickness.

The mechanism may fail to operate, even though the motor turns, if one of the gear-case parts (worm gear or main reduction gear, for example) has broken. The procedure for dismantling the appliance for access to the gear box is given in the preceding section, and is to be followed at this step.

## 9.22. Wringer Turns, but Agitator Will Not

Again, this fault may be due to a defective gear within the gear case. With the gear case open for inspection, consider the possibility of one of the following:

Broken Pitman arm
Broken agitator-drive gear
Broken drift pin fastening gear to agitator shaft
Defective agitator OFF-ON lever and associated mechanism

Outside the gear box, there is the possibility that the agitator-drive block has become unfastened from its shaft. Numerous methods are used on the different models for fastening the drive block to the shaft, including setscrews, splined shaft and block, flats machined on shaft, and Woodruff keys. If any one of these devices has failed, and the agitator-drive block is not being driven by the shaft and gear-box mechanism, a test which will reveal this condition is as follows: With the agitator OFF-ON lever in the ON position and the motor deenergized, attempt to turn the agitator by hand. If it turns readily, the fault just mentioned is indicated. As verification, remove the agitator-drive block—it should come off easily—and examine it for the defect responsible for its faulty performance.

## 9.23. Agitator Operates, but Wringer Does Not

There is always the possibility that the one (or at most two) gears within the gear box which drive the wringer may be the cause of this defect; however, it is more likely to be due to a fault within the wringer. The following test will help make a distinction between the two possible causes. Remove the wringer from its post. With the appliance in operation, look down inside the wringer post and see if the wringer shaft is turning (a pocket flashlight is helpful). If it is not turning, the fault lies in the gear case; if it is turning, the wringer contains the defective component. Gear-case repair has already been discussed. The most likely causes of failure within the wringer are these:

Broken part in wringer gear case
Broken roll coupling
Loose shaft on roll

Considering the above in the order given, the defect in the wringer gear box requires that the gear box be opened and the parts cleaned off and examined for wear and breakage. The contents of a typical wringer gear box are illustrated in Figure 9-7. Almost any of the parts shown can, if worn out or broken, cause the wringer to become inoperative; and, of course, replacement on any or all defective parts will be required to restore satisfactory operation. Fresh lubricant and a new gasket are essential in making this repair.

The wringer lower roll (Figure 9-9) is the driven roll. The roll shaft has flats machined on it at the gear-box end. Connecting roll shaft to gear-box shaft is a coupling made of either cast iron or pressed steel. To maintain adequate lubrication of this coupling is difficult, since it is located where soapy water can and does splash onto it, resulting in rusting and wear. The roll coupling is easily accessible for examination and servicing. All that is necessary is that the wringer top bar and upper roll be removed; then the lower roll is lifted out of place. It is now possible to reach into the space at the end of the wringer gear housing and lift out the coupling. If coupling replacement is necessary, the new one should be covered with a heavy grease —one that will cling well, since the longer the lubricant remains in place the greater will be the life of the coupling as well as the parts with which it is associated—the wringer roll and gear-drive shaft.

As is to be expected, the wringer roll shaft (the steel shaft onto which is molded the rubber) will become rusted as a result of constant exposure to water. The rust can "creep" along the shaft under the rubber and eventually loosen the shaft from the rubber roll. When this occurs, the wringer will appear to behave normally until clothes are fed into the roll; then the roll will stop turning. If this trouble is suspected, it may readily be verified by clamping the roll shaft in a vise and giving the roll a twist by hand. Turning the roll under these conditions indicates a loose roll. Incidentally, it might be mentioned that every washing machine repaired in the shop should be tested by running clothes through the wringer to show up the possibility of the roll's being loose on its shaft. A short piece of 1/2-inch lumber tapered all around can be used to simulate a clothes load for this test.

## 9.24. Other Wringer Troubles

Perhaps the most important part of the wringer is the safety-release mechanism which removes all tension from the rolls when a lever is depressed. To avoid injury to the operator of the machine, it is essential that the safety release be in good operating condition at all times; thus, it is imperative that the repair man examine carefully the operating parts of this mechanism when repairing the wringer. Any evidence of rust, bent parts, or worn latches is sufficient cause for replacement of these parts. A thin coating of grease placed on the moving parts of the release mechanism will prolong their useful life. The design of some wringers incorporates the use of springs in the release mechanism. Be sure that any of these which have become rusted are replaced with new galvanized springs. If adjustments are provided, they should be set so that a very light pressure will operate the release mechanism.

Wringer-roll tension is obtained from a heavy spring steel

bar pressing on the bearings of the upper roll. Seldom does this spring lose its tension, but roll pressure will be reduced if the wood bearings wear to the extent that the rolls can move farther apart. Almost all complaints of too little pressure between the rolls can be remedied by replacement of the wooden bearings, both upper and lower. Bearing replacement is quite easy. The upper roll bearings are exposed for removal when the safety release is disengaged and the top bar lifted out. The lower bearings come out of place when the lower roll is lifted, and are removed with the roll.

Beneath the wringer is the flipper board, the purpose of which is to deflect the wrung-out water into the proper tub—that is, the tub at the side of the wringer into which the clothes are being fed. The flipper board is hinged at its center so that it may be tipped or slanted to deflect the water onto one side or the other of the wringer. This operation is usually automatic, being performed by a friction device attached to the lower roll. This is a simple device, the behavior of which is readily comprehended upon observation. As with most wringer parts, it is susceptible to rust, and in consequence may either break or jam. Replace the defective part with a new one to restore operation.

## 9.25. Automatic Washing Machine Will Not Start

As with the nonautomatic machine, this may be caused by such things as a defective cord or plug, open-circuited motor, and so on, and the servicing procedure is the same as that for the nonautomatic washing machine (Sec. 9.19). An additional possible cause of failure to start is a defect in the timer used on the automatic machine. Servicing the timer is an electrical problem, and a voltmeter is the proper test instrument. Considering that the timer is a clock-operated OFF-ON switch with numerous contacts, its function is to supply continuity to the motor and solenoids. Proceed as follows:

Remove the back panel of the appliance; this makes the motor accessible for servicing and testing.

Remove the small cover plate from the motor end bell, thus giving access to the motor terminals for voltage measurement.

Take the steps necessary to make the timer and lid-interlock switch terminals accessible. This may involve removing the metal rim around the upper part of the machine, removing the timer and allowing it to dangle in front of the machine by its lead wires, or other dismantling procedures as dictated by the design of the machine. If the dismantling required is such as to make operation of the machine a hazard, disconnect the motor from its coupling or belt before testing.

Place a jumper around the interlock switch (if there is one), plug in the cord, and set the timer. If the motor now operates, the interlock switch is the defective component. If the motor does not operate, measure the voltage at the input (attachment cord) end of the timer. Full-line voltage measured here absolves the cord and plug. Measure the voltage at the output (motor) end of the timer. Circuit identification of the proper terminals requires the assistance of the wiring diagram, a copy of which is customarily cemented onto the inside of the back panel. If no voltage is measured here, the timer is defective and must be replaced. If line voltage is measured at these terminals, check further, at the motor. No voltage at the motor indicates a defective cord between timer and motor.

If the timer is faulty in any switch position, the fault can be detected by this voltmeter test. Repairs to the timer itself are not practical; it must be replaced with a new one.

## 9.26. Automatic Washing Machine Will Not Change Speed

Low speed for washing, high speed for spin drying, are obtained from the same motor through change of pulley or gear ratio, accomplished by a solenoid and clutch combination. If the machine will not change speeds, the solenoid may be at fault: either through jamming or because of an open-circuited coil.

Test with a voltmeter at the solenoid terminals to determine if power is being supplied to the solenoid. If not, the timer is defective (Sec. 9.25). If the solenoid voltage is present, a humming or vibrating sound can be detected at the solenoid; it is trying without success to draw in its plunger. Examination will reveal the cause of jamming. If the solenoid does not hum, it should be disconnected and tested with an ohmmeter for continuity. An open-circuited solenoid should, of course, be replaced.

## 9.27. Water Supply

The automatic washing machine has hoses attached for the water supply, both hot and cold, and does its own mixing of water to obtain a temperature determined by the setting of a thermostat. The following is a summary of possible water supply troubles and their causes:

> If the water supply is inadequate, check as a possible cause the condition of the hoses and pipes, the solenoids operating the water valves, and the valves themselves, for possibility of a clogged condition.
>
> If the water is too hot or too cold, examine first the valves and solenoids to be sure that both hot and cold water are being delivered; then check the thermostat. A defective thermostat or one with an improper setting will cause incorrect water temperature.
>
> If the water rises too high or not high enough in the tub, examine for defective operation the mechanism which determines the water level. Since this device differs on the various brands of automatic washing machines, it is impractical to attempt to give more specific information here.

## 9.28. Washing Machine Shocks User

This condition is particularly disturbing on washing machines because the soapy water used in the machine is a good conductor of electricity. This fact, along with the frequent use of the washing machine in a basement with a damp floor, can cause a rather severe shock. The source of the fault is a defect in the insulation on the electric wires within the machine, a defect in the motor, or a defect in some control device such as timer, switch, and so on. The general procedure is to follow a continuity check. There must be an electrical connection between the circuit wiring and the frame of the machine to produce a shock, and this connection must be isolated and removed. Begin at the cord and test with either ohmmeter or series test lamp between the plug prongs and the frame of the machine. Next, remove the motor from its mounting and place it so that it does not touch the machine. Finally, remove the control devices from their fastenings and locate them so as to prevent contact with the appliance. If at any one of these steps the continuity between plug cap and frame disappears, the fault lies in the part just removed, and it must be either replaced or, in the case of the motor, repaired or rewound.

Within the motor, the fault may lie in the winding, the centrifugal switch, or the site at which the cord enters the motor. The latter two can be repaired. The winding, however, must be replaced.

## 9.29. Trouble-Shooting Chart: Washing Machines

| SYMPTOM | CAUSE | TEST | REMEDY |
|---|---|---|---|
| Motor will not turn. | Open circuit in motor | Check motor for continuity at terminal block. Normal resistance is two to five ohms. Visual examination may reveal broken wire in motor. | Repair or replace motor. |
| | Open attachment cord | Test for cord (Sec. 4.9). | Replace cord set. |
| Motor hums but will not turn (may blow fuses). | Open starting winding in motor or defective centrifugal switch | Dismantle motor; examine switch for defect. Test starting winding for continuity with ohmmeter or series test lamp. | Replace switch or motor. |

| SYMPTOM | CAUSE | TEST | REMEDY |
|---|---|---|---|
| | Worn or dry bearings in motor | Visual examination. | Replace bearings (Sec. 7.7). |
| | Jammed mechanism: a. gear box | Turn motor coupling by hand. If it will not rotate, mechanism is jammed. | Replace defective part(s). |
| | b. wringer | Remove wringer from post. If coupling now turns, trouble is in wringer. Dismantle gear box and/or wringer head. Examine for defective part(s). | |
| Motor turns, but mechanism will not. | Broken or loose coupling or belt | Visual examination. | Replace coupling or belt. |
| | Worn or broken gear in gearcase | Dismantle gearcase. Visual examination will reveal defective item. | Replace worn or broken gear(s). |
| | Broken agitator On-Off lever | Same as above. | Same as above. |
| Wringer turns, but agitator will not. | Broken agitator On-Off lever | Same as above. | Replace or repair defective part. |
| Agitator operates, but wringer will not. | Broken wringer coupling | Dismantle wringer head and determine by visual examination which is defective part. | Replace defective part(s). |
| | Broken wringer gear | Same as above. | Same as above. |

| SYMPTOM | CAUSE | TEST | REMEDY |
| --- | --- | --- | --- |
| | Broken wringer roll shift lever | Same as above. | Same as above. |
| | Wringer roll rusted loose from shaft | Remove lower roll, examine for rust on shaft. Place milled end of shaft in vise and attempt to turn rubber by hand. | If rubber is loose, replace roll. |
| Loud thump each time agitator reverses. | Worn gears | Visual examination of interior or gear-case. | Replace worn parts. |
| Oil leaks from gear-case. | Probably caused by water getting into gearcase owing to too high water level in tub | Same as above. | Replace bushing in agitator post, agitator drive shaft and water flinger. Clean and relubricate gear-case. |
| Wringer cannot be moved to various locations about tub. | Rusted index mechanism | Visual examination. | Replace defective parts. |
| Water spills into wrong tub while wringing. | Jammed flipper board—probably due to rust | Visual examination. | Replace defective parts. |
| Wringer safety release will not operate. | Safety release jammed—probably due to rust | Visual examination. | Replace defective parts. |
| Automatic washing machine will not start. | Motor defect (see above) or defective timer | Check voltages at timer and motor according to circuit diagram accompany-ing machine. | Replace timer. |

| SYMPTOM | CAUSE | TEST | REMEDY |
|---|---|---|---|
| Automatic machine will not change speed. | Defective trip solenoid | Check voltage at solenoid. | Replace solenoid or switch. |
| Automatic machine does not properly mix water. | Defective solenoid or thermostat | Test voltages at solenoids for mixing water. | Replace defective component |
| Appliance shocks user. | Ground in motor or switch (most likely due to moisture in motor or switch) | Disconnect motor from switch—check independently for ground. | Replace or repair defective component. NOTE: Occasionally a *temporary* repair can be affected by reversing plug cap in receptacle. |

# IRONERS

## 9.30. Units of the Ironer

The ironer (Fig. 9-14) is manufactured in a number of styles, from huge gas-heated models suitable for institutional use to the newest style, which is light enough to be easily carried by one person. The ironer consists of the shoe, the roll, the reduction-gear unit, and the motor.

## 9.31. The Ironer Motor

The motor is identical with that used on a washing machine except that its size is smaller. Whereas a 1/4 hp motor is required for washing-machine service, a 1/6 hp or less is sufficient to handle the ironer load. Servicing procedure for the motor is exactly the same as that outlined for the washing-machine motor.

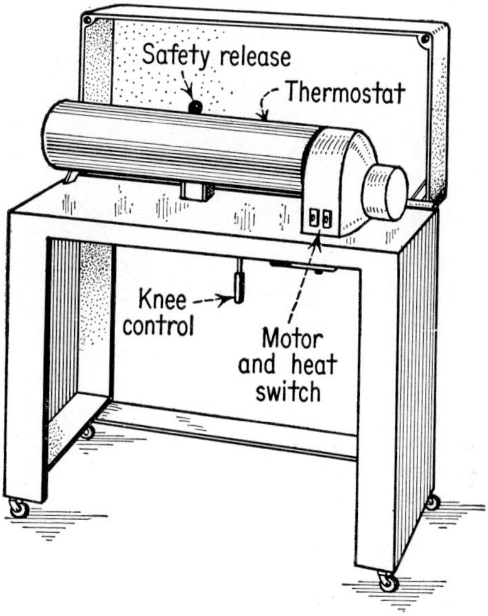


FIG. 9-14. (Courtesy, Landers, Frary, & Clark)

## 9.32. Roll Drive and Shoe Pressure

The motor is attached to the gear case by means of a standard flexible coupling. The gear case provides the drive for the roll, as well as a pressing and lifting action applied to the nichrome-element heated shoe.

The ironer roll moves at a rather slow speed: slow enough to provide the proper feed speed which allows the clothes to remain under the shoe long enough to be pressed (5 to 10 rpm). This slow speed is obtained by a series of reduction gears, beginning with a worm gear driven by a direct coupling to the motor. Some makes of ironers terminate the gear train by a chain drive onto the roll shaft, in order to obtain flexibility. The fundamentals of such a system are shown in Figure 9-15 (page 298). The worm drives two reduction gears and a chain which turns the roll. Attached to one of the reduction gears is a control plate for the ironer shoe. It is fitted with an eccentric block, and rotation of the eccentric will operate a series of levers causing the ironer shoe to move to and away from the roll. If this control plate were allowed to move constantly with the rotation of the reduction gear, the result would be a constant to-and-fro action imparted to the ironer shoe.

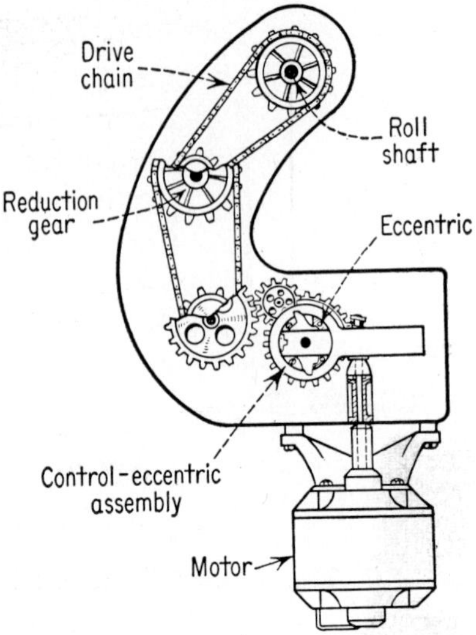


FIG. 9-15. (Courtesy, Landers, Frary, & Clark)

Now, it is necessary that the shoe remain pressed against the roll while ironing rather than jump up and down. To accomplish this, the control-eccentric assembly (Fig. 9-15) is arranged so as to move independently of the reduction gear. The fingers protruding from the side of the control assembly will, when depressed, put into operation a ratchet whose teeth hold on to the reduction gear for one half of a revolution only, then release. Thus, the ironer shoe may be left in the down or in the up position at will, and moved only when the control ratchet finger is pressed in. As shown in the diagram (Fig. 9-14), a knee control operates the lever which depresses the ratchet and controls the shoe.

The system just described provides fully automatic operation of the ironer shoe. Many of the less elaborate styles of ironers are provided with a lever for manual operation of the shoe.

Ironer shoe pressure is usually about 100 pounds. A latch is often provided on the back of the shoe which, when released, will remove the shoe pressure. This is for emergency use, and should be reset before the ironer is again used.

The ironer shoe is heated by a nichrome heating unit. Depending upon the brand, it may consist of one, or a number, of heating elements. One popular brand has two heating elements in parallel, each controlled by a thermostat. This arrangement permits individual control of the temperature of each end of the shoe, a practical convenience when one end of the shoe is being given more use than the other.

Some few models have a sealed-unit heating element; on these, replacement of the entire shoe is necessary when breakdown occurs. Most, however, are supplied with a mica-encased separate unit, which easily becomes accessible when the screws on top of the shoe are removed. If the shoe is thermostatically controlled, the thermostats are reached in the same manner.

The roll drive is in operation as long as the motor turns. It is often desirable to stop the roll while ironing in order to adjust the garment, or for pressing portions of garment which cannot be satisfactorily finished by the ironer. To stop, the roll must be disengaged from its source of power, the motor. This is usually accomplished by a sliding-gear clutch as a part of the reduction-gear train. A foot- or hand-control lever moves the clutch so as to engage or disengage the roll, or roll and intermediate drive gear. The exact location of this control part varies between brands, but may be determined either by inspection or by referring to the manufacturer's manual.

## 9.33. Current Requirements

The wattage of the ironer may be in excess of 1,500, most of which is consumed by the heating element (Fig. 9-16). The motor requires less than 5 amp for its operation, whereas the heating element uses over 10 amp. As a result of such large current consumption, it is unwise to use this appliance in the same circuit with other heavy-duty appliances, or even with a number of smaller-wattage devices. Many modern homes are wired with a special 20-amp No. 12 wire-appliance circuit, and this circuit should be used for ironer operation.

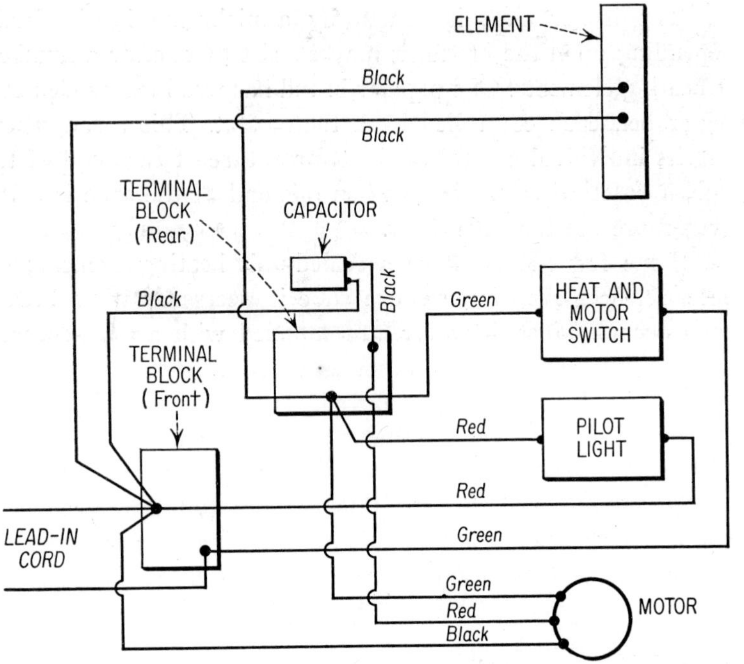


FIG. 9-16.

## 9.34. The Roll

The ironer roll has three different coverings. Next to the roll itself is a jute or burlap pad, one end of which is either cemented or clipped into place. When this padding is replaced, the ironer should be put into operation, and the rotation of the roll with the shoe down used to feed the padding into place. After the jute padding is rolled on, it is followed by a length of cotton padding. Start the cotton padding by placing a short length of it under the burlap, and let the ironer feed the remainder on over the burlap. Next, a muslin cover should be placed on the roll, starting it with a short length (6 inches) under the cotton padding, letting the ironer feed the remainder on the roll as a top covering. Permit the ironer to operate for a minute or more to smooth out the padding. Finally, draw up and fasten the drawstrings that hold the muslin cover in place (Fig. 9-17).

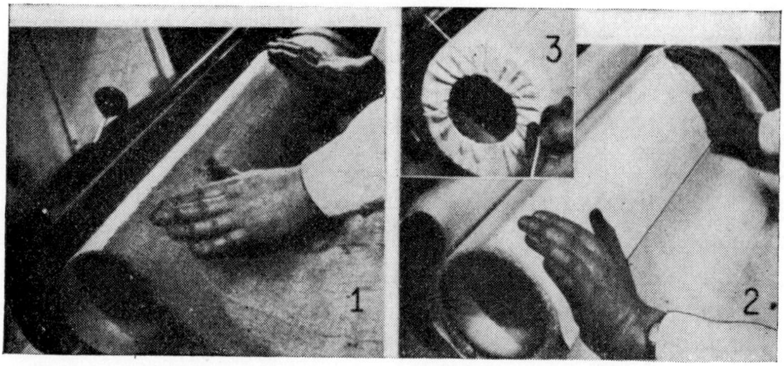


FIG. 9-17. (Courtesy, Landers, Frary, & Clark)

Ironer lubrication follows the same principles as those outlined for washing machines. The gear case holds about a pint of oil. The roll bearings should be well greased, but not to such an extent that the lubricant will seep out onto the clothing.

## REPAIRING IRONERS

### 9.35. General Discussion

The electric motor used on an ironer is the same type (split-phase motor) as that used on the washing machine. This type motor is described and its operation explained in Sections 6.4 and 9.2, and the servicing procedure given in Sections 9.3, 9.13, and 9.14. The troubles and servicing procedure for the motors on ironers are fundamentally the same as that listed in the above references and need not be repeated here.

*Roll Will Not Turn*

This fault may be caused by one of the following:

Broken motor coupling
Broken roll-drive jaw
Broken drive chain
Fault in gear case

The defective motor coupling can be detected by observation. It may be necessary to lay the ironer on its back to gain access to the motor, which, in some models, is mounted in an inconspicuous location below the machine. The obvious repair is replacement of the motor coupling; or if, as occasionally happens, the setscrew has just become loosened, tightening it down will restore operation.

The rotation of the motor is transmitted through the gear train to a long shaft, at the end of which is a block or jaw which engages the roll, causing it to turn. If this jaw has become damaged or loose on its shaft, the roll will fail to turn. As with the motor coupling, this defect can be detected by observation, and the nature of the fault will indicate the type and extent of repairs necessary.

Of course, the roll may be unable to turn due to a faulty drive mechanism: either the chain or reduction gears. Fortunately, most ironers are so designed that the removal of a panel covering the accessible side of the gear box allows a view of the mechanism in operation; thus the faulty part can be spotted by direct observation, and steps necessary for repair taken. If it is necessary to remove the gear-box panel, this should be done with care, and provision be made for catching the oil as it pours out of the gear case. Positioning the ironer so the panel being removed is uppermost simplifies this procedure. For purpose of observation the gears can be operated with the oil removed from the gear case, utilizing the lubricant clinging to the gears; however, oil supply should be renewed during final reassembly. If the defective component in the gear case is difficult to locate, it may be necessary to take apart the contents of the gear case, cleaning each one and examining it for wear or breakage. Replace defective parts with new ones.

## 9.36. Shoe Will Not Open or Close on Roll, or Shoe Oscillates

Linking the knee control (Fig. 9-14) with the transmission assembly (Fig. 9-15) is a rod called the shifter rod. As the shifter rod is operated, the ratchet engages the clutch for half a revolution. The clutch rotates the eccentric to produce motion of the eccentric arm, say to lift the shoe from the roll. When the shifter rod is again operated, the eccentric is rotated another half-revolution, this time to lower the shoe onto the roll. Any of the gears, springs, levers, clutch, or eccentric mechanism involved in this operation will, if damaged, cause failure of the iron shoe to move in response to pressure on the control lever. Repair of this defect requires that the gear case be opened and its parts examined, both individually and in operation with neighboring parts. Upon replacement of defective parts, the precaution of adequate lubrication and gasket renewal should be observed.

If the control rod has become bent, this duplicates a condition in which the operator applies continuous pressure to the control rod. The shoe eccentric mechanism will repeat its half-revolutions in rapid succession, and the shoe will repeatedly open and close onto the roll. The obvious cure is to straighten the bent control rod, or, if it is too badly distorted, to install a new one.

## 9.37. Shoe Does Not Heat Properly

This fault may be caused by defect in the wiring (Fig. 9-17), the heat switch being faulty, or trouble within the shoe itself. It can be isolated to one of these three in the following manner: Place a jumper around the heat switch and plug in the cord. If it now heats, the switch was faulty and must be replaced. If the shoe still will not heat, measure the voltage at the terminals where the cord attaches to the shoe. No voltage at this point indicates defective wiring; if line voltage is measured here, the fault lies within the ironer shoe.

Faulty wiring requires that the wiring be traced from shoe to line cord, each section being tested for open circuit or poor terminal connection. An ohmmeter is used to test the several lengths of cord for continuity. Faulty wire must be replaced; poor terminal connections must be renewed.

Within the ironer shoe are located the heating element and thermostat(s). Some ironers have two heating elements, parallel-connected, each with its own thermostat, allowing separate control of the temperature of left and right ends of the ironer shoe. The shoe must be opened up to permit access to the thermostats and elements for testing and replacement. The thermostat is tested with an ohmmeter after having been disconnected from the circuit. The ohmmeter should register zero ohms with the thermostat knob set in the high-heat position, infinity with the thermostat in the off position.

The heating element also is tested with an ohmmeter, and should have a resistance value compatible with the wattage rating of the shoe ($R = E^2/W$). The defective heating element must be replaced with one of identical resistance value.

## 9.38. Trouble-Shooting Chart: Electric Ironers

Note: Motor troubles, tests, and repairs are generally the same as on washing machines.

| SYMPTOM | CAUSE | TEST | REMEDY |
|---|---|---|---|
| Roll will not turn. | Broken roll-drive jaw (located at free end of roll) | Visual examination. | Replace defective part. |
| | Broken drive chain | Visual examination. On some machines a cap is located on housing which, when removed, allows examination of chain. | Repair or replace. |
| | Broken motor coupling | Visual examination. If coupling is broken, none of controls, except heat, will operate. | Repair or replace. |
| | Broken part in gear case | This defect requires more dismantling of gear case than the above, and should be deduced by elimination. | Replace defective part. |

| SYMPTOM | CAUSE | TEST | REMEDY |
|---|---|---|---|
| Shoe will not move to and fro. | Broken eccentric | Visual examination. | Replace. |
| Shoe oscillates. | Bent control rod | Visual examination. | Straighten; or, if too badly bent, replace. |
| Shoe will not heat, or heat is too low. | Open thermostat (defective contacts) | Visual examination and/or test with ohmmeter. Zero ohms in ON position. | Replace thermostat. |
| | Open heating element | Test with ohmmeter. Resistance may be calculated from wattage: $R = E^2/W$. | Replace heating element; or, if sealed unit, replace entire unit. |

# ELECTRIC WATER HEATERS

## 9.39. General Discussion

There is a definite trend toward the use of electricity for heating purposes, particularly in areas where the cost of electricity is low (1.5¢ per kw hour or less). The numerous benefits of electric heating—cleanliness, ease of delivery, ready application of automatic-control devices—has resulted in the appearance of many appliances which, while not new in principle, are newcomers to the electrical-appliance field. One such appliance is the electric water heater. No new principles will be encountered in the water heater; the electrical production of heat by a nichrome element has been frequently encountered in the preceding pages. The purposeful arrangement of parts and the circuitry will be the main topics of our examination of this appliance.

## 9.40. Tank

In order to compete with other forms of water heating, the electric water heater must do its job efficiently, allowing as little heat as possible to escape into the outer air. The actual container of water must be well insulated. (Heat insulation, of course, is the meaning of *insulation* here.) The outer shell, seen when the heater is externally observed, is just a protective

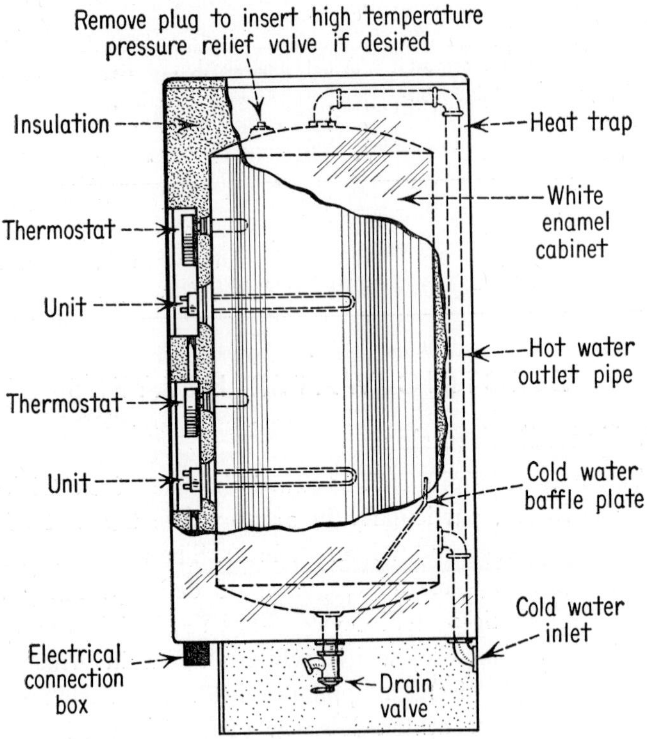


FIG. 9-18. (Courtesy, Landers, Frary, & Clark)

cover to hold the insulating material in place. Its styling is such as to enhance the over-all appearance of the appliance. The actual water container lies within the insulating layer (Fig. 9-18).

Loss of heat by the water may occur in three different ways: conduction, convection, and radiation. Conduction occurs when an object which is at a higher temperature than its surroundings transfers some of its heat to adjacent objects which, in turn, pass heat on to their neighbors. For example, if a brass rod is held over a flame, the portion of the rod being heated transfers heat to the adjoining part of the rod until the hand holding the rod feels the metal getting warmer. The possibility that conduction may lower the temperature of the water within the heater calls for an insulating layer between water and outer air, of such a nature that it will not readily conduct heat. Fiber glass is the material most commonly used for this purpose.

Convection takes place in circulating fluids, either liquid or gaseous. It is known that warm air is lighter in weight than cool air, and that within an enclosed area containing both, the warm air will rise, while the cooler air drifts downward. If the tank of the electric water heater were unprotected, the air surrounding the tank, upon being heated by the water within the tank, would rise, allowing cooler air to take its place; thus, by circulating air (convection currents, so called) the tank would be cooled. Even with an outer cover, air circulation could take place within the space between the cover and the tank. The use of glass wool as an insulator between tank and shell causes many small pockets of air (air is a good heat insulator) to be trapped within the spaces of the glass wool, thus reducing loss of heat by convection.

The reader might try the following experiment. Place a heating element in a socket, allowing it to hang vertically. While it is glowing, place the hand a few inches *below* it and notice how suddenly the hand is warmed. The same effect can be observed with a lamp bulb while glowing. Conduction, especially through air, proceeds too slowly to account for this heating effect; convection would produce an *upward* draft of air. One is led to the conclusion that the form of heat here observed is quite different from the two previously described, and operates much more rapidly. This is radiant heat: heat by *radiation*. This is the form of heat the earth receives from the sun. It travels at the speed of light (186,000 miles per second), and is similar to light in many respects. It can be focused as can a beam of light. It is reflected by a shiny surface—polished metal or a mirror. If the inside surface of the electric heater tank, or even the outer cover, is made of a shiny substance such as aluminum, porcelain, mirrored glass, or stainless steel, this will serve to reflect the radiant heat back into the water, making for less costly heating. Experiments indicate that heat will radiate from a dark surface more rapidly than from one which is bright or light in color. This means that if the white porcelain or enameled surface of the heater is allowed to become dirty, heater efficiency is thereby lowered. Many manufacturers use a stainless-steel tank, and a white-enameled outer cover is universal practice.

When the heater is serviced, nothing should be done by the repair man which will impair the retention of heat. The matter of darkening or dirtying the surface has just been mentioned. Packing the insulation too tightly, omitting it entirely, replacing it with an inferior substitute, or allowing it to get wet, will reduce heater efficiency and increase the cost of operation.

## 9.41. Heating Units

The sealed-unit type of heating element is most frequently used in water heaters. Figure 9-18 shows this type of heating element. The smallest size used is 600 w, the largest 3,000 w at 220 v. The sealed unit contains a nichrome heating element imbedded in a white powder, magnesium oxide, which substance is undamaged by heat, and, furthermore, is an excellent electrical insulator. The outer sheath of the sealed unit is made of stainless steel. This assembly is quite durable; the materials of which it is made do not readily deteriorate under conditions of ordinary usage, and the element is protected from corrosion. Two units are used, one near the top, the other toward the bottom of the heater (as may be observed in the cutaway view, Figure 9-18). The wattage rating of the upper element supplies approximately 30 w per gallon of tank capacity; the bottom unit, 20 w per gallon of tank capacity. Each heating element has its own control thermostat, which may be adjusted by the service man to fit the consumer's needs. The range of thermostat settings is from a low of 120° F. to a high of 170° F. A normally satisfactory setting is 150° F.; indeed, the factory setting is at this temperature.

## 9.42. Circuits

In many municipalities the electric power company allows a special low rate for the electricity used for water heating, provided the heater operates only during periods of otherwise low power consumption, which hours are specified by the power company. An extra meter is installed by the power company which records electric-heater kw hours only. This submeter, as it is called, contains a clockwork-operated switch which limits operating time to the controlled hours. Figure 9-19 shows the connection of a submeter. The submeter is usually located beside the regular meter.

The upper and lower heating elements of the electric water heater are generally paralleled across the 220-v single-phase a-c service from the submeter in either of two ways. One connection, the *limited demand,* is that in which the thermostats of the two heating elements are interlocked in such a fashion that only one can operate at a time. The upper thermostat controls a double-pole double-throw switch. As can be seen from the diagram in Figure 9-19A, when the upper element is in operation the circuit of the lower element is disconnected. When the upper thermostat turns off the upper element, at the same time it connects the lower element into the circuit. Name-plate data on the heater will list the higher-wattage heating element as producing the maximum current requirement, or *demand,* with the limited demand connection.

Figure 9-19B illustrates a circuit-wiring diagram which differs from the foregoing only in the connection of the lower heating-element wire to the upper thermostat-terminal block. Notice that this connection is now such as to allow the operation of the two heating element units to be electrically independent of each other; thus, both heating elements may be in the circuit at the same time. The maximum demand with the connection of Figure 9-19B is the sum of the wattages of the two heating elements.

At the time of installation the circuit is wired in whichever of the above schemes better fits the needs of the user.

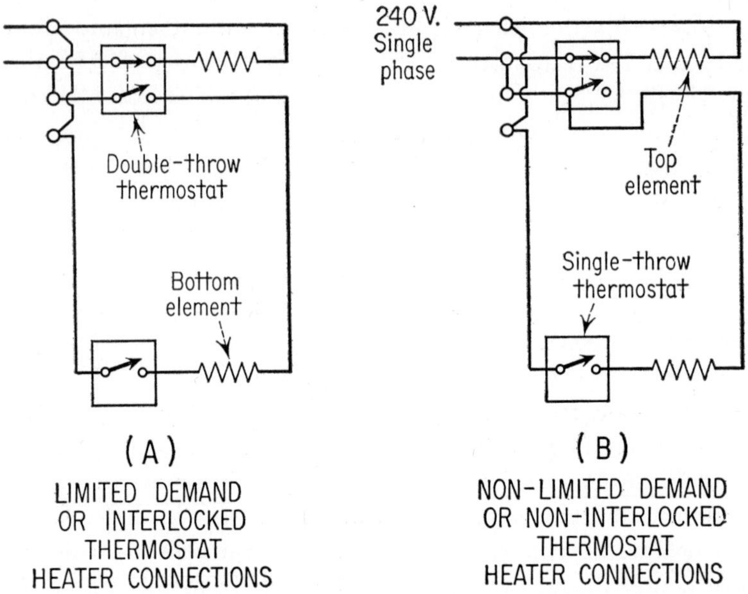


FIG. 9-19.

Seldom will it be necessary for the repair man to change the connections from one to the other type of demand. To avoid inadvertent changes, wires which must be unfastened to allow repair work to be done should be marked in such a fashion as to allow proper reconnection. If the electric water heater is of such a design as to permit easy circuit tracing, perhaps a sketch of the circuit wiring will suffice.

## 9.43. Installation

Although the installation of the electric water heater will probably be done by someone other than the person called in to make repairs, it undoubtedly is helpful for the repair man to understand the requirements to be met in installation, since it will enable him (1) to do more intelligent servicing, and (2) to recognize a defect or trouble due to installation causes.

The electric water heater should be installed as close as is reasonable to the tap from which the hot water will be drawn. Copper tubing is recommended because of its durability. If placed in the basement, the water heater should be located

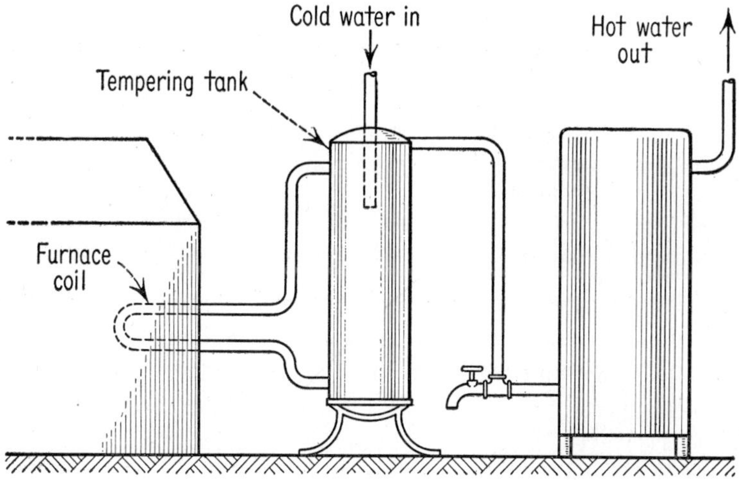


FIG. 9-20.

directly under the kitchen sink so the shortest possible run of pipe to faucet can be installed. The reason for this arrangement is that hot water remaining in a noninsulated pipe will rapidly cool; within half an hour the water will have cooled to room temperature. It is impractical and costly to heat water electrically which will subsequently be cooled in an exposed pipe line. Thus the use of insulation on the pipe is advisable, especially if the run is long. Furthermore, it is suggested that the smallest-size pipe which will deliver an adequate flow be used; the smaller the pipe, the less the volume of metal which must be heated.

If a furnace coil is used to heat water during the winter months, it must not be connected directly to the electric water heater tank. There is placed between furnace and heater a "tempering" tank; a noninsulated 30-gallon tank into which the hot water from the furnace coil is run (Fig. 9-20). The tempering tank serves the further purpose of bringing cold water up to room temperature when the furnace is not in use. thus reducing the temperature rise demanded of the heater coils.

When an electric water heater is installed, all plumbing must be finished before electrical connection is made to the service mains. The water-heater tank should be thoroughly purged of air and filled with water before the heating elements are fired up. Operating the heating elements when the tank is empty may severely damage the heating coils. This precaution should be observed by the repair man whenever it becomes necessary to drain the tank in order to make repairs.

### 9.44. Relief Valve

The operation of an electric water heater is wholly automatic and, barring defects or failures, the appliance will operate indefinitely without attention. The thermostats provide proper water temperature and the water supply inlet is open at all times. However, in some communities the local code requires that a relief valve be installed on the electric water heater. The purpose is to allow the escape of water in the event of overheating due to thermostat failure. The relief valve is customarily located in the top part of the tank and may be made accessible by removing the top cover or, in some models, by removing a small cover plate located immediately above the valve. While the valve setting is adjustable, the adjustment is usually factory-made, and no alteration of this setting is necessary.

## *Servicing Water Heaters*

### 9.45. General Discussion

The principal troubles which develop in electric water heaters are those resulting from corrosion, indicated by a leakage of water. Corrosion commonly occurs at connection points.

Where the thermostat is mounted in the heater, the recessed receptacle, or thermostat well, may become corroded and allow water leakage. The same difficulty might occur at the relief valve. These parts must be removed and replaced with new parts.

Be sure to use the proper tool for removal, since these parts were firmly fitted upon assembly and may have become fragile from corrosion, so that removal will be difficult at best. Use of the right tool is the best insurance against causing further damage while servicing. For example, if the thermostat well is fitted with a hexagon nut, it should be approached with a socket wrench rather than a pipe wrench or an adjustable wrench. Upon replacement of a part which fits into the tank, pipe compound should be used to prevent leakage. If the fitting is gasketed, a new gasket should by all means be used rather than the old one, which may no longer be serviceable.

The complaint that water is not hot enough may result from electrical difficulties: either a defective thermostat or a defective heating element. On the other hand, it may be due merely to the fact that water consumption exceeds the rating and ability of the heater to supply hot water. If the trouble is of an electrical nature, it can be tested by metering the circuit. An ammeter placed in the line will indicate reduced current flow. A voltmeter placed across the line will indicate whether low heat is due to low voltage.

A defective heating element may be located with an ohmmeter. A 1,200-w 240-v heating element, for instance, should have 48 ohms. If such an element tests as having infinite resistance on the ohmmeter scale, it is obviously open-circuited. If it measures twice as much as normal (96 ohms, in the foregoing example), it consists of two parallel elements, one of which is burned out. In this fashion the heating units can be tested and the defective one isolated. If the heating elements prove to be satisfactory, and the line current is too low, then, by elimination, the thermostat is indicated as the defective component. However, before deciding to replace the thermostat, observe whether someone has tampered with the temperature adjustment. Such an alteration will, obviously, cause the water temperature to be too high or too low.

Water that is too hot may be caused, as mentioned above, by an altered thermostat setting. Also, stuck contacts on the thermostat, either upper or lower, will produce the same effect. Thus, if the water temperature is unusually high, and the heater is still drawing current, as indicated by the submeter, then one of these conditions is to be suspected.

If the sealed-unit heating element has four terminals shunted in pairs, it is a two-heating-element parallel-connected unit. Should one of the elements of this unit burn out, the other will provide heating, but at a reduced wattage. This is a possibility which the service man should never fail to investigate.

## 9.46. Trouble-Shooting Chart: Electric Water Heaters

| SYMPTOM | CAUSE | TEST | REMEDY |
|---|---|---|---|
| Water not hot enough | Defective heating element | Calculate resistance from wattage rating data. Test with ohmmeter. | Sealed unit repairs not practical. Replace with new element. |
| | One-half heating element burned out (parallel-connected elements) | Remove wires or jumpers which parallel elements. Check with ohmmeter or series test lamp. | Same as above. |
| | Defective thermostat | Voltmeter test: voltage at input but not at output terminals of thermostat. (Adjust thermostat to maximum setting and repeat test.) | Replace thermostat. |
| | Thermostat setting tampered with | Observation. | Reset. |

| SYMPTOM | CAUSE | TEST | REMEDY |
|---|---|---|---|
| | Defective insulation: insulation wet from leak in tank. Insulation too tightly packed | Observation: outside of tank is warm. | Replace insulation. |
| Water too hot | Thermostat contacts stuck together | Examine contacts if thermostat can be uncovered. Continuity check with line switch open. | Replace thermostat. |
| | Thermostat setting too high | Observation. | Reset to proper temperature. |
| Too little water | Pipes clogged with mineral deposit | Open valve at bottom of tank; compare rate of flow with water delivered to tap. | Replace pipe. |
| Leaky tank | Corrosion | Observation: look especially at places where fittings are attached. | Replace corroded part. Seal with gasket or pipe compound. |

## Now that you have read this chapter, can you answer these questions?

**1.** What damage, if any, will occur if the motor on a washing machine rotates in the wrong direction?

**2.** The replacement motor for a washing machine has the wrong direction of rotation. How would you remedy this?

**3.** Why are wood bearings used in the wringer of a washing machine?

**4.** The rolls of a wringer turn normally until clothes are fed into them, then they refuse to turn. There is nothing wrong with the drive gears. What is the probable trouble?

**5.** Describe the procedure for drying and reinsulating the winding of a motor which has been subjected to excessive moisture.

**6.** Why is it often possible to stop a washing machine temporarily from shocking by reversing the plug in its receptacle?

**7.** What damage will occur if water is allowed to get into a washing-machine gear case?

**8.** Describe the construction and function of an oil seal.

**9.** What is meant by torque?

**10.** What test will reveal if a washing machine is overloaded?

**11.** What damage will occur from overloading a washing machine?

**12.** Explain the significance of the safety release.

**13.** Why do wringer rolls stick together if the roll pressure is not removed between washdays?

**14.** What is the drain board? The flipper board?

**15.** Describe the washing-machine spinner mechanism.

**16.** Why does not an ironer require a motor of as great a horsepower as that of a washing machine?

**17.** In what way does the automatic washing machine differ from the nonautomatic machine?

**18.** What is a solenoid?

**19.** Why is low voltage detrimental to the operation of the automatic washing machine?

**20.** How can it be determined that a machine is operating on low voltage?

**21.** What is meant by an assembly?

**22.** What is the purpose of the agitator (turbulator, dasher, activator)?

**23.** If the washing machine has been stored in a cold place what steps should be taken to insure safe operation?

**24.** What are the causes of clothes being torn while laundered?

**25.** How might the attachment cord of an ironer become the cause of low heat?

*chapter* **10**

# Miscellaneous Small Appliances

There are a few small appliances whose operating principles differ from those already explained. These are the electric razor, the bottle warmer, and electric door chimes.

## ELECTRIC RAZORS

### 10.1. General Discussion

Servicing procedure for electric razors differs from that for other motor-driven appliances mainly in that greater care must be exercised in assembly and disassembly because of the small and delicate parts.

Three types of driving units are employed in the various models of razors. They are the universal motor; a special motor developed for razors based on the principle of an electromagnet with interrupted current; and a vibrator. The first model to be considered is that with a universal motor.

### 10.2. The Universal-Motor Type

This model, needless to say, works equally well on a-c and d-c. A recognition feature is the fact that brush-holder caps are externally accessible. The universal motor is self-starting, and has at its cord end a movable section of the case, to which are connected the necessary elements and contacts which will cause it to serve as an off-on switch.

The motor armature and field (Fig. 10-1) are quite small, and an extremely fine wire is used for the windings. It is much too tedious a task to attempt to rewind field or armature with the ordinarily limited facilities of the appliance repair shop, since a reasonable exchange price is allowed by most manufacturers. The usual growler and ohmmeter tests will indicate defective field and armature coils.

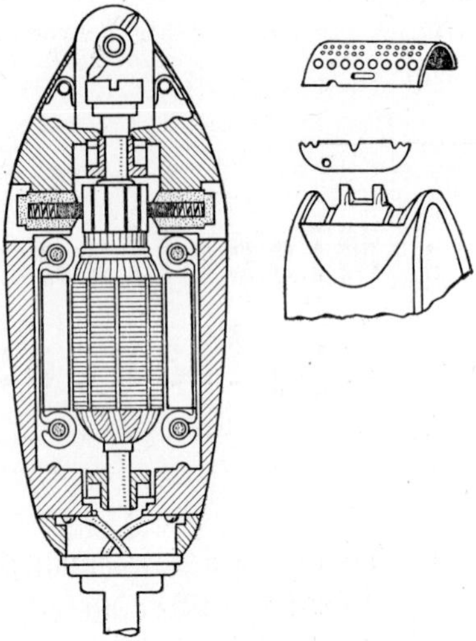

Fig. 10-1.

The armature drives an attached bolt and eccentric pin. The oscillating motion of the eccentric pin is transmitted to the cutter and cutter holder. The cutter is covered by a screened housing called the comb.

The case is in one piece. To disassemble the razor, the comb and cutter are slipped off; the metal sheath beneath the cutter holder is pried loose, exposing two screws. Loosening these screws allows removal of the cutter-holder assembly. The eccentric drive nut is screwed off the armature shaft. When the screws holding the switch onto the cord end are removed, the armature and field are exposed. The armature now may be slipped out of its bearing, leaving the razor disassembled except for the field coil. Loosening two retaining bolts allows removal of the field assembly.

## 10.3. The Electromagnet Type

While the universal motor is self-starting, the electromagnetic type of motor used in shavers will not start by itself; an external lever or wheel must be given a preliminary spin, after which the motor will continue to run of its own accord.

This motor (Fig. 10-2) contains but one field coil, encircling an iron field core of a horseshoe shape. The rotor is a laminated iron assembly mounted on a shaft and shaped so as to fit within the faces of the field poles. There is no coil or

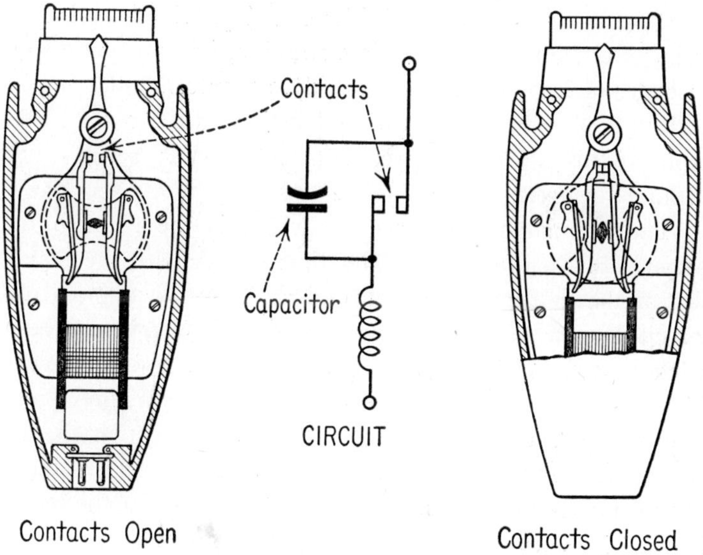


FIG. 10-2.

winding of any sort on the rotor. Current is conducted into the field coil through a set of contacts actuated by a cam on the rotor shaft; the cam opens and shuts the contacts for each half revolution of the rotor. The action is as follows:

Assuming that the contacts are closed, current through the field coil makes an electromagnet of the field poles. The rotor, being a magnetic substance, will align itself with this electromagnet.

As the rotor turns, the cam on the rotor shaft opens the contacts in the field circuit. The electromagnetism ceases.

Inertia gained by the rotor due to magnetic attraction of its iron parts causes the iron to move past the pole faces. Ultimately its movement will be sufficient to allow the cam-actuated contacts to close. The rotor is now attracted farther in the original direction of rotation by the renewed magnetism allowed by the closing contacts.

Once this process is started in a certain direction, it is self-sustaining. The motor is stopped by disconnecting its current source—that is, by pulling out the attachment-cord plug.

It is apparent that the initial speed provided by the field, causing one fourth of a complete rotation, is inadequate to sustain continued rotation. Consequently, an external starting knob or wheel is placed in an accessible location on the razor housing. A spin of this wheel will give the motor a start; it will continue to rotate by itself.

The laminated-iron assembly which is the rotor is not a magnet. Hence, it is not at any time repelled by the magnetic poles of the field: merely attracted as is any iron piece placed near either pole of a bar magnet. From this fact it may be concluded that a field pole resultant from an alternating current will attract the rotor iron equally well as does a direct-current energized field. The determining factors as to whether the motor will serve better when operated from a-c or d-c are (1) the wire size and number of turns of the field coil, and (2) the tendency of contact points to draw and sustain a severe arc on d-c and not on a-c. The arcing of the contacts in the razor motor is generally so great as to preclude d-c operation. Unless otherwise specified by the name plate or legend on the razor, it should be operated on a-c only.

In spite of the fact that a-c contact arcing is less severe than d-c, the amount of arcing that does occur is sufficient to cause two undesirable effects: shortened contact life because of the disintegrating action of the arc, and radio interference. Both effects are materially reduced by use of a capacitor connected across the contact terminals. The value of capacity used is adequate to absorb the arc caused by a-c but not that caused by d-c. The manner in which the capacitor accomplishes this is described in Section 1-16.

The outer case of this type of razor is in two parts, held together by small bolts. When the case is opened, internal construction and assembly are clearly revealed, and further dismantling is simple.

## 10.4. The Vibrator Type

The third type of razor mechanism consists merely of an electromagnet and vibrating reed (Fig. 10-3). The reed moves to and from the electromagnet at the speed of the changing 60-

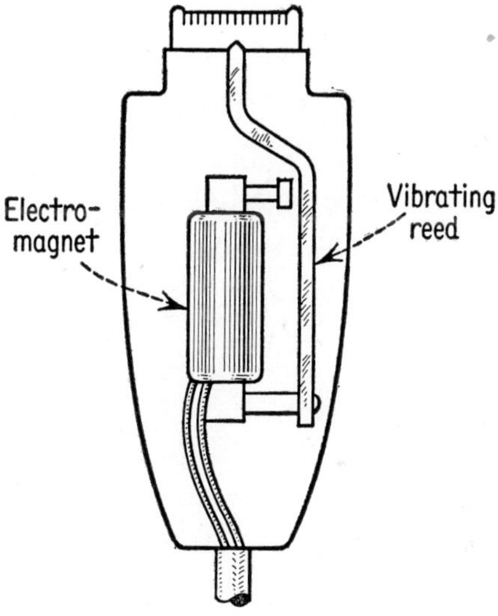


FIG. 10-3.

cycle alternating current applied to the electromagnet. The natural springiness of the reed causes it to move away from the electromagnet during the portion of the cycle when the alternating current is reversing its direction. Thus, the reed vibrates 120 times a second.

This vibratory motion is transferred to the blade attached to the reed. At the high speed of the vibration of the reed, its stroke is relatively short. This type of razor is relatively noisy compared with the two preceding types, and hence has had only a limited popularity. Because of its fewer moving parts, however, it is less expensive.

## *Servicing Electric Razors*

### 10.5. Motor Will Not Run

The usual causes of failure of a motor to operate are to be suspected here. They the following:

Defective cord and/or plug
Defective switch
Open circuit in motor

The procedure to follow is the same as has been previously described in connection with other motor-driven appliances. The cord and plug can be tested either indirectly, by substitution with a test cord, or directly, with ohmmeter or series test lamp. The motor can be tested for continuity with an ohmmeter; and it should normally possess a rather high resistance because of the fine wire in its field and armature. A continuity test of the motor by means of the series test lamp is not always conclusive, since the amount of current drawn by the razor motor may be inadequate to cause the lamp to glow. The customary recommendation that all defective parts be repaired or replaced must be amended here; often the value of the motor represents the major cost of the appliance, and it may not be economically advisable to replace the motor when for a small additional sum a new razor could be purchased. In any event, the repair man should use his own judgment in this regard.

### 10.6. Motor Runs Too Slowly

The cause of this fault will vary somewhat with the type of motor. If the capacitor associated with the type of motor shown in Figure 10-2 is defective, that will cause the motor to run slowly. If the armature or brushes of the series motor are faulty, the speed will also be reduced. In either type, dry bearings will cause a reduction of speed.

In Section 10.3 is discussed the action of the electromagnetic type of motor. The circuit, shown in Figure 10-2, is that of an interrupted coil with the interrupter contacts shunted by a capacitor. If this capacitor develops an internal short, the action of the switch contacts is partially or totally eliminated, and the magnetism of the field will not be cut off. The usual effect on razor performance is a severe reduction in speed. If this is suspected to be the fault, merely unsoldering one of the capacitor wires will provide quick verification, since the motor will then run at full speed. The capacitor should be replaced before operating the razor for a prolonged period, as the arcing produced with the capacitor absent will rapidly deteriorate the contacts.

Slow speed in a universal-motor type of razor resulting from defective armature can be serviced in the manner outlined in the chart in Section 7-11 for universal motors. A defective armature must be replaced, because armature and wire are so small as to require special techniques and equipment to rewind.

Reduced speed due to dry or gummed bearings can be detected upon dismantling the razor, since the shaft will not turn readily. Cleaning both bearing and shaft with carbon tetrachloride, and relubricating, will generally cure this trouble.

## 10.7. Trouble-Shooting Chart: Electric Razors

| SYMPTOM | CAUSE | TEST | REMEDY |
|---|---|---|---|
| Motor will not run or runs slowly. | Open circuit in<br>a. motor field<br>b. cord | Test with ohmmeter or test lamp for continuity. Remove cord. Fasten wires together and test at other end with series test lamp or ohmmeter for continuity. | Replace with new field coil.<br><br>Replace with new cord. |
| | Worn or damaged motor brushes or brush springs | Visual examination. | Replace brushes and/ or springs. |

| SYMPTOM | CAUSE | TEST | REMEDY |
|---|---|---|---|
| | Shorted capacitor | Test for capacitors given in Section 7.4. | Replace capacitor. |
| | Dry or gummed bearings | Visual examination. | Clean and lubricate. |
| | Defective switch | Open-type switch—checked by examination. | Replace all defective switch parts. |
| | Defective armature (open, short, grounded) | Armature test (Sec. 7.6). | Replace armature. |
| | Open-circuited coil on vibrator-type razor | Test coil for continuity with ohmmeter. (Coil normally has relatively high resistance.) | Replace coil. |
| Appliance blows fuses. | Short in cord or motor | Check at plug cap with ohmmeter. Zero ohms indicates short. | Dismantle razor, testing for short at each step. When short disappears, defective component is indicated. |

# ELECTRIC BOTTLE WARMERS

## 10.8. General Discussion

Developed expressly for the purpose of keeping the contents of an infant's nursing bottle at the proper temperature, the bottle warmer (Fig. 10-4) operates on the principle that water which is not 100 per cent pure will conduct a current. The water obtained from a city supply system contains dissolved mineral salts in sufficient quantity to make it a conductor. The addition of a small quantity of table salt will increase still further the conductivity of the water (decreases its resistance). If a current is passed through the water, heat will be generated in proportion to the current flow and the water resistance. (calories of heat $= 0.24\ I^2R\ t$.) Under the proper condition of conductivity, the heat generated will be sufficient to raise the water temperature to the boiling point. Hence, the water temperature may be controlled by varying the percentage of dissolved mineral salts in the water.

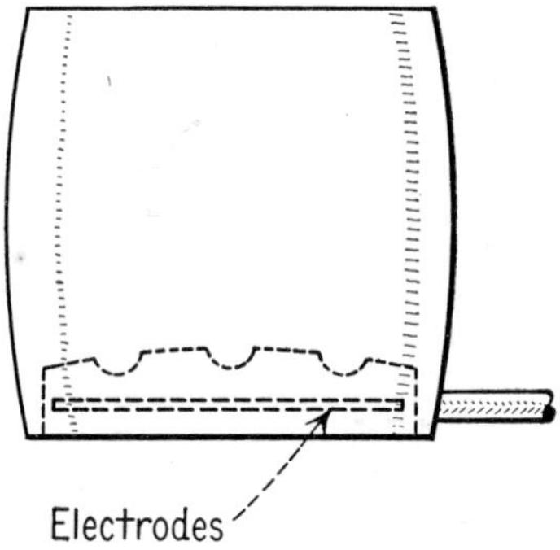


Fig. 10-4.

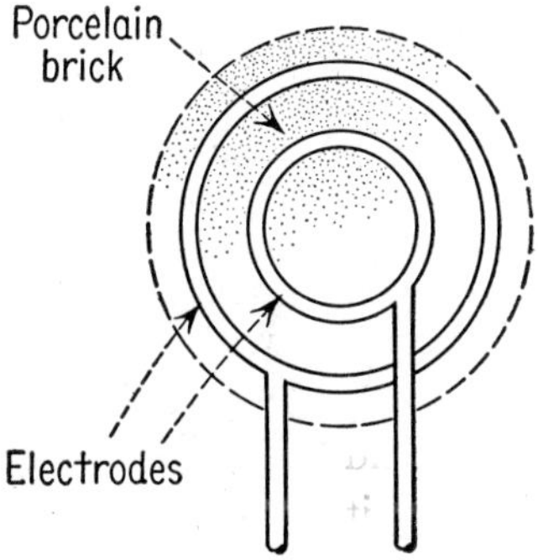


Fig. 10-5.

The bottle warmer contains two electrodes. These are of copper wire, insulated from each other by a porcelain brick in which they are mounted. To each electrode is connected one wire from the line cord. In this condition, if the appliance is plugged in, there will be no current flow through the open circuit (Fig. 10-5).

In operation, a quantity of water (instruction as to amount is supplied by manufacturer's literature enclosed with appliance) is placed in the bottle warmer, and a small amount of table salt added to the water so as to make it more conductive. The appliance is plugged into a receptacle, and the current flow through the water produces sufficient heat to warm the water—even cause it to boil. A bottle placed in the warmer will have its contents warmed in proportion to the length of time the current is allowed to flow. Under prolonged use, it may be necessary to replenish the supply of water, which evaporates rapidly at a high temperature.

This appliance may also be used as a vaporizer to provide

medicinal fumes in a sickroom. A medicated solution is placed directly in the appliance and allowed to boil.

### *Repairing Bottle Warmers*

### 10.9. Replacing Parts

The electrical circuit of the bottle warmer is quite simple. There is little to cause trouble in such a circuit other than natural deterioration of wire and terminal connections resulting from age and corrosion, or breakage of the porcelain insulator in which the electrodes are mounted. Repair will consist of replacing any and all worn, deteriorated, or damaged parts. Care should be taken in assembly to avoid short circuits by properly spacing the electrodes with respect to each other.

## ELECTRIC CHIMES

### 10.10. General Discussion

Figure 1-11 illustrates the operation of an electromagnet, which is described as being a piece of soft iron around which is wrapped a coil of wire, current being sent through the coil. As long as the current flows, the piece of iron remains a magnet; when the current is interrupted, the magnetism ceases. Why does the piece of iron become a magnet?

Figure 1-9 shows that a current-carrying conductor has a magnetic field surrounding it, and illustrates the method of determining its direction. The cross section of a coil through which a current is flowing, together with the plotted magnetic field of each turn of wire, will give evidence that the over-all effect of the addition of all these magnetic fields is a continuous flux threading through the coil from one end to the other: that is, the coil itself acts as a magnet, and its magnetism is transferred (induced) into the iron core.

### 10.11. The Solenoid

The coil by itself, as we have just seen, is a magnet. It is called a solenoid, and has the property of drawing magnetic substances to itself just like any bar magnet. If an iron rod is placed at one of the openings of the coil, it will be sucked into its center when current passes through the coil. The same thing will occur at the coil's other end. Therefore it makes no difference what the coil polarity may be; it is still attractive to mag-

FIG. 10-6. (Courtesy, Nutone, Inc.)

netic substances. Since this is true, an alternating current may be applied to the solenoid and it will still draw a piece of magnetic material to its center; the changing polarity will not detract from the constant magnetic pull of the solenoid magnetic flux.

The principles just outlined are those which apply to the electric chime. The works are shown in Figure 10-6, and are seen to consist of a solenoid, a soft iron plunger with attached spring, and two pieces of chime metal. The spring holds the plunger in such a position that the center of the plunger metal is not aligned with the center of the solenoid. When current flows through the solenoid, the plunger moves against spring pressure so that its center *does* align with the center of the solenoid; and in the process, a small fiber tip on the plunger bumps against one of the pieces of chime metal, producing a musical note. Interruption of the current allows the spring to pull the plunger back, and the overshoot of the plunger causes its other fiber-tipped end to bump against the other piece of chime metal, thus producing another musical note.

The magnetic behavior of the solenoid is controlled by a push button. When the push button is pressed, the solenoid

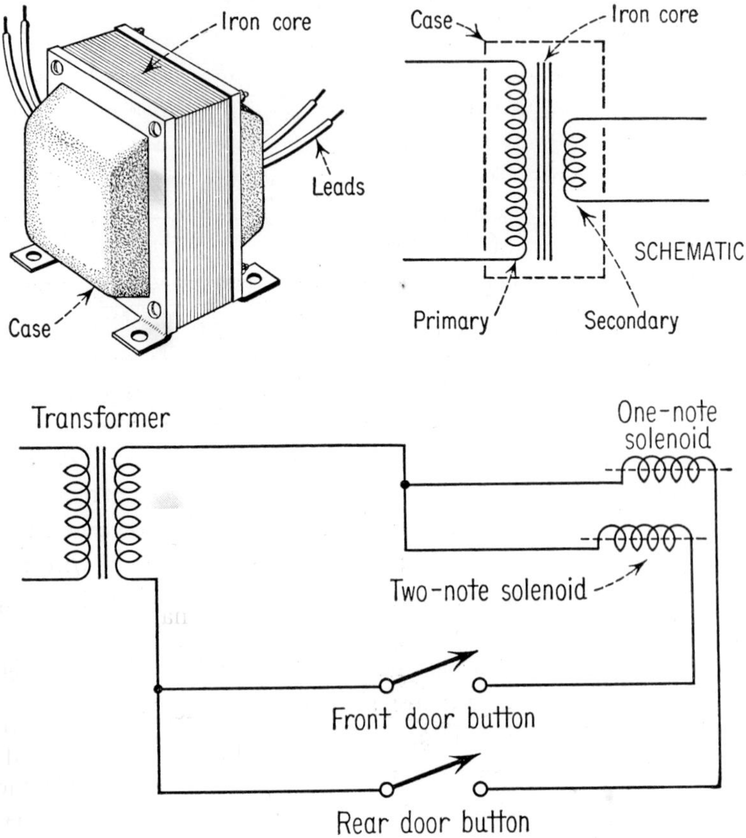


Fig. 10-7.

circuit is completed and one note sounds; when the button is released, the other note sounds.

## 10.12. The Transformer

Like the ordinary doorbell, the electric chime is operated at a low voltage, yet is connected into the regular 120-v house-wiring circuit. This is accomplished by means of a transformer. The transformer is an a-c-operated (only) device used to increase or decrease the voltage. As used with electric chimes, the transformer lowers the voltage from 120 v to 15 v a-c.

The transformer (Fig. 10-7) consists of two windings of insulated wire, each winding being insulated from the other, and an iron core on which the windings are wrapped. The core is made of many pieces of thin iron strips stacked together. This type of construction is called a laminated core, and is necessary to insure cool operation (Sec. 11.3). The winding with the greater number of turns is connected across the 120-v line, and is called the *primary*. The winding with the lesser number of turns is called the *secondary,* and to it are connected the chime solenoid and the push button. The only connection between primary and secondary is through the magnetic field within the iron core. The magnetic flux is produced by the primary current, and interlaces the secondary winding, producing a voltage in the secondary turns.

The value of the voltages across primary and secondary windings is a function of the number of turns, and is directly proportional to the turns ratio. If, for example, there are one tenth as many turns on the secondary as is on the primary, there will be one tenth the voltage across the secondary that there is applied to the primary. Suppose that the primary has 600 turns with 120 v applied. That would be 1/5th v per turn. At the same 1/5th v per turn, the secondary must have 75 turns to produce the 15 v for operating the chimes. The voltage ratio of a transformer does not depend upon the size of wire used. Wire size is a consideration only in that it must be adequate to carry the current required without overheating and burning the insulation.

The chime transformer is called a *step-down* transformer in applications where the primary has the fewer turns; where a higher voltage is obtained by its use, it is called a *step-up* transformer.

Although the transformer will provide a higher voltage than the source voltage (step-up), there is no power actually created by this device; except for the slight losses that occur, the power (product of volts times amperes: watts) put in is equal to the power taken out. When no power is being delivered —as, for example, when the chime transformer secondary is open-circuited by the push button in its normally open state— there is very little power being put into the transformer. This no-load condition results in such a minute current flow through the primary coil that it can be permanently connected to the 120-v line without heating the transformer (and without causing a noticeable increase in the electric bill at the end of the month).

Most electric chimes have two solenoids, each with its own plunger. The two are identical except for an arrangement whereby one plunger hits against a felt bumper when released by the solenoid, so that a second note is not produced. When used in the circuit hookup shown in Fig. 10-7, this chime will produce two notes when the front door button is pressed, but only one when the visitor is at the rear door, enabling the owner to know which door to answer.

## *Repairing and Servicing Electric Chimes*

### 10.13. General Discussion

Most chime sets are designed with the expectation that the solenoid coil itself will last indefinitely. The most common reason for failure to operate is wear produced by the back-and-forth sliding of the plunger, so that it eventually binds instead of sliding smoothly in its cylinder. The solenoid and plunger—

or, in the case of the less expensive chime, the entire set—should be replaced. Do not lubricate the plunger. Oil causes the plunger to stick in its cylinder or to move sluggishly, and does more harm than good. If lubrication is necessary, graphite should be used. Dirt may also cause the plunger to be sluggish in its movement. Cleaning the solenoid and plunger will, of course, remedy the trouble.

Electrical troubles are more likely to be found in the transformer and switch than in the chimes proper. A faulty switch may be checked by disconnecting its leads and touching them together. If the chime operates, then the switch is defective. The transformer may be checked while in the circuit by means of a voltmeter connected across its secondary terminals. Around 15 v should be indicated by the meter. If a voltmeter is not available, another set of chimes. a doorbell, or a low-voltage bulb may be connected across the transformer secondary. If the test device operates, the transformer is satisfactory.

If transformer, button, and chimes are all good, the only remaining possible cause of failure to operate is defective wiring. The wiring may be tested for continuity with an ohmmeter; or it may be "rung out." Ringing out a circuit is accomplished by a device consisting of a buzzer (or bell) and four dry cells, all connected in series. To the ends of the circuit are connected a pair of rather long test leads. If the test-lead ends are connected together, the buzzer will buzz. If in any other manner the circuit between the two test lead ends is completed, the buzzer will buzz. So it is possible, if the test-lead wires are long enough, to connect one to each end of a length of wire whose continuity is doubtful, and test it for possible breaks. When using this device to test the chime's transformer secondary-circuit wiring, be sure to disconnect the chime circuit from the transformer.

The methods described above for trouble-shooting the low-voltage chime circuit apply to the same type of circuit as used to operate an ordinary doorbell or buzzer

## 10.14. Trouble-Shooting Chart: Electric Chimes

| SYMPTOM | CAUSE | TEST | REMEDY |
|---|---|---|---|
| Will not chime. | Open solenoid | Check solenoid coil with series test lamp or ohmmeter. Normal resistance is a few ohms. | Replace coil, or rewind coil, or replace chime set. |
| | Defective switch | Remove switch. Clip wires together. Chimes should sound. | Replace switch. |
| | Open-circuited or shorted transformer | Place low-voltage lamp (Christmas-tree lamp) or voltmeter across transformer secondary. No voltage indicates defective transformer. | Replace transformer. |
| | Blown fuse | Test across primary of transformer with voltmeter. No voltage indicates blown fuse. | Replace fuse. |
| Chime note is very faint. | Worn plunger hole | Visual examination. | Replace chime set. |
| | Plunger hole dirty or gummed | Same as above. | Clean, but do not oil. |
| Chimes one note only. | Worn or broken spring or plunger | Same as above. | Replace spring. |
| Chime set hums constantly but will not sound. | Jammed or defective switch (Button may be stuck.) | Remove switch and test and examine. | Replace or repair switch. |

# ELECTRIC CLOCKS

Repairs to electric clocks can be made in the appliance repair shop if the trouble is of an electrical nature. It may be well to state at the outset that repairs to clock gears, bearings, and other clockwork parts are not feasible; this type of repair is more in the realm of the watchmaker. Actually, repairs to an electric clock consist mainly of replacement of defective electrical parts: motor, cord set, and, on a few models, a pilot lamp. Before discussing these repairs in more detail, let us examine the motors used in electric clocks.

## 10.15. Clock Motors. The Manual-Start Motor

Clock motors can be classified roughly as self-starting and manual-starting. Clocks containing the manual-start motor are equipped with a knob or lever which must be spun or tripped to start the rotor turning. The rotor (Fig. 10-8) consists of a toothed steel disk placed between similarly toothed steel field poles. The rotor is spring-loaded with a heavy brass disk of approximately the same size as the rotor. A single-field coil magnetizes the field poles. Sixty-cycle a-c is required for the field supply; it will energize the field poles (make them magnetic) 120 times per second. With the rotor set into motion in a clockwise direction, assume that rotor tooth (A) is aligned with field tooth (1) at a time when the field magnetism is as shown in Figure 10-8. The tooth (A) will be attracted to pole tooth (1). Half a cycle (or 1/120th of a second) later, the poles will have reversed; tooth (A) will again be attracted to the field, and if the velocity of the rotor is correct, tooth (A) will be attracted by tooth (2). Again in

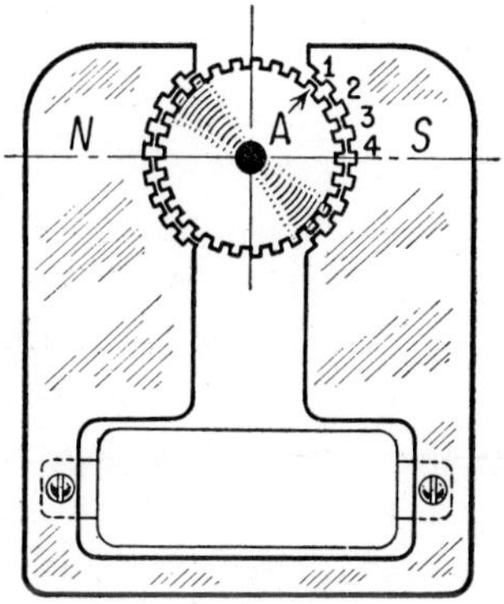

Fig. 10-8.

1/120th of a second, tooth (A) will be attracted, this time by tooth (3), and so on. Thus, if the rotor is initially spun at a correct speed it will lock into step with the changing polarity of the field poles, which speed is determined by the fact that the alternating current is 60 cps. If the rotor is initially rotated at a speed higher than this synchronous speed, it will, on slowing down, lock into step with the changing field polarity at synchronous speed.

The rotor itself would be totally halted by the attraction of the field pole. The (nonmagnetic) brass disk attached to the rotor through a spring is not attracted by the field and does continue to rotate, tightening the spring. The energy thus stored in the coiled spring imparts a thrust to the rotor during periods when the poles are changing magnetic polarity; that is, when the poles are demagnetized. The action just described occurs at all the field teeth and corresponding rotor teeth, and their cumulative effect provides the motor torque.

The speed of the rotor is too high to drive any of the clock hands directly. An alternating current of 60 cps produces 7,200 pole reversals per minute, and, although there are numerous teeth in the rotor and field poles, the number is far less than 7,200, so a gear train is used to reduce the rotor speed to that required for the hour, minute, and sweep-second hands.

## 10.16. The Self-Starting Motor

The shaded-pole principle of starting is employed in the self-starting clock motor (Fig. 10-9). Upon reviewing the principle of the shaded-pole motor (Sec. 6.3), it will be found that within the field structure of this motor there is produced a rotating magnetic field for which the a-c used is responsible. Also mentioned is the matter of slip—the difference in speed between the rotating magnetic field and the rotor within it. To eliminate this slip, and cause the rotor to have the same velocity as the rotating magnetic fields (3,600 rpm in a two-pole motor), the clock motor is equipped with a hard-steel nonlaminated rotor. In some types this rotor is a steel ring surrounding the field pole iron. Being hard steel, the rotor becomes a *permanent* magnet, with poles which lock in with the rotating poles of the field, thus accomplishing synchronous rotation. The

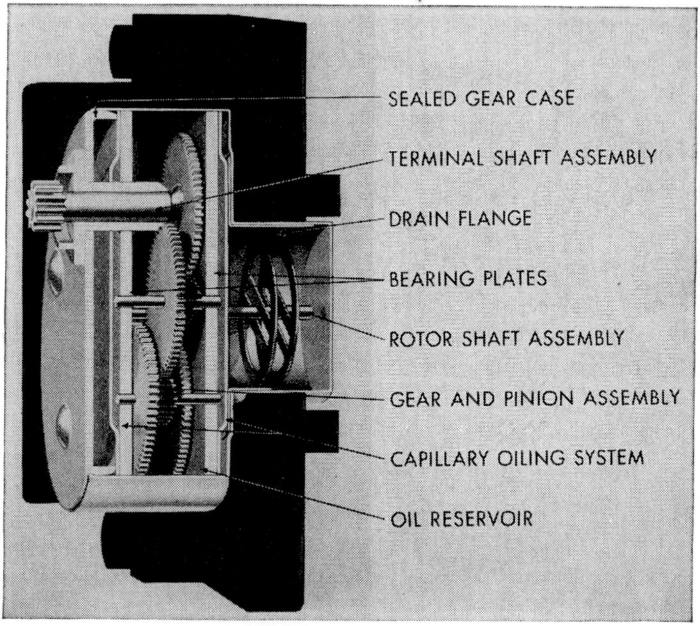


FIG. 10-9. (Courtesy, Telechron)

use of a steel (rather than a laminated iron with imbedded copper bars) rotor reduces the power of the motor, but this fact is relatively unimportant in a clock motor, considering the extremely low power required to turn the gears and hands of a clock.

The self-starting clock motor is available with built-in gears which lower the shaft speed to any desired value. Usually the shaft speed chosen is 1 rpm, and the sweep-second hand of the clock is fastened directly onto the motor shaft. Additional external gears are required for the lower speeds of the minute and hour hands.

## Servicing Electric Clocks

### 10.17. General Discussion

As has been mentioned, repairs to the electrical portion of the clock can be made in the repair shop. The electrical circuit of the clock consists merely of a line cord connected directly to the motor coil, and a continuity test will show if coil or cord is open-circuited. But a word of caution in making this test: if the series-test lamp is used, a very low-wattage lamp should be used in the tester. Otherwise, the opposition offered to a-c by the motor field coil will limit the current to such a low value that a moderate- or high-wattage lamp will remain totally dark, causing a perfectly good circuit to appear to have a break. More positive results are obtained by using an ohmmeter for the continuity test. From 500 to 1,000 ohms is typical of the field-coil resistance.

If the continuity check indicates that the circuit is complete, but the clock still does not run, remove the motor and, with the cord plugged into 120 v a-c, test the field for magnetism with a piece of iron (knife blade or hack-saw blade). If the test piece is felt to vibrate, the most likely cause of failure to operate is a gummed or jammed motor. Provided the motor is not enclosed, it can be soaked in carbon tetrachloride for two or three minutes, being agitated meanwhile to loosen the mechanism. If this only partially frees the motor, it can be set to running while immersed in carbon tetrachloride; this is often more effective in aiding the dissolving of gummed oil or dirt which interferes with motor operation. Carbon tetrachloride is not a conductor and will not ignite. A nonmetallic container for the solvent, such as a soup dish or glass tray, should be used to prevent shorts from metallic contact. And be sure that *only* carbon tetrachloride is used. Other solvents are almost invariably highly inflammable, and must never be used where an electric arc or spark might occur. This is sufficiently important to bear repetition. *If the motor is allowed to run while immersed in the solvent, be sure the solvent is carbon tetrachloride*

If the clock motor can be put in order by the foregoing procedure, it should be lubricated with a special clock oil (obtainable from a jeweler's supply house) before replacing it in the clock. If the motor still will not operate, it will be necessary to replace it with a new one. Repairs should not be attempted on the inner parts of a sealed-unit motor or sealed-unit rotor assembly; instead, a new unit should be installed. Motor and/or sealed unit rotor assembly are obtainable upon an exchange basis either from the appliance parts outlet or from the manufacturer.

It is inevitable that the nature of repairs will necessitate, in many instances, complete dismantling of the clock. Many clock mechanisms require that the hands be removed in order for the motor to be removed. Customarily the hands are held to their shafts by friction. The shaft which turns the hour hand also operates the alarm release. When the hour hand is replaced it must be pressed onto its shaft in an angular position to correspond with the time-position of the alarm release. It may be necessary to operate the alarm a few times to determine the correct hour-hand position on its shaft. It is advisable to acquire the habit of giving a test run on a newly repaired clock *with alarm button pulled out* to avoid overlooking the foregoing possibility, which might otherwise not make itself noticeable in a test run. If you would like to see a thoroughly disgruntled customer then return to him a clock which, when set for six-thirty a.m., goes off at two o'clock in the morning!

The direction of rotation of a clock's hands have given rise to the terms clockwise and counterclockwise, used to describe directions of rotation in general. In setting a clock it seems only natural to cause the hands to turn in a clockwise direction, approaching the correct time from time past; this is accomplished by rotating the set knob in a counterclockwise direction (from the rear of the clock). To accommodate this natural tendency, the set knob is screwed onto its shaft with a left-hand thread. The appliance repair man should not forget this fact in removing the knobs, lest a tight one be damaged, or the shaft twisted and broken, by forcing a tool against the direction of removal. A normal right-hand thread is customary for the alarm reset knob.

## Now that you have read this chapter, can you answer these questions?

**1.** The capacitor across the terminals of a shaver motor has become short-circuited. How will the shaver behave?

**2.** Will all types of electric razors operate on both a-c and d-c? Explain.

**3.** What type of cord is used on an electric razor?

**4.** What is the basis of the operation of a bottle warmer?

**5.** What is an electrode?

**6.** Describe the operation of a solenoid.

**7.** Why is a transformer used with electric chimes?

**8.** Why is the push button for chimes placed in the low-voltage circuit of the transformer?

**9.** What is meant by the voltage ratio of a transformer? How is it related to the number of turns of the windings?

**10.** What would be the probable effect of a short circuit across the secondary terminals of a door-chime transformer?

**11.** How is a transformer checked for faulty operation?

**12.** What precaution must be observed when testing the interconnecting wiring of a door chime wiring system?

**13.** Will chimes operate on d-c? Explain.

**14.** Draw the circuit of a set of chimes with front- and back-door push-button switches.

*chapter* **11**

# Fluorescent Lamps

As modern in appearance as in its application to present-day living, its high efficiency, illumination without heat, and close approximation to actual daylight in color value make the fluorescent style of lighting highly desirable for use in both home and industry. To an ever-increasing extent, the fluorescent lamp is becoming an appliance rather than a fixture. It is a not uncommon sight to see table lamps equipped with fluorescent units, and a modern kitchen is considered incomplete unless illuminated by this method, which eliminates shadows.

The fluorescent lamp is actually an electronic device. A discussion of its operation must necessarily be based upon the theory of current flow through a gas rather than the conventional metallic conducting path. Consequently, a number of new terms will be introduced in this chapter.

## 11.1. The Parts of a Fluorescent Unit

The parts of a fluorescent unit are shown in Figure 11-1. While not an actual picture of the complete fixture itself, this figure depicts the essential parts required to operate a fluorescent tube better than would a picture of the working unit, as it illustrates some essentials not visible in a photograph of the appliance. The most conspicuous and necessary part is the tube itself.

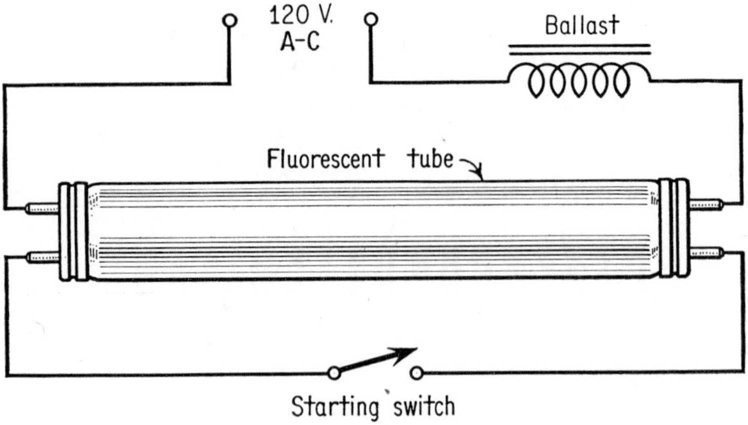


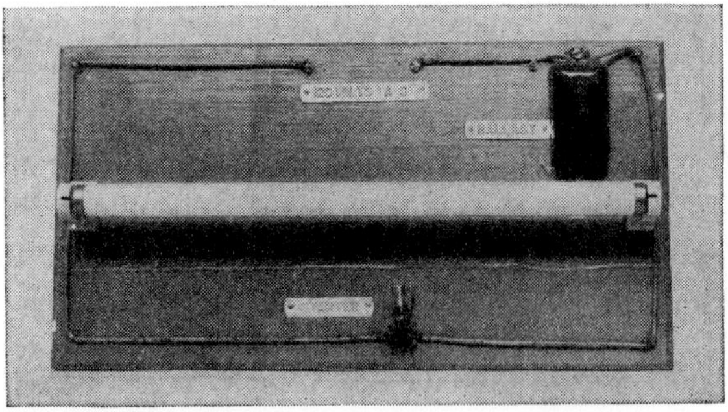

Fig. 11-1.

## 11.2. The Fluorescent Tube

At either end of the fluorescent tube is a pair of prongs through which electrical contact is made from the power source to the tube. As may be seen by the cutaway, Figure 11-2, each pair of prongs is connected to a small filament. Note, however, that there is no internal connection throughout the complete length of the tube. As will be subsequently explained, these filaments glow only during the brief period when the lamp is being ignited. They are not, therefore, designed for continuous current flow, and any condition which may occur to allow prolonged operation of the filaments will materially reduce the life of the tube.

During construction, the tube is evacuated, then filled with argon gas at less than atmospheric pressure; that is, there is a partial vacuum in the tube. Also, there is introduced into the

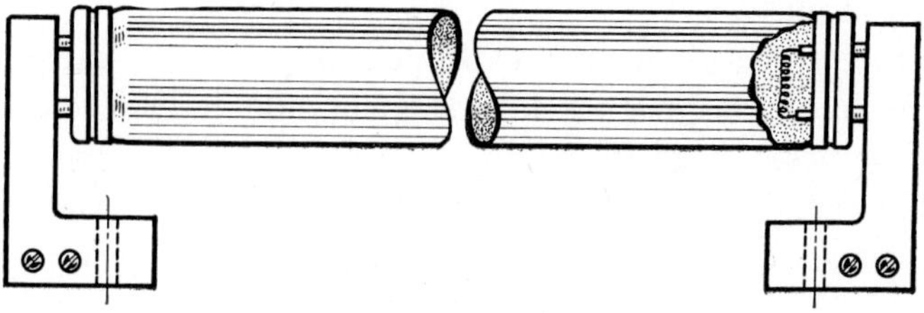

FIG. 11-2.

tube a small amount of metallic mercury, which, due to the reduced pressure inside the tube, becomes mercury vapor. It is this combination of gases which will, under the proper conditions, support the flow of an electric current.

The tube itself is clear glass. The white appearance of the tube is due to a chemical coating inside the tube. This chemical is one of a group known as *phospors,* and has the quality of glowing brightly when subjected to ultraviolet light. The glow from this chemical coating is the actual visible light of the fluorescent lamp.

## 11.3. The Ballast

One of the essential parts of the fluorescent unit as shown in Figure 11-1 is the *ballast.* The ballast, also known as the auxiliary or the reactor, consists of a coil of wire wrapped around a stack of iron strips. This type of construction is known as a laminated core. The use of alternating current through this coil results in the setting up of currents in the iron core itself (eddy currents). The magnitude of these currents and their resultant overheating of the iron core is minimized by making the core from a stack of thin iron strips rather than from a solid piece of metal.

The ballast is placed in series with the fluorescent tube. In this position it will, because of its ohms, control the amount of current which will flow through the tube. This is quite important, since the tube itself, by its nature as a conductor, will, if not protected by the ballast, draw so much current as to destroy itself.

In Chapter 1 it was explained that a wire carrying a current has a magnetic field set up around it. The combined magnetic fields of all the turns of a coil form an electromagnet, whose strength depends upon the magnitude of the current flowing through it. If the current flow is suddenly interrupted, as by the opening of a switch, the magnetic field around each turn of the coil will suddenly collapse, producing a momentary high voltage. This is called the inductive kick. The inductive kick of the ballast in a fluorescent circuit will produce an arc through the tube. Once the arc is produced, current will continue to flow through the tube, and a much lower voltage is adequate to keep it flowing: less than the 120 v of the power circuit.

## 11.4. The Starter

To produce the high voltage of the inductive kick, it is necessary that the current through the ballast be suddenly interrupted. This is accomplished by a switch called the starter. As shown in Figure 11-1, the starter is parallel with the tube. When the tube is nonconducting (not glowing), the starting switch alone is in series with the ballast, and when opened will break the circuit of the ballast.

Both manual and automatic starters are in use. The manual switches are to be found on desk and table lamps. The ceiling fixture is equipped with the automatic starter. The manual starter is a push-type momentary-contact switch. The automatic switch is thermostatically operated. The details of the operation of the automatic starter will be discussed later in this chapter.

## 11.5. Cycle of Operation

Referring to Figure 11-1, the inoperative tube and open-contact starter make the unit open-circuited. The line voltage (110–120 v) is insufficient to strike an arc across the tube. When the starting switch is closed, it completes a circuit through the ballast and the two filaments in the tube all in series, and the filaments heat up.

The present-day theory of the nature of electricity is that it consists of negative electrical particles called *electrons*. These electrons are present in all matter, and their motion through a conductor constitutes a current flow. Just as particles of vapor in the form of steam escape from boiling water, so, also, these electrons will boil off certain materials when they are heated. The filaments in a fluorescent tube are coated with electron-emitting materials. Heating of the filaments causes them to emit electrons into the tube. When the starting switch is opened, the inductive kick provides the electromotive force necessary to force the emitted electrons through the tube from one end to the other, thus establishing a current flow through the tube. The current having started through the tube, there occurs an electrochemical change in the argon- and mercury-vapor gases called *ionization*. An ionized gas is a good conductor; hence, the initial flow of current produces its own self-sustaining effect, and it will continue to flow until the circuit is broken. Thus the fluorescent lamp is lighted. The starting switch is open, and it remains so until it is necessary to light the lamp again.

## 11.6. Fluorescence

Ionization of the mercury vapor in the fluorescent tube, accomplished by the current flow, is a process which produces light. The mercury-vapor light is quite poor from the standpoint of usable illumination; it is, however, rich in an invisible type of light, ultraviolet. As the ultraviolet light shines on the fluorescent chemical coating in the tube, it causes the chemical to glow with a brilliant light. The ultraviolet light cannot penetrate the glass of the tube, but the fluorescent can, and does, providing a highly efficient light. By varying the chemical composition of the fluorescent powder, almost any color can be obtained. The two colors known as "natural white" and "daylight" are the most popular.

The amount of usable ultraviolet light generated within the fluorescent tube is a function of the pressure of the gases therein. As the temperature of the tube changes, an accompanying change of pressure takes place. Tubes are manufactured so as to be most efficient at room temperature. A severe variance from this temperature, such as operation out of doors on a winter day, will cause lowered brilliance of the fluorescence. If the unit is to be used in an application such as this, a tube having gas pressure such as to allow efficient operation under low temperatures should be obtained.

## 11.7. The Automatic Starter

A number of automatic starters have been used, but that kind which outnumbers all others in popularity is the glow starter, shown in Figure 11-3A. The socket into which the tube fits is made so that the starter can be clipped into it and is thereby connected into the proper place in the circuit. From the cutaway in Figure 11-3B it is seen that the starter consists of a glass tube containing two thin metal pieces. These metal parts are bimetallic strips tipped with small contact points. When heated they will bend, moving together and closing the circuit in which the starter is placed.

In addition to the bimetals, the tube contains neon gas. The purpose of the neon may be best explained by observing the circuit conditions in Figure 11-4. If the switch contacts are open, the voltage across the switch is the line voltage, 120 v a-c. Any voltage in excess of 50 v a-c will cause the neon bulb to fire (glow). The small quantity of heat produced by the glowing neon tube is sufficient to cause the bimetallic strips to bend, completing the filament-ballast circuit. The closing of these contacts removes the voltage from the neon bulb, and it extinguishes.

With the heat source removed, the bimetallic elements retract and the contacts open, producing the inductive kick from the ballast necessary to start the fluorescent tube glowing.

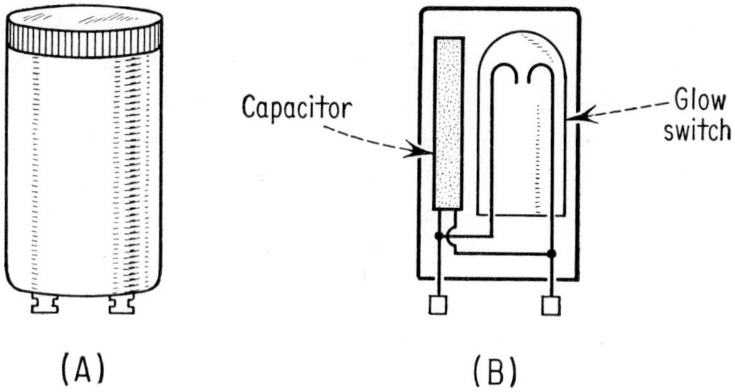


Fig. 11-3.

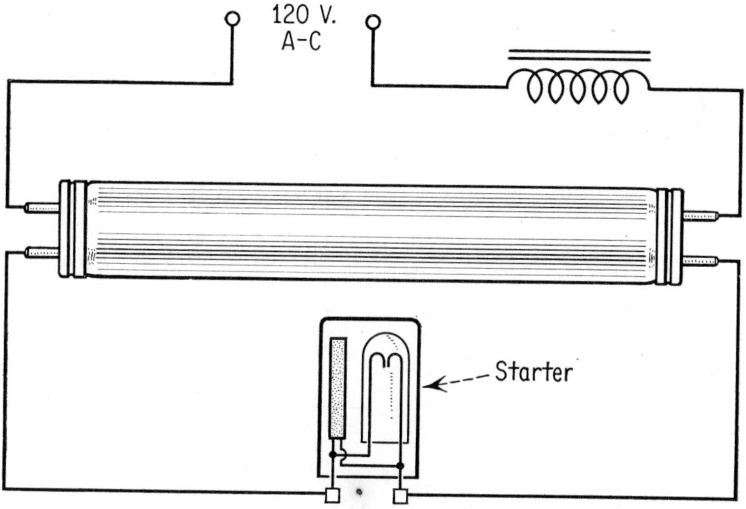


Fig. 11-4.

The starter is in parallel with the conducting fluorescent tube, and the voltage across the conducting tube (line voltage minus the voltage drop across the ballast) is not sufficient to fire the starter neon bulb; thus, the starter contacts remain open.

Contained within the capsule of the neon glow starter is a small capacitor. This capacitor is wired across the switch contact points. In absorbing the arc formed when the contacts open, the capacitor serves the dual purpose of increasing contact life and reducing the radio interference caused by an arc.

Among the troubles that may occur in a fluorescent unit are welding together of the starter contact points or shorting of the capacitor. Either condition would result in permitting a constant current flow through the tube filaments and their subsequent burnout. To protect the tube from damage resulting from starter failure, the starter contains an auxiliary thermostat, operated by a small resistor, which will eventually open the starter circuit and save the fluorescent tube.

## 11.8. Stroboscopic Effect

Although the fluorescent circuit may be designed for direct-current operation, it is more economically adapted to use with alternating current. Furthermore, the almost universal trend toward a-c for household wiring dictates that this type of current be used to operate the fluorescent fixture. The ordinary incandescent lamp gives no evidence of the use of a-c or d-c, its operation being apparently identical on either. This is not true of the fluorescent lamp. The reversal of the current flow, each alternation of a-c, is accompanied by a brief period, right at the reversal time, when current flow ceases, then resumes in the opposite direction to that of the preceding interval. The glow of the fluorescent tube almost extinguishes at this reversal time, only to start up again as the current increases. Thus, a flicker, at a rate of 120 cps occurs while the lamp is in operation. A flicker at this speed is much too fast to be observed with the eye as such; however, its effect is noticeable. A rapidly moving object passing by the illumination of a fluorescent lamp is observed as a series of objects rather than as a single object in motion. The blade of an electric fan operated by an induction motor, such as the shaded-pole motor, appears to stand still or to move slowly backward, since an induction motor's speed is a function of the frequency of the applied alternating current.

This is called the stroboscopic effect of the fluorescent lamp. A refinement of this principle is utilized to observe machinery in motion for the purpose of detecting operating flaws, since the proper speed of stroboscopic flicker rate will cause moving objects to appear to stand completely still. This effect does not exist in the incandescent lamp. Although it is subjected to the same current fluctuations, the incandescent filament cannot lose its glow rapidly enough for a flicker to occur.

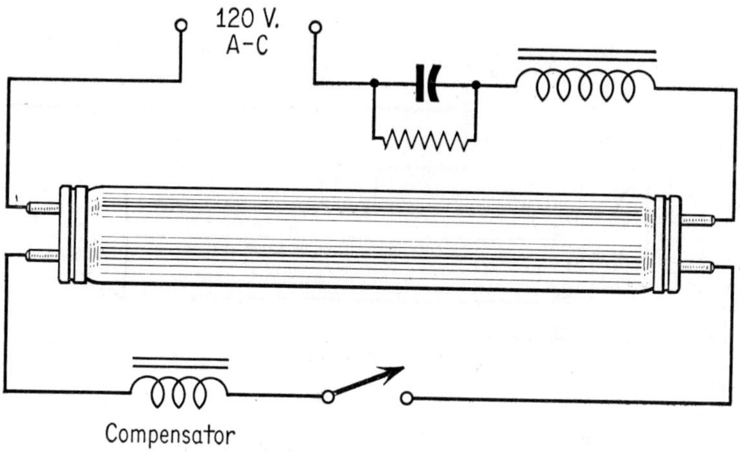


FIG. 11-5.

## 11.9. The Leading Lamp

Under certain conditions the stroboscopic flicker becomes objectionable. If it is used as illumination for work of an exacting nature, irritation of the eyes may result. This condition may be corrected by use of a fluorescent unit containing two lamps, one of which is connected in the circuit as previously discussed, while the circuit of the other contains a series capacitor (Fig. 11-5). The characteristics of a capacitor are such that it tends to change the time of current flow in an a-c circuit.

Therefore, the *time* of current reversal in this unit will differ from that of the other lamp, with the result that the flicker of the two lamps will overlap, so to the eye there does not appear to be any flicker at all. The lamp with the capacitor in its circuit is called the leading lamp, for its current "leads" the current of the other lamp.

## 11.10. The Compensator

Although the capacitor effectually removes the stroboscopic flicker, it does at the same time absorb the inductive kick of the ballast, making it necessary to insert additional in-

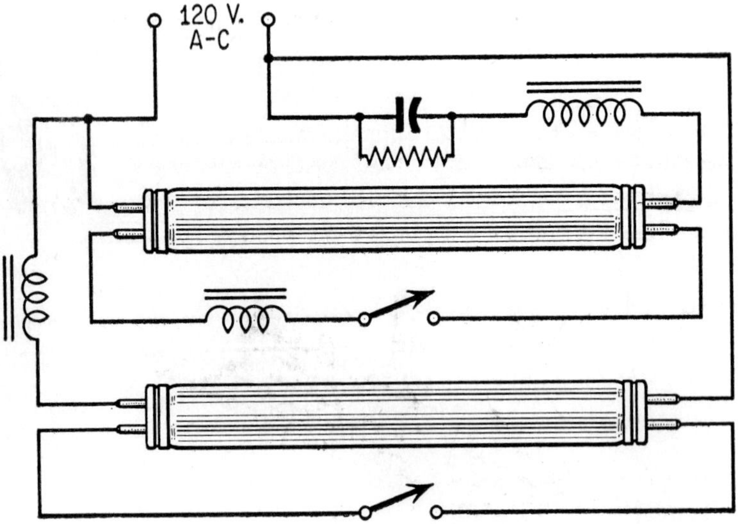


FIG. 11-6.

ductance in the circuit. The compensator, a ballast placed in the starter circuit, serves this purpose; it does not influence the behavior of the capacitor, since the compensator is not in the circuit of the lamp while it is glowing. Figure 11-6 shows the circuit of a two-lamp unit containing both ordinary lamp and leading lamp.

## 11.11. Filtering

The flow of current through the gases in the flourescent tube produces radiations of the type that causes radio interference. A radio operating near a fluorescent lamp will have a loud

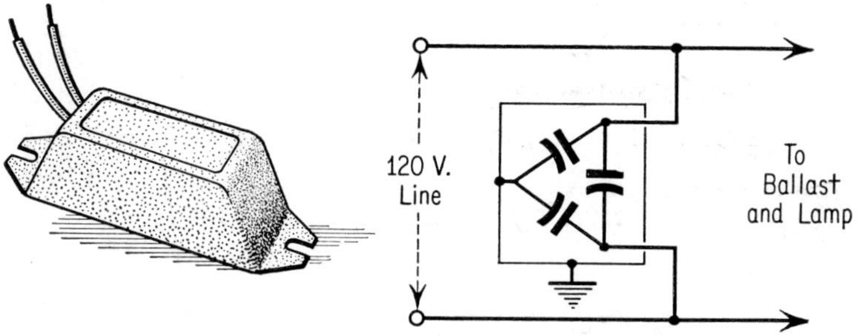


FIG. 11-7.

hum at the 120-cps interruption rate of the current through the fluorescent tube. This noise may be eliminated by placing a capacitor-type filter across the 120-v line as it enters the fixture. A typical filter and its circuit are shown in Figure 11-7.

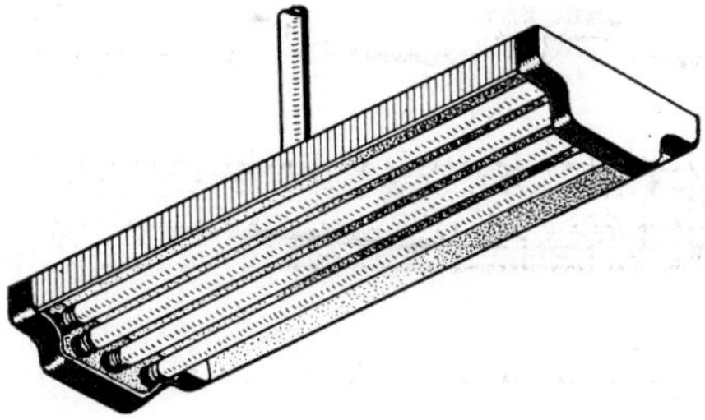

FIG. 11-8.

## 11.12. The Fixture

When the electrical and electronic parts thus far described are assembled in a completed unit, it appears as shown in Figure 11-8. This is a ceiling fixture using four lamps in a V-shaped framework which acts somewhat as a reflector. Contained within the framework are the ballast, capacitor if used, and the interconnecting wiring. The lamps are removed from their sockets by giving them a quarter-turn and sliding the pins out through a slot provided for that purpose. When a lamp has been removed, its starter is visible, extending through a hole in the framework. It also is removed by a quarter twist. If it is necessary to remove the ballast, the fixture framework may be dismantled by prying it apart. The fixture is so designed that this may be done without damage to the finish.

## *Servicing Fluorescent Lamps*

### 11.13. General Discussion

From the servicing standpoint, the fluorescent unit may be considered to consist of four parts: the lamp, the starter, the auxiliary equipment, and the wiring. The accessibility of these parts is in the order named, and this should be given consideration when trouble-shooting the unit. Much valuable time may be lost otherwise in checking the wiring and ballast when only the tube is at fault and when its replacement will effect the necessary repair.

Since the tube and starter are the parts most easily reached, they should be checked first. The easiest and most effective manner of testing the quality of these two parts is by the substitution method: that is, by replacing them individually and separately with parts from another fixture known to be good, or by trying the suspected part in the other working unit. If this method proves both starter and tube to be in satisfactory working order, it is then necessary to dismantle the fixture. Check the wiring with a series test lamp (be sure to disconnect fixture from line) to eliminate this possible source of trouble. All that remains is the ballast. If no other cause of trouble has been found, the ballast is the defective component (assuming, of course, it has been determined that the trouble is not external to the fixture, such as in receptacle, fuse, and so forth).

Checking the ballast indirectly, by eliminating all other

possible sources, is the easiest method of tracing the trouble to this component. A ballast with an internal short will not work. It will, however, test the same as a good one with the series test lamp. If the resistance of the ballast is known, and an ohmmeter is available, it may be tested in this manner, but this is not generally convenient outside the shop.

A fluorescent tube may be defective and yet the filaments be complete. This tube will glow faintly at each end because of the heated filaments, yet refuse to "fire." The starter will keep on trying to ignite the tube, to no avail. If such a condition is allowed to exist for very long, the starter, which is designed for occasional use only, will be ruined. A fixture that behaves in this manner should have a new tube installed immediately, or else the defective tube should be removed until a new one can be obtained.

## 11.14. Trouble-Shooting Chart: Fluorescent Lamps

| SYMPTOM | CAUSE | TEST | REMEDY |
|---|---|---|---|
| Does not burn. | Burned-out lamp | Replace with known good lamp or try faulty lamp in working fixture. | Replace lamp. |
| | Defective starter | Replace with new starter, or try faulty starter in working fixture. | Replace starter. |
| | Defective ballast | Dismantle fixture to point where ballast is accessible. Remove and insert new ballast in circuit. Test. | Replace ballast. |
| | Defective wiring | Check by eliminating other possibilities (see above). | Repair or replace wiring. |

| SYMPTOM | CAUSE | TEST | REMEDY |
|---|---|---|---|
| Lamp flickers and refuses to ignite. | Defective or aged lamp | Try faulty lamp in working fixture. | Replace lamp. |
| | Defective starter | Try faulty starter in working fixture. | Replace starter. |
| Appliance is noisy (hums). | Loose laminations in ballast | Visual and aural examination. | Replace ballast. |
| Appliance blows fuses. | Internal short (cord or accessories) | Disconnect line wires. Test with ohmmeter. Zero ohms indicates short. | Replace offending component. |

## Now that you have read this chapter, can you answer these questions?

**1.** Give two reasons for the use of a ballast in a fluorescent fixture.

**2.** Describe the ballast.

**3.** Draw the circuit of a fluorescent unit using a manual starter.

**4.** Why is not a SPST wall switch used as the starter in a fluorescent fixture?

**5.** With the starting switch open, there is no apparent complete circuit for the current flow. What actually completes the circuit?

**6.** What is it that glows in a fluorescent lamp?

**7.** Why does this lamp have a more noticeable flicker than an incandescent lamp?

**8.** What happens if the starter is wired in backward?

**9.** What happens if the ballast is wired in backward?

**10.** Describe the glow-type starter.

**11.** What is a compensator? A leading lamp?

12. Will one ballast serve for use with two fluorescent lamps? Explain.

13. Why will a fan blade driven by a shaded-pole motor appear to stand still or move slowly when viewed by the illumination of a fluorescent lamp?

14. Will it damage the auxiliary equipment of a fluorescent unit if the tube is removed without disconnecting the source of power?

15. Why does a fluorescent lamp have cooler operation than an incandescent lamp?

16. What is the meaning of inductive kick? How does it occur?

17. Why is a fluorescent lamp less efficient in a cool room than in a temperate one?

18. Discuss the relative merits of incandescent and fluorescent lighting.

19. How would you test a defective fluorescent unit?

# chapter 12

# Refinishing Methods

Most repair jobs are of a routine sort, where the repair man's experienced eye can quickly spot the cause of trouble from the behavior of the appliance. However, occasionally an unusual "trouble" will be encountered which will require all the skill and ingenuity of the appliance man to isolate and remedy. The ability to handle such jobs is the criterion of the repair man's craftsmanship. Unfortunately, the finished product gives no evidence of whether the repairs needed were elaborate or minor. The appliance looks the same as it did when it was received from the owner. Indeed, paradoxically, the job which requires the most effort and material may give the least outward evidence of improvement. Hence it adds a finishing touch to a good repair or rebuilding job to improve in some way the general appearance of the appliance; and the owner will appreciate such effort.

## 12.1. Cleaning

There are a number of ways to give an appliance a "like new" finish. What is most generally needed is just plain washing. The owner may have been timid about applying soap and water to an electrically operated appliance; the repair man need not be, for, knowing the electric circuit as he does, he is capable of washing the appliance without doing any damage to the circuit itself. Furthermore, appliances will sometimes get dirty just in the process of repair. Appliance repair is not clean work; it is often difficult to avoid leaving greasy finger marks on a white surface, for example, and these ought to be removed at the conclusion of the job.

Any nationally advertised brand of soap powder or flakes, or detergent, dissolved in water and applied with a clean shop towel, will remove most ordinary dirt and grease from a painted surface, and all except permanent stains on porcelain. The soaping or application of detergent should be followed by clear water to prevent streaks. If the painted surface remains dull and dingy after the above treatment, a paint-cleaner, such as Duralacque, may be used, care being taken to follow the instructions on the box.

## 12.2. Painting

If the paint is chipped or scratched, it is advisable to repaint the appliance. The new paint should be sprayed on, not brushed. However, before applying a spray coat, certain preliminaries must be taken care of. If the old paint is chipped or scratched, the scar will be not only visible but conspicuous, through the new coat. If the piece to be painted is small, such as the body of a mixer or the top bar of a wringer, a motor-driven wire buffing wheel can be used to remove all the old paint. Some pieces (the skirt of a washing machine, for example) are too big to put to a wire wheel, and, even so, too much time would be required to buff off all the old paint. The larger pieces may be prepared with a paint-remover solution, or by feather sanding.

Feather sanding entails the use of a very fine grit of so-called "wet or dry" sandpaper. The wet paper is applied to the rim of the cracked paint spot or scratch. The purpose of this process is to remove the abrupt change of level from paint to metal by gradually thinning the paint coat as it approaches the bare metal. Thus the paint appears to blend into the metal surface with a gradual decrease of thickness of the paint coat. It may then be sprayed over with a new coat of paint, and no blemish will show through the new coat.

Paint spraying requires much practice to master. It is wise to practice on a number of objects before attempting to put a finish on a repair job. Supplies needed include a compressor and air tank, hose and paint gun, and a supply of paint and thinner. The paint should be thinned almost to the consistency of water. A pressure of 25 to 40 pounds of air is quite satisfactory. The gun should be moved to and fro in even strokes to apply a uniform layer of paint. The quantity of paint to apply to any one area is important. Too little paint will dry to a powdery dull surface; too much will run. The best finish is obtained when the quantity sprayed on is just enough so that individual globules of paint fuse together, and the surface being painted assumes a glossy appearance. Even a slight bit more will cause the paint to run, so caution must be exercised. The spray gun should be held about 2 feet from the surface being painted. This distance allows the paint to dry partially before it hits the metal surface.

Ordinary lacquer or enamel, with thinner used as a solvent, dries rapidly but remains elastic for a few hours. Painted parts should be allowed to dry overnight. This allows a safe margin of time, with the assurance that the painted surface will be dry enough to handle without marring when the appliance is reassembled. The spray gun must be cleaned after each use lest it clog and refuse to operate. A small container of thinner can be set aside for this purpose. The clinging paint can be cleaned from the gun by using a small paintbrush dipped in the cleaning thinner. After all visible paint has been cleaned off, what remains in the nozzle can be removed by spraying a little thinner through the gun.

Any electrical fixtures installed in the spray-painting booth must be of the explosion-proof type as prescribed by the National Electric Code.

## 12.3. Polishing

Metals that will corrode or rust are plated with a noncorrosive material, but some materials which are themselves noncorrosive are to be found on appliances, notably aluminum and "white metal." Motor end bells, ironer shoes, and vacuum-cleaner castings are examples of such use. Restoring the original polish and luster to these parts improves immeasurably the appearance of an appliance. A motor-driven cloth polishing wheel is used to renew these metal surfaces.

Two types of cloth wheels are available. The "hard wheel" consists of a number of circular pieces of cloth sewn together to build up the desired thickness. The stitching extends spirally from the center shaft hole to the outer edge. The amount and closeness of the stitching gives the wheel its stiffness. A "soft wheel," on the other hand, has stitching only at the center, so that the outer perimeter remains quite flexible.

An abrasive compound is used with the cloth wheel. A number of compounds such as emery, pumice, tripoli, and jeweler's rouge are available, in a wide variety of grits. They are prepared in cake form, and are applied to the wheel by holding the block of abrasive against the wheel while it is spinning. Too much abrasive applied too vigorously will result in waste, since much of it will fly off the wheel and be lost. Only as much as will cling to the wheel should be applied. The abrasive holds on to the wheel rather well, and considerable polishing may be done before it becomes necessary to apply more.

The hard wheel is used with a coarse abrasive—pumice, emery, or carborundum—for preliminary or rough polishing. Surfaces that have been scratched or marred may be smoothed to a dull finish with the coarser abrasives. The dull finish can be given a mirrorlike polish with the softer wheel and a fine abrasive—either whiting, or jeweler's rouge. Extremely soft metals will assume a high polish when applied to the soft wheel with no abrasive.

The object to be polished should be held against the wheel with only moderate pressure. Pushing it against the wheel too hard slows the motor and distorts the cloth-wheel shape, both of which reduce polishing efficiency. The work should be moved across the wheel in slow, even strokes, taking care that areas polished overlap each time, thus assuring an even, streakless sheen. Do not hold one spot against the wheel for a prolonged period of time, since this will cause the metal to heat and discolor.

Surfaces that have been plated may be repolished, provided the surface is not too badly worn or marred, and due care is exercised. Plating is rather thin, and easily penetrated by the polishing wheel. A very fine abrasive, if any, should be used, with the soft wheel, and polishing should be held to a minimum so as to remove as little as possible of the actual plating metal.

## 12.4. Replating

Occasionally it becomes necessary to replace a part whose only defect is a slight rusting. An example is the replacement of a wringer drain board, which, when it acquires even a slight coat of rust, will stain clothes. It is not necessary to discard these parts, which may be taken to a plater and be refinished. Cadmium plating is inexpensive, and will make the piece as serviceable as when new.

Parts used where food is present, such as the shelves of a refrigerator, or the beaters of a mixer, should be tinned rather than plated, since the tinning process does not involve the use of the poisonous chemicals that are required for many types of plating.

Another process that is best handled by a specialist in that line is the refinishing of an aluminum agitator. The agitator itself is of too awkward a shape to use a wire wheel, and the imbedded soap causes the buffed or polished agitator to become streaked. An agitator should never be painted, for paint will come off and stain the clothes being washed. A sand blast will restore the agitator's original velvetlike appearance, hence the services of a sand-blaster should be sought when such refinishing becomes necessary.

## 12.5. Porcelain

The porcelain finish to be found on washing-machine tubs, ranges, and some smaller appliances is actually a coating of colored glass which has been melted, or fused, onto a base of sheet iron. Being glass, its behavior is that of glass. It does not readily stain or scratch, but once this damage occurs it cannot be made good as new. Porcelain finish is easily cleaned with soap and water. It is brittle, and will chip or shatter. The original material cannot be patched without returning it to the smelter for refiring, which, of course, is impractical. Consequently, appliances having porcelain finish should be handled with care to prevent damage of any sort.

One temporary method of repair is possible. A number of porcelain "patch" materials are on the market, all of which are applied like paint. While it is possible to use these materials to repair a porcelain crack or chip to an extent that will require close examination to reveal the patch, the patching materials discolor more rapidly than the porcelain, as they are more severely attacked by acids, heat, and stains than is the original. Individual taste should dictate as to whether a patch is preferable to the uncovered blemish.

## 12.6. Solvents

At the other end of the scale is the matter of cleanliness that does *not* meet the eye. While it will neither add to, nor detract from, the appearance of the finished product, the conscientious workman will be as zealous about the cleanliness of the inner works of the appliance as he is about the surface finish. There is no denying that a clean mechanism will give performance superior to one that is rusty, or which contains unclean lubricants. To properly examine gears and the like for defect or wear, it is necessary to remove all dirt and grease from these parts.

For general cleaning of metal parts, a solvent should be used which is available in a moderately large quantity at a reasonable cost, and which will not readily evaporate, explode, or catch fire. While gasoline and similar volatile substances are reasonable in cost, the hazard attendant to their use is well known. Carbon tetrachloride is an excellent cleansing agent, as well as being noninflammable; it is, however, quite expensive, and must be kept sealed when not in use, since it evaporates rapidly. A fluid known as *distillate,* obtainable from dealers in refinery products, is best suited to general use in cleaning dirty metal parts. It is no more inflammable than motor oil, yet is thin enough to flow readily, making cleaning easy, and is somewhat in the same price range as kerosene or coal oil.

It is advisable to have two or three small tanks of this solvent available for parts cleaning. The major portion of the grime can be removed by the first wash, while cleaner fluid is used as a rinse. A system of this sort will reduce the quantity of solvent that becomes too dirty for further usefulness. Experience will make it apparent what types of brushes will be most handy for this cleaning method. The small hardware is easily cleaned by putting it in a soap-saver (obtainable at the five-and-ten-cent store) and moving it briskly to and fro through the solvent. The same soap-saver may be used to keep all the hardware from one appliance together, from time of disassembly until it is ready to reassemble.

Distillate evaporates very slowly. It is necessary to wipe off the parts that have been cleaned; or, if sawdust is available, it may be used to soak up the excess fluid. An air gun used in conjunction with the paint-spray compressor will blow off the sawdust, leaving the part as clean as when new except for rust, which can be removed by a wire wheel.

After the parts have been cleaned in this manner it will be easier to compare them with new ones and determine which parts are so worn that they might cause trouble at a future date unless replaced. If all moving parts which show signs of undue wear are replaced, it is evident that the appliance will possess the same working quality as when new, and should give the same performance, and period of trouble-free operation, as a new one.

Motor armatures, field, coils, and other wired or wound assemblies should not be cleaned in the slow-drying solvent, nor should rubber or any assembly containing rubber be allowed to come in contact with this fluid. A faster-evaporating solvent is indicated for use with these parts: one which dries before insulation or rubber deterioration can begin. Either gasoline or carbon tetrachloride is suitable, preferably the noninflammable carbon tetrachloride.

# Index

# Index